Well
NHS HAI
2006/07

Twentieth edition

Editor
Peter Merry

JMH Publishing Ltd
www.wellards.co.uk

Twnetieth edition published 2006 by
JMH Publishing Ltd
Bramblebank
Turners Green Road
Wadhurst
East Sussex
TN5 6EA

ISBN 0-9544991-8-2

Contents

Preface
Acknowledgements

Chapter 1: The changing structure
& management of the NHS
— The Department of Health 1
— Executive agencies 2
— Non-departmental public bodies 2
— Special health authorities 2
— Developments in Scotland 5
— Developments in Wales 8
— The NHS in Northern Ireland 11
— NHS boards & their functions 12
— NHS Appointments Commission 17
— Strategic health authorities 19
— Primary care trusts 19
— Personal medical services 24
— NHS walk-in centres 25
— Care trusts 26
— NHS trusts 28
— Foundation trusts 29
— Treatment centres 33
— Arm's length bodies 34
— Acts of Parliament 35

Chapter 2. The NHS workforce
— The human resources agenda 39
— Pay modernisation 41
— NHS Employers 46
— The NHS Institute for Innovation and ..
   Improvement 47
— Managers 47
— Medical staff 49
— Nursing staff 58
— Dentists 61
— Optometrists 62
— Professional & support staff 62
— Health & safety 67

Chapter 3: Implementing NHS strategy
— The NHS Plan for England 72
— Implementation checklist 78
— National planning framework 79
— The NHS improvement plan 79
— Out of hospital care 81
— The NHS Plan in Scotland 82
— The NHS Plan in Wales 83

Chapter 4: Involving patients
— The Commission for Patient and Public
Involvement in Health 84
— Patient and public
   involvement forums 84
— Patient choice 86
— Choose and book 88
— The expert patient programme 89

Chapter 5. The advance of clinical
governance
— Overview 93
— Main elements of clinical
   governance 95
— Clinical effectiveness 96
— NHS research & development 99
— The National Institute for Health and
Clinical Excellence 102
— The National Patient Safety Agency 107
— Risk management 110
— Clinical negligence 111
— Complaints 112

Chapter 6. The public health agenda
— Overview 117
—Strategies for health 117
— Screening 121
— Choosing health 123
— Spearhead primary care trusts 125
— Reducing health inequalities 126
— The clean hospitals programme 129
— Campaign to tackle smoking 130
— Control of infectious diseases & health
   protection 133
— The Health Protection Agency 141

Chapter 7. New approaches to care
— Acute services 143
— Intermediate care 147
— Clinical care networks 151
— Maternity services 152
— Child health services 158
— Mental health services 166
— Services for people with learning ....
   difficulties 173
— Services for black & minority ethnic ....
   people 175
— Services for older people 181

— Supportive & palliative
   care services 184
— Dental services 189
— Ophthalmic services 191
— Pathology services 194
— X-ray & imaging services 199
— Pharmacy services 202
— Ambulance services 213
— The management of long-term ....
   conditions 216
— Genetic services 219
— Drug misuse 220
— Sexual health 221
— Transplant services 223
— Blood transfusion services 225

Chapter 8. Performance management
— Overview 227
— Healthcare Commission 228
— The national patient & user survey 230
— National service frameworks 235
— The NHS cancer plan 236
— The national service framework for ....
   children 239
— The national service framework for ....
   coronary heart disease 241
— The national service framework for ....
   mental health 243
— The national service framework for ....
   older people 244
— The national service framework for ....
   renal services 247
— The national service framework for ....
   long-term conditions 248
— The national service framework for
diabetes 249

Chapter 9: The partnership imperative
— Overview 250
— Local authorities & healthcare 252

— The Commission for Social Care ....
   Inspection 252

Chapter 10. Working with the private sector
— Independent healthcare 254
— Nursing & residential care 255

Chapter 11. Financing the system
— Financing the system 256
— Distribution of funds 258
— Payment by results 261
— Capital and private finance 266

Chapter 12. Communications
— Openness & accountability 270
— The press & the NHS 272

Chapter 13. Healthcare information
— Connecting for Health 275
— Clinical decision support systems ... 278
— Confidentiality 279
— NHS library and knowledge services 282
— NHS Direct 284

Chapter 14. Support services
— The NHS estate & facilities
   management 289
— Sterile services & decontamination 292
— NHS supplies & procurement 293
— Security in the NHS 295

Chapter 15: Reference
— NHS fact file 302
— NHS jargon explained 312
— Abbreviations & acronyms 320
— Index 332

Preface

For this edition of *Wellard's NHS Handbook* we have changed the format and produced a more compact publication but in every other respect the formula remains as before. The National Health Service refuses to stand still and with each succeeding year the need to have a clear guide to the structure and organisation of the service remains as strong as ever. To understand how the NHS works and moves it is important to have a grasp of current innovations and this is what the Handbook sets out to outline.

The *NHS Handbook* was originally created by the National Association of Health Authorities in 1980 to act as a guide for those people new to the health service, particularly members of health boards, and for anyone else who had a need to learn more about how the system operated.

By 1994, with input from JMH Publishing, the publication was turned into an annual to reflect the ongoing rapid rate of change within the service. JMH Publishing, under the brand name Wellards, has also in recent years turned to electronic formats, producing an extensive web-based output for organisations needing to know about the NHS. But there remains a need to provide in-depth information about the many complex areas of the NHS and the Handbook does that.

The revised and updated text in the twentieth edition draws on the official sources of information about the health service and the organisations which support it.

The Wellard's team once again will welcome your feedback on the twentieth edition and on how the task of describing the NHS can be further enhanced.

Peter Merry
March 2006

Acknowledgements

The process of updating and revising the Handbook each year has become an in-house task for the Wellard's team. Particularly thanks therefore go to John Heath, Ed Birch, Clare Grant, Oliver Hudson and Hilary Heath.

Much of the text is built on input from a number of experts and we are grateful to those individuals.

Peter Yuen of the Office of Health Economics kindly provided the material for the NHS fact file section.

Wellard's NHS Handbook 2006/07

Recent years have seen the NHS undergo several major structural and organisational changes. These have gone hand-in-hand with the devolution of power to Scotland, Wales and Northern Ireland. The outcome has been increasing diversity in the organisation of health and social care in the UK.

The NHS

The NHS was established by the National Health Service Act of 1946. Under the Act, the Secretary of State for Health is responsible for the provision of health services in England. Parliament holds the Secretary of State to account for the functioning of the NHS and the use of resources.

The NHS Plan for England, published in July 2000 (chapter 3), sets out a programme for investment and reform designed to rebuild the NHS over 10 years. At the heart of the plan is a commitment to increase spending on the NHS and to use the additional funds to increase staffing and provide more beds and equipment. There is a major emphasis on ensuring that services are designed around the patient and offer personalised care.

The Department of Health

The Department of Health supports the Secretary of State and health ministers in carrying out their functions. It is responsible at a national level for the NHS, public health and social care. Its work is centred in Leeds and London.

The Department is lead by its permanent secretary Sir Nigel Crisp, who is also NHS chief executive.

The Department's role in relation to the NHS is different from its role in relation to social care. Local authorities are the bodies responsible to their communities for the provision of social care. By contrast, the Department is the strategic headquarters of the NHS and has been directly involved in the running of the NHS and overseeing its performance. The current view is that detailed management of the health service should not attempted from Whitehall and that more decision-making should be taken at the local level.

There is a different relationship again in the field of public health where the Department works through the NHS, local government and other agencies to promote the health of the population. A public health group is located in each of the nine governments offices of the regions and each has a regional director of public health responsible to the chief medical officer.

In line with major structuring reforms which have been implemented across the NHS in England, the Department has redefined its role. It is concentrating on:
• setting overall direction
• ensuring national standards are set
• securing resources
• making major investment decisions
• driving choice for patients and users.

The change programme reduced core Department staff from 3,600 to 2,245 by 2004. Half of the cuts were achieved by efficiency savings while the rest resulted from transferring posts to other national bodies.

The Department has also reviewed its arm's length bodies which employed over 19,000 people. It has looked at how efficiently they are operating and how they can reduce demands on frontline services.

DH management board

In 2006 the Department was changing the make-up of its departmental board. From July 2006, its membership will be:
• chief executive/permanent secretary
• chief medical officer/standards and quality

The changing structure and management of the NHS — 1

- departmental management
- finance
- chief nursing officer
- communications
- director of commissioning (new post)
- director of provider development (new post)
- social care (new post)
- policy and strategy (new post)
- workforce/HR
- Connecting for Health/IT
- commercial
- two non-executive directors.

DH national clinical directors
National director for emergency access
National director for mental health in England
National director for heart disease
National clinical director for patients and the public
National clinical director for primary care
National director for valuing people
National director for older people's services
National cancer director
National clinical director for diabetes
National clinical director for children.

DH key specialists
Chief dental officer
Chief health professions officer
Chief pharmaceutical officer for England
Chief scientific officer

Executive agencies
There are three executive agencies, which are part of the Department and responsible for particular business areas:
- Medicines and Healthcare Products Regulatory Agency
- NHS Connecting for Health
- NHS Purchasing and Supply Agency.

Non-departmental public bodies
The Department also has responsibility for a number of non-departmental

public bodies (NDPBs). They are independent and provide specialist advice to the government. Examples include:
- Commission for Patient and Public Involvement in Health
- Council for Healthcare Regulatory Excellence (CHRE)
- Commission for Social Care Inspection (CSCI) (until 2008)
- General Social Care Council
- Healthcare Commission
- Human Fertilisation and Embryology Authority (until April 2008)
- Human Tissue Authority
- Monitor (independent regulator of NHS foundation trusts)
- National Biological Standards Board (until April 2006).

Special health authorities
There are a number of special health authorities in England, each of which has a unique function and some of which have remits that extend beyond England. They include the:
- Dental Vocational Training Authority
- Health Protection Agency
- Health and Social Care Information Centre
- Mental Health Act Commission
- National Institute for Health and Clinical Excellence
- National Patient Safety Agency
- National Treatment Agency for Substance Misuse
- NHS Appointments Commission
- NHS Direct
- NHS Institute for Innovation and Improvement
- NHS Litigation Authority
- NHS Logistics Authority (until April 2006)
- NHS Professionals
- Postgraduate Medical Education and Training Board.

Strategic health authorities
Merger proposals published in July 2005

2

The changing structure and management of the NHS — 1

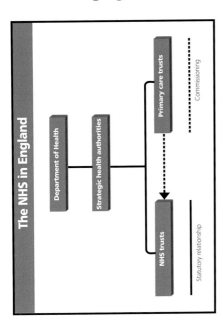

The NHS in England

Department of Health

Strategic health authorities

NHS trusts

Primary care trusts

Commissioning

Statutory relationship

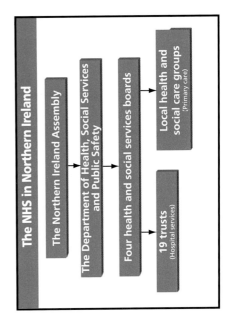

The NHS in Northern Ireland

The Northern Ireland Assembly

The Department of Health, Social Services and Public Safety

Four health and social services boards

19 trusts
(Hospital services)

Local health and social care groups
(Primary care)

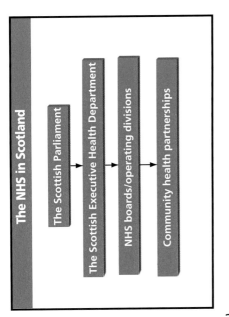

The NHS in Scotland

The Scottish Parliament

The Scottish Executive Health Department

NHS boards/operating divisions

Community health partnerships

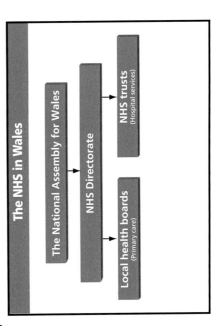

The NHS in Wales

The National Assembly for Wales

NHS Directorate

Local health boards
(Primary care)

NHS trusts
(Hospital services)

will lead to the number of strategic health authorities (SHAs) being reduced to about 11. In January 2006, transition arrangements were announced to oversee the creation of the new system. Eleven transition leads for clusters of SHAs were appointed as an interim measure.

There are currently 28 SHAs in England each serving on average a population of 1.5 million. They have the responsibility for overseeing the development of the NHS and social care. SHAs broker solutions to local problems and hold local services to account through the performance management of NHS trusts and primary care trusts.

SHAs have a board of directors comprising a chair and non-executive directors. They appoint the chief executive and executive team whose members include the finance director and the director of public health.

NHS trusts

There are around 240 NHS trusts in England responsible for managing the provision of hospitals, mental health and ambulance services and other specialised services. Acute trusts are often large and complex organisations overseeing local services in one or more hospital. Mental health services are provided from a host of community facilities, hospital psychiatric units, regional secure units and specialist hospitals.

The work of each trust is overseen by a board of directors whose membership comprises a chair and non-executive directors, and an executive team led by the chief executive and including a finance director, a medical director and a nursing director.

NHS trusts are self-governing organisations with responsibility for the services they control and they are expected to work in partnership with primary care trusts and other agencies. There is also a duty on trusts to balance their budgets, to ensure high standards in the delivery of care and to consult the public. They work in partnership with other local health and social care organisations (including 150 social services departments in local government). NHS trusts work within the framework of local delivery plans and contribute to their development.

NHS trusts receive the major part of their income from service agreements negotiated with primary care trusts for the provision of healthcare.

Primary care trusts

Just over 300 primary care trusts (PCTs) in England are charged with improving the health of local people, developing primary and community health services and commissioning hospitals services. Merger proposals published in July 2005 will lead to the number of PCTs being reduced to about 120–160. PCTs provide a means of involving GPs and other primary care and community health staff in the planning and commissioning of services.

PCTs secure the full range of services for their resident populations, and have the responsibility for the management, development and integration of all primary care services including medical, pharmaceutical, dental and ophthalmic services. They also take lead responsibility for developing and sustaining partnerships with other agencies, including local authorities, voluntary organisations and private sector providers.

PCT boards, through their chairs, are accountable to their strategic health authority, and ultimately the Department of Health and Secretary of State.

Some PCTs have become care trusts which are responsible for a range of health and social care services.

Patient involvement

The main theme of the NHS Plan is the necessity of creating a patient-centred health service. The Health and Social Care Act 2001 places a duty on NHS trusts, primary care trusts and strategic health authorities to make arrangements to involve and consult patients and the public in service planning and operation, and in the development of proposals for changes.

This process is supported by arrangements such as the creation locally of patient and public involvement forums and patient advice and liaison services.

Variations in the UK

Differences in approach to the organisation of the NHS are widening as a consequence of devolution. While the Westminster Parliament retains power over the constitution, defence, the economy and other major areas, devolution is giving the Scottish, Welsh and Northern Ireland governments considerable influence over areas such as health and social care. The Scottish Parliament has greater powers than the Welsh Assembly because of its ability to enact primary legislation and raise some revenue, but in both countries there is an opportunity to develop policies that are adapted to differences in need.

Developments in Scotland

The Scottish Executive controls the planning, organisation and funding of the Scottish NHS (including the ability to raise or lower income tax).

The Scottish Executive Health Department (SEHD) is responsible for the leadership of the NHS and for implementing health and community care policies. It develops strategy,

allocates resources and performance manages the system. Accountability is to ministers and the Scottish Parliament.

SEHD is also responsible for:
- The Scottish Ambulance Service
- NHS 24 — telephone advice service
- State hospital at Carstairs, Lanarkshire — providing secure healthcare
- NHS Health Scotland — public health
- NHS Education for Scotland — training for NHS staff
- NHS Quality Improvement Scotland — monitoring clinical standards
- Social work policy and in particular for community care and voluntary issues.

The Scottish Executive Health Department is accountable to the Scottish ministers, who are in turn answerable to the Scottish Parliament.

Trevor Jones is the chief executive of the Scottish Executive Health Department. As the accountable officer, he is directly answerable to the Scottish Parliament for financial matters and holds responsibility for the efficient and effective use of SEHD and NHS Scotland resources.

Unified health boards

Health boards are strategic bodies, accountable to the SEHD and ministers. The main function of the unified NHS boards is to ensure efficient, effective and accountable governance of the local NHS system and to provide strategic leadership and direction for the system as a whole.

Unified NHS board functions comprise:
- strategy development
- resource allocation
- overseeing implementation of the local health plan
- performance management of the local NHS system.

The unified boards are charged with improving the health of local populations and delivering healthcare. Membership of the boards includes nominated NHS staff, chairman and chief executives of the trusts and representatives of local authorities.

From 2002/03, local health plans were established in each health board area. These three-year plans include:

- action points for each local authority area in which the health board operates
- healthcare plans covering primary, community, secondary and tertiary services
- financial strategy.

Fifteen unified NHS boards oversee divisional management teams, which run Scotland's hospitals and primary care services locally.

Community health partnerships (CHPs) deliver a wide range of community health, such as GP and pharmacy services and community nursing. The roles and responsibilities of CHPs vary across Scotland. They have control of budgets, are devolved from health boards, and have representation from frontline staff as an integral part of their management structure.

They are also intended to promote closer partnership working with local authorities and other agencies. Management of CHPs is drawn from a range of backgrounds including healthcare professionals, local authorities, patients and carers and the voluntary sector.

Human resources

NHS Scotland employs over 143,000 staff, making it Scotland's largest employer. This includes 63,000 nurses, midwives and health visitors, 8,500 doctors and 7,000 family practitioners (that is, doctors, dentists, optometrists and community pharmacists). *Learning together* (December 1999) is the strategy encompassing education, training and lifelong learning for all NHS Scotland staff.

It aims to:

- ensure personnel have the right skills, knowledge and attitudes
- ensure personnel are supported and encouraged to learn
- help personnel respond to new ways of caring and the demand for new services
- encourage ways of working and learning together
- provide career progression and job satisfaction.

Funding

The Scottish Executive's Finance and Central Services Department (FCSD) is responsible for coordinating relationships with the UK government and advising ministers on the allocation of the Scottish budget.

The Scottish Parliament agreed to spend £7.9bn on the NHS for 2004/05 (the equivalent to one-third of the country's total budget), £8.6bn in 2005/06 and £9.3bn in 2006/07. The highest healthcare expenditure is staffing costs — running at about 75 per cent of the total budget.

Scotland traditionally spends more per head on the NHS than England and Wales. The 2001/02 budget represented the equivalent of £1,217 per person living in Scotland — 20 per cent more than the equivalent figure in England and Wales (but in line with other European countries).

Over the past two decades the growth in NHS expenditure has been measured at 6 per cent a year (compared with England's 3 per cent). The Scottish Executive has defended its allocation by demonstrating a greater need for funding.

UK health statistics illustrate

Scotland's higher:
- death rates
- cancer incidence
- hospitalisation rates
- number of people living in deprived and rural areas.

Government expenditure on health and community care can be divided into three categories:
- hospital, community health services and family health services (for example, wages, drugs bill)
- community care (for example, voluntary bodies)
- other health services (for example, public health and research).

The *Fair shares for all* report established the formula for allocating funds to each of the 15 health boards, taking into account the following factors:
- fairness
- population and demographics of each health board
- level of deprivation
- remote and rural areas.

Almost 90 per cent of the money allocated to NHS boards is calculated in this way. NHS boards must use their funding to tackle the Scottish Executive's 12 key priorities for NHS Scotland, as set out in *Partnership for care*:
- cancer
- coronary heart disease/stroke
- delayed discharges
- financial break-even
- healthcare associated infection
- health improvement
- mental health
- patient focus/public involvement
- service re-design
- waiting times
- workforce development/staff governance
- 48-hour access for primary care

The number of annual priorities is set at a maximum of 12.

Quality

NHS Quality Improvement Scotland (NHSQIS) is special health authority that decides on its own work programme. It promotes high-quality care in all parts of the NHS across Scotland through clinical audit, clinical guidelines and best practice statements.

NHSQIS sets clinical and non-clinical standards. It:
- advises on health interventions that are value for money
- collects and publishes data about clinical performance, and investigates serious service failures
- supports implementation of clinical governance.

The NHS Quality Improvement Scotland management team is led by chief executive Dr David Steel and the organisation is chaired by obstetrician Lord Naren Patel.

NHS boards need to meet NHSQIS standards as part of their annual performance assessment. The Scottish Executive has instructed boards to take account of NHSQIS advice and ensure that recommended medicines and treatments are made available.

NHSQIS interprets National Institute for Health and Clinical Excellence (NICE) guidance for use in Scotland. NICE technology appraisals are issued to NHS Scotland at the same time as they are issued to the health service in England and Wales. NHSQIS comments on any implications for NHS Scotland arising from NICE guidance.

The Scottish Intercollegiate Guidelines Network (SIGN) was formed in 1993 but since January 2005 has been part of NHSQIS. It publishes evidence-based guidelines containing recommendations for effective practice in the management of clinical conditions. As of February 2006, SIGN had a programme of 79 guidelines which have

The changing structure and management of the NHS — 1

either been published, are in development or are under review. SIGN guidelines cover a wide variety of topics and are developed by multidisciplinary working groups.

The Scottish Medicines Consortium (SMC) is part of NHSQIS. SMC advises NHS boards and their area drug and therapeutics committees across Scotland about the status of all newly licensed medicines, new formulations and any major new indications for established products. The appraisal process begins when the manufacturer is seeking a licence.

Managed clinical networks (MCNs) are linked groups of health professionals and organisations from primary, secondary and tertiary care working on a particular disease area. They are intended to work in a coordinated way to ensure that everyone has access to the same standard of care, regardless of where they live. There are national, regional and local clinical networks. All health boards are required to have MCNs in diabetes and in coronary heart disease.

NHSQIS is responsible for endorsing managed clinical networks, supporting them and monitoring their progress.

Further information
Scotland's health on the web
www.show.scot.nhs.uk

Scottish Intercollegiate Guidelines Network
www.sign.ac.uk

Scottish Medicines Consortium
www.scottishmedicines.org.uk

NHS Quality Improvement Scotland
www.nhshealthquality.org

Fair shares for all. 1999.

www.scotland.gov.uk/fairshares

Improving health in Scotland. 2003.
www.scotland.gov.uk/library5/health/
ihis-00.asp

Learning together. 1999.
www.scotland.gov.uk/learningtogether/
leto-00.htm

Our national health. 2000.
www.scotland.gov.uk/library3/health/
onh-00.asp

Partnership for care. 2003.
www.scotland.gov.uk/library5/health/
pfcs-00.asp

Developments in Wales

Leadership
Brian Gibbons, Assembly cabinet minister for health and social services, is head of the Health and Social Care Department and leader of the Welsh NHS. His responsibilities are:
- setting health resource levels from within the Welsh budget
- monitoring and responding to the health of the nation
- promoting good practice in health services and holding them to account
- canvassing and acting upon the views of staff, carers and patients
- staffing NHS Wales.

As leader of the Welsh NHS, he is counterpart to the English Secretary of State for Health.

Strategic leadership of the Welsh NHS is the responsibility of the National Assembly for Wales. The Assembly, which is based in Cardiff Bay, decides policy and funding. It has powers to create and amend secondary legislation and to determine spending priorities. The Assembly says that it aims 'To promote the health and wellbeing of everyone living in Wales and provide effective and efficient health services'.

The NHS Directorate is the head office of the NHS in Wales and is responsible for advising and implementing the National Assembly's policies on health services. Its head is Ann Lloyd.

Dr Tony Jewell is chief medical officer. He advises the Assembly cabinet minister for health and social services on professional and medical matters.

Quality

Under the Health and Social Care (Community Health and Standards) Act 2003, the National Assembly for Wales has powers to review and investigate the provision of healthcare by and for Welsh NHS bodies. Powers to require documents, information and explanation are delegated to a National Assembly inspectorate — Healthcare Inspectorate Wales (HIW — pronounced as the name Huw), which on 1 April 2004 took over most of the Welsh work of the Healthcare Commission.

HIW promotes continuous improvement in the quality and safety of patient care within NHS Wales.

HIW's main duties are to:
• inspect NHS bodies and service providers against national standards, agreements and clinical governance guidance in Wales
• assess management arrangements for clinical governance and NHS services
• assess quality of NHS services across agencies/sectors using, for example, networks, patient journey tracking.

HIW is independent of the Welsh Assembly and the NHS. Its inspection reports are given to the chief executives of the inspected organisation, who then publish them and make them available to the Welsh Assembly.

HIW works to the national

healthcare standards set by the advisory board and assesses against clinical governance guidance issued in Welsh Healthcare Circular 69. It must also work with other organisations:
• Care Standards Inspectorate for Wales
• Healthcare Commission
• National Audit Office
• Welsh Audit Office
• Social Services Inspectorate Wales.

HIW can access health bodies in England where cross-border commissioning is concerned.

Other responsibilities of HIW include safeguarding and promoting the rights of children. However, HIW does not investigate individuals or respond to complaints. The chief executive of HIW is Peter Higson.

Guidance issued by the National Institute for Health and Clinical Excellence (NICE) is not compulsory in Wales, but it is used where it is deemed applicable.

Wales has its own public health arrangements in the form of the National Public Health Service for Wales.

Commissioning care

In 2003, local health boards (LHBs) took over from local health groups. They are statutory bodies responsible for commissioning, securing and delivering local healthcare. They are analogous to primary care trusts in England.

Specialist services such as cardiac surgery, emergency ambulance services and some children's services are not planned for by the LHBs. Health Commission Wales (Specialist Services) organises these services nationally. There is an LHB in each of the 22 local authority areas of Wales, and each LHB reports to one of the three regional offices.

Fifteen NHS trusts (including one ambulance trust) are accountable to the regional offices for patient care, efficiency and finances. The trusts manage 135 hospitals, comprising 15,000 beds (17 major acute hospitals contain over 8,000 beds).

Strategy

The evidence-based programmes that make up the Welsh national service frameworks (NSFs) are built upon the Assembly's priorities in healthcare. The NSFs, which detail what patients can expect to receive from the healthcare service in the major health areas, are supported by guidance from NICE.

There are NSFs on:
- children, young people and maternity services
- coronary heart disease
- diabetes
- mental health
- older people
- renal services
- national cancer plan.

For more on NSFs, see chapter 8.

The All-Wales medicines strategy group (AWMSG) advises the Welsh Health Minister on strategic medicines management and prescribing issues. AWMSG is accountable to the Welsh Assembly and is required to make the Assembly aware of developments in drugs and prescribing and ensure that a consistent cost-effective approach to prescribing is in place across Wales.

In every Welsh NHS trust there is a community health council (CHC) to:
- tell the public about the NHS and the NHS about the public's needs
- monitor service from a patient's point of view and to hold NHS bodies to account
- provide independent help to anyone who has problems with NHS services.

The Welsh Assembly takes advice from the Association of Community Health Councils on patient concerns.

The association gets its funding through the NHS allocation. It answers to the Assembly cabinet minister for health and social services.

Important documents about NHS Wales are:
- *Improving health in Wales*, launched in 2001, outlines the long-term strategy for NHS Wales. Additional implementation plans have been published.
- The Welsh pharmacy plan (*Remedies for success: a strategy for pharmacy in Wales*). 2002.
- Welsh Assembly Government. *Designed for life: creating world class health and social care for Wales in the 21st century*. May 2005.

Funding

Around 80 per cent of the health budget goes to local health boards (LHBs). These are analogous to English primary care trusts and are responsible for commissioning care from hospital trusts and other organisations.

Hospital trusts secure their funding in much the way as English hospital trusts through service agreements to provide care.

Further information

All-Wales medicines strategy group
www.wales.nhs.uk/awmsg

Healthcare Inspectorate Wales
www.hiw.wales.gov.uk

Health of Wales information service
www.wales.nhs.uk

Improving health in Wales: a plan for the NHS with its partners. 2001.
www.wales.gov.uk/subihealth/content/keypubs/pdf/NHSStrategydoc.pdf

National service frameworks

www.wales.nhs.uk/sites/
home.cfm?orgid=334

*Remedies for success: a strategy for
pharmacy in Wales.* 2002.
www.wales.nhs.uk/documents/
PharmacyStrategy.pdf

The NHS in Northern Ireland

The administration of the Northern
Ireland NHS lies with the Department of Health, Social Services and
Public Safety (DHSSPS), which implements three main areas of policy
and legislation:
• health and personal social services —
  primary and secondary care, community health and personal social services
• public health — protecting public
  health and wellbeing
• public safety — the fire authority,
  food safety and emergency planning.
   The aim of DHSSPS is to improve the
health and wellbeing of the people
living in Northern Ireland and to set
priorities for healthcare delivery.
   The Department is split into several
groups and one agency:
• planning and resources group
• management group
• professional groups
• health estates.
   In 2005 the DHSSPS employed some
850 staff, with over 41,000 staff in the
health and social services sector.
   In November 2005 in response to a
review of public administration in
Northern Ireland, Health Minister Shaun
Woodward announced a major reor-
ganisation of the NHS which will create
18 organisations from 47. The plans
include:
• a smaller government department
• a strategic health and social services
  authority to replace the four health

social services boards
• 18 NHS trusts reduced to five by April
  2007 (the ambulance service to remain
  as a separate trust)
• seven local commissioning groups,
  taking on roles from the four boards
  and the 15 local health and social care
  groups, which will be abolished
• one patient and client council
  replacing the four health and social
  services councils.
   The commissioning groups would
involve a partnership of the strategic
health and social services authority and
GPs and other primary care professionals, and they would share their boundaries with the seven district councils.
   The new NHS trusts would promote
links between hospital and community-
based services.
   Mr Woodward said that the existing
management cost was £155m a year
and he was keen to reduce that. From
January 2006 the reconfiguration
programme board would start work.
   Four health and social services boards
commission and purchase health and
social care services for their populations.
   The NHS trusts manage 135 hospitals, including 17 major acute hospitals
with over 8,000 beds. A number of local
or community hospitals also provide a
restricted range of services, though
none are able to deal with emergencies.
They provide GP supervised intermediate care beds, outpatient surgery and
medical clinics, day surgery and minor
injuries units.
   The clinical resources efficiency
support team promotes clinical efficiency in Northern Ireland.
   The new geographical coverage
of the five health and social services
trusts are:
• the western area — covering Sperrin
  Lakeland, Foyle, and Altnagelvin
  health and social services trusts

The changing structure and management of the NHS — 1

- the northern area — covering Homefirst Community, Causeway and United Hospitals HSS trusts
- the southern area — covering Craigavon area hospital group, Craigavon and Banbridge Community, Newry and Mourne and Armagh and Dungannon
- the Belfast Area — which will amalgamate the Belfast City Hospital, Royal Group of Hospitals, Mater Infirmorum and Greenpark Trusts, and North and West Belfast Trust, part of South and East Belfast trust and part of Down Lisburn HSS trust
- the south eastern area — covering the Ulster Community and Hospitals trust, part of South and East Belfast Trust and part of Down Lisburn trust.

NHS boards & their functions

The NHS is a major public sector organisation directed by the Department of Health acting in accordance with the policies of the government of the day. The executive line of authority is clear from the chief executive of the NHS and the Department of Health in Whitehall, down to the chief executives of strategic health authorities, NHS trusts and primary care trusts (the other constituent parts of the UK have a similar hierarchy).

Such a clear managerial structure might be considered sufficient to ensure the proper management of the NHS except that it would run against the traditions of the British public sector where the involvement of non-executives in one form or another has always been a feature. These non-executives, whether as elected councillors in local government, nominated members of health organisations or school governors, or appointed magistrates, all seek to do one thing: safeguard the public interest.

Some 3,600 UK citizens are currently serving as non-executive directors of NHS boards, which were introduced in April 1991 in their present guise following the NHS and Community Care Act 1990. More recently non-executives have been appointed to the boards of primary care trusts.

Non-executive directors, working corporately with the chairman, the chief executive and the other executive directors, are accountable for the proper management of the strategic health authority (health board in Scotland), NHS trust, primary care trust within the spirit of Lord Nolan's seven principles of public life (box 1). This means that every aspect of the work is potentially available to their scrutiny including clinical outcomes, providing of course that patient confidentiality is observed. Given the complex nature of the work it is necessary to decide how each member of the board is to contribute to the healthy running of the board's affairs.

Roles

The chairman. The chairman (or chair), is described as the head of the organisation but in fact he or she shares many aspects of the leadership with the chief executive (and in the case of primary care trusts also with the chair of the professional executive committee). They have to decide between them how the organisation communicates with the press, other public bodies, and local politicians. In many cases it will be more practical for the chief executive to be the spokesperson for the board but there may be sensitive political situations where the chairman is preferable as it is not advisable for an executive board member to make an statement which might imply political affiliation. The chairman's role in managing board meetings is unequivocal. This means that he or she ensures that the business is transacted in a manner which allows full discussion while at the same time making reasonably brisk progress through the agenda. Very lengthy meetings lead to tiredness and this can mean that important issues at the end of the agenda are given inadequate attention.

The chairman therefore has to make sure that all members of the board are being effective at meetings and in particular that the non-executive's contribution is useful. Outside the board meeting he or she will keep an eye on the non-executives' involvement to make sure that they add value to the board's work but do not get too embroiled in day-to-day management.

Ultimately the chairman of a strategic health authority, NHS trust, or PCT, is accountable up the line to the government for the satisfactory imple-

Box 1. The seven principles of public life

Selflessness
Holders of public office should take decisions solely in terms of the public interest. They should not do so in order to gain financial or other material benefits for themselves, their family, or their friends.

Integrity
Holders of public office should not place themselves under any financial or other obligation to outside individuals or organisations that might influence them in the performance of their official duties.

Objectivity
In carrying out public business, including making public appointments, awarding contracts, or recommending individuals for rewards and benefits, holders of public office should make choices on merit.

Accountability
Holders of public office are accountable for their decisions and actions to the public and must submit themselves to whatever scrutiny is appropriate to their office.

Openness
Holders of public office should be as open as possible about all the decisions and actions that they take. They should give reasons for their decisions and restrict information only when the wider public interest clearly demands.

Honesty
Holders of public office have a duty to declare any private interests relating to their public duties and to take steps to resolve any conflicts arising in a way that protects the public interest.

Leadership
Holders of public office should promote and support these principles by leadership and example. These principles apply to all aspects of public life. The Nolan committee set them out for the benefit of all who serve the public in any way.

Source: *Standards in public life: first report of the committee on standards in public life.* Chairman: Lord Nolan. TSO, 1995.

mentation of government policies within the resources made available. But he or she has to do this while maintaining credibility with the local community and with the staff.

The chief executive. The chief executive is usually a career NHS manager who will bring a vast amount of experience to the board's affairs. He or she will be expected to know what happens at every level of the NHS. Although not usually a clinician by background, the chief executive will also be able to demonstrate an understanding of clinicians' work, not only that of doctors but all the other people in a therapeutic role. Indeed the government hold him or her accountable for clinical performance. The ability to gain the respect of clinical staff is therefore vital and those who have failed to command this have often found this a reason for not being able to continue in the chief executive role.

The chief executive is also responsible for the proper management and administration of the organisation, ensuring that it runs within the resources available and is both efficient and effective. He or she has to ensure that the quality of healthcare is maintained and improved and that patients and the public are involved and consulted on the organisation. He or she has to combine a strategic view with a firm managerial grip of the day-by-day work. It is also important that the chief executive is able to motivate the organisation to work hard in their shared objective of doing the best they can for the patients in their care.

Executive directors. The maximum number of executive directors on a strategic health authority, NHS trust or PCT board is five, including the chief executive. In NHS trusts there must always be directors of finance, medicine

and nursing and in strategic health authorities there must be a finance director and a director of public health.

Primary care trusts are expected to include a director of public health in their executive team. The number of GP executives on such a board cannot exceed three and may only be two in number. A PCT board is supported by a team of functional directors and a professional executive committee of up to 15 members who are predominately from the health professions. There is some cross membership within the trust board.

It is up to the chief executive to recommend what other directors should be on the board. It is not obligatory to fill all five places and there may be directors of certain functions who do not have a seat on the board.

It is important the executive directors understand the difference between their corporate role as board members and their functional role as head of an aspect of the organisation. This requires a fine judgement at times particularly if they find themselves disagreeing with their own manager, the chief executive. The paradox is that they are equal in the boardroom but subordinates outside. It is helpful if this issue is discussed at some point in a board meeting to make sure it is clear how such disagreements are to be handled. After all, it is in the interests of the proper working of the board that a full-ranging discussion is allowed even if this leads to different points of view.

Non-executive directors. Non-executive directors bring a knowledge of the wider world to the board. They are able to provide a more objective view and user their own experience to challenge what may have become institutionalised attitudes within the NHS itself. Nevertheless this ability to bring something extra must always be focused and should not be used to challenge executive directors for the sake of it. This balance can only be attained by making sure that the non-executive directors are well educated in the ways of the NHS. For instance, the procedures for financial control may well be different from what someone in industry is used to. It is unhelpful to suggest that they be changed given that they are part of a national accounting system within the NHS.

Constant challenges can also be demoralising for the executives; they often need support in difficult and stressful circumstances. Nevertheless such support must not lead to complacency and probity has constantly to be safeguarded.

Non-executive directors have been concerned about their potential personal liability particularly in a situation where probity may be under question. The Department of Health has issued guidance which says:

A chairman or non-executive member or director who has acted honestly, reasonably, in good faith and without negligence will not have to meet out of his or her own resources any personal civil liability which is incurred in further-ance, or purported furtherance, of the execution of the NHS Acts.

As a board sometimes has to make highly controversial decisions regarding local facilities, this at least protects them from being held personally liable for the consequences of such decisions.

The board's corporate role

There are therefore four roles within each board, each with their own responsibilities. But they are expected to join together to act corporately,

which means that they are jointly and indivisibly responsible for key decisions. But about what?

Strategy. Strategy broadly is concerned with how tomorrow will be different from today. It can be separated from tactics which are more concerned with process. Strategy is about the vision which gives an organisation a sense of direction. The art in strategic management is to keep the vision intact while adapting to changing circumstances. The government has given some help to this by providing a three-year rather than one-year financial framework thus allowing a less frantic and volatile approach to planning.

Making choices. One of the board's most important roles is to make choices. To do this it needs enough — but not too much — information. On occasions, it also needs courage to do what may be necessary but unpopular. Deciding resource priorities is always part of any board's function. It is more difficult when such decisions involve people in pain and suffering.

Monitoring results. Boards do not just allocate resources; they have to be assured that the use of those resources has been effective. This is by no means easy as the indices of effectiveness are very varied and at times, debatable. Concentrating only on outcomes is insufficient. Boards need to be concerned with *how* people were treated — the quality of care — just as much as what happened to them in the end. There is increasing pressure on government for boards to concern themselves with effectiveness and this means that clinical outcomes are a legitimate area for board members to probe. But it is a delicate matter to ask a doctor about his or her practice without appearing to be challenging them from an inexpert position. The board first ensures that there is a structure for clinical governance where clinical procedures and outcomes are routinely examined. A trust board must receive regular reports from their clinical governance committee but care should be taken to anonymise it to protect patient confidentiality.

Trust boards are required to produce a statement of internal control annually which is audited by their external auditor. They also have to make an annual declaration to the Healthcare Commission that their organisation is achieving NHS core standards. The trust's annual report, a public document, will indicate where there are matters for concern and the action being taken.

Boards are expected to draw up an assurance framework and to make sure that it is embedded in their activities.

Social responsibility. Corporately the board is responsible for safeguarding the common good. What is meant by this will vary according to circumstances but all boards need to be able to demonstrate to the public that the organisation is responsive to their wishes and that there are rigorous procedures in place which limit the likelihood of any sort of financial wrongdoing.

Most health organisations are relatively large employers in their own areas and being an ethical employer sets a good example to the local community. Unfortunately this is difficult to demonstrate on occasions when boards are faced with having to curtail services and limit staff numbers accordingly.

Boards have a duty to obey the law. Many of the topics covered by the statement of internal control are legal requirements.

Some trust boards have got into difficulty with the contracts of their most senior staff. It is imperative that the remuneration committee scrutinises the terms of such contracts to ensure that they comply with employment law and that they neither exploit the post holder or conversely give them terms of employment — particularly concerning fringe benefits and severance pay — which are disadvantageous to the service as a whole.

The Public Interest Disclosure Act 1998 gives protection to whistle-blowers who have shown genuine (that is, not malicious) concern regarding the mistreatment of patients, financial irregularities, abuses of care, and health and safety cover-ups. Boards are required to designate a senior manager to deal with employees' concerns. Gagging clauses in staff contracts are prohibited.

Board members have to be clear-headed about what the press call cover-ups particularly as in some cases allegations may lead to the health organisation being sued. Nowhere is this more important than in the proper handling of patient complaints. Any sort of prevarication will threaten a board's reputation.

Codes of conduct

Throughout public life in recent years there has been concern regarding proper conduct. In June 1999 the Hampel code on corporate governance was published incorporating the main principles previously circulated following the 1992 Cadbury and 1995 Greenbury guidance.

In January 2003, Derek Higgs reported to the Secretary of State for Trade and Industry and the Chancellor of the Exchequer on the role and effectiveness of non-executive directors (www.dti.gov.uk/cld/non_exec_review). The report recognised the important role that non-executives play.

The NHS has not been exempt from scandals regarding the proper use of public money and questionable proce-dures. In 1994 the then Health Secretary Virginia Bottomley issued a *Code of conduct* and *Code of accountability*. Attached to this booklet was an Executive Letter EL9(94)40 addressed to all chief executives giving more detailed guidance on:
- audit committees
- remuneration committees
- publication of details of remuneration
- decisions reserved for the board and schemes of delegation
- financial and performance reporting
- annual reports by health authorities.

The *Code of conduct* has three main components: accountability, probity and openness.

Accountability is about being *answerable to* and *answerable for*. So boards must be prepared to give an account of their actions up to the strategic health authority, the Depart-ment of Health and thence to the government and to Parliament. But there are others to *answer to* as well. NHS trusts and PCTs are expected to answer to the patients they treat. Patients' expectations continue to rise with the increase of public knowledge. Trusts are also answerable to the primary care trusts which buy their care.

All types of boards are *answerable for* the proper management of public funds. To be able to do this effectively every member of the board, executive or non-executive, must be able to understand how the funds are man-aged. It is also necessary to have an audit committee, comprising some of the non-executive directors, to look in more detail at financial and commercial matters. Outside scrutiny is provided by independent auditors — often the Audit Commission, whose reports are published. In addition, the National Audit Office may pursue matters of particular concern and report to government.

But being *answerable for* is not just a matter of finance. All professions are governed by their own codes of conduct and boards must be aware what standards are required. In addition there are bodies, such as the Healthcare Commission, set up to encourage high

The NHS Appointments Commission

The NHS Appointments Commission was established in April 2001. The commission specialises in recruit-ment, training and appraisal of people for board level appointments to NHS bodies (such NHS trusts), ministerial advisory bodies and non-governmental organisations in England.

The commission is made up of a chairman, Sir William Wells, eight regional commissioners and the chief executive Roger Moore. The commis-sion receives £3.5m annually from the Department of Health and the majority of its activity is on behalf of the Health Secretary.

It recruits up to 1,000 people a year. Short-listed candidates are interviewed by panels that include an independent assessor. The commission board meets monthly to consider panel recommendations and make appointments.

NHS Appointments Commission, Cheapside House, 138 Cheapside, London EC2V 6BB. Tel: 020 7615 9300. www.appointments.org.uk

The changing structure and management of the NHS — 1

quality standards and to protect the interests of patients. The patient and public involvement forums need to be consulted and provide direct feedback on services. These in turn are supported by the patient advice and liaison services.

Probity concerns honesty and integrity. So, for instance, each board member must be explicit about their own business interests and these must be recorded in a register held by the board's secretary. The role of the board secretary is important in assuring pubic confidence that matters are being handled honestly.

More widely, boards need to ensure that their procedures are sound. Standing orders and financial instructions are obligatory and need to be kept up-to-date. This is a suitable task for the audit committee. The remuneration committee keeps an eye on the salaries of the top executives.

Probity also concerns the appointment of the non-executive directors. It has often been said that public life relies unduly on the contribution of a narrow social band of people who have the leisure or the personal resources to give time to being non-executives. While this altruism can be applauded it is also important that appointments to public boards are made fairly and come from all parts of the community.

The Commissioner for Public Appointments — currently Dame Renee Fritchie — a previous NHS chairman — scrutinises board appointments. In response to a critical report by her in 2000, the NHS Appointments Commission now makes all chair and non-executive appointments to NHS trusts, primary care trusts and strategic health authorities. Regional commissioners take part in the process of appointing new non-executive directors and make

sure they are equipped for their role. The commissioners must demonstrate that such appointments are made strictly according to merit after fair and open competition.

Openness assures staff, patients and the public generally that a board is conducting itself properly in the common interest, and, in those circumstances where difficult decisions have to be made, a proper account has been taken of all the relevant facts and opinions.

The public have a legal right to attend full board meetings but the meeting may be closed when matters concerning named individuals — staff or patients — are discussed or when the details of a contract for goods or services are commercially sensitive.

It is useful to remember that *meetings in public* are not the same as *public meetings* in that the prime duty of the board is to manage its business openly providing the listening public with an opportunity to learn about their health service and in so doing protect their interests.

Being an effective board member

Being effective on a board is not innate, it requires the development of particular skills and aptitudes.

Preparation. The NHS is extremely complicated. Board members therefore have to spend time understanding how it works as part of our social and political system, and its policies and priorities. In addition the ability to understand the contribution of each group of staff is important if stereotyping of attitudes is to be avoided.

Prioritising. One of the most difficult aspects of board work is to sort the important from the less important. It is made more difficult sometimes because what is urgent is not necessarily that important. Clear-thinking is therefore imperative as is a conscientious approach to giving each subject the appropriate time for consideration.

Good humour. Board work is challenging but it need not be gloomy. A board which learns to enjoy its work will often find that work less onerous. The executive directors in particular will be likely to work more effectively at board level if they do not feel they are perpetually on trial by the non-executive directors.

The future

Structural reform of NHS organisations continues with the creation of foundation trusts, and the merger of primary care trusts and strategic health authorities. Chairman and non-executive directives of foundation trusts are being appointed by their board of governors. Yet the manner of working is still expected to conform to the standards discussed above.

The prime duty of boards is to develop effective partnerships so that all can work together to ensure that the NHS continues to meet its constantly challenging task of treating illness and promoting health.

Further reading

Department of Health/NHS Appointments Commission. *Governing the NHS. A guide for NHS boards.* June 2003.

Strategic health authorities

From October 2002, 28 strategic health authorities (SHAs) in England covered an average population of 1.5m. The authorities had responsibility devolved to them from the eight NHS regional offices for performance managing the local healthcare system, including primary care trusts and NHS trusts.

In July 2005 in *Commissioning a patient-led NHS*, NHS chief executive Sir Nigel Crisp proposed radical structural changes to SHAs, so that their number would be reduced from 28 to about 11, and they would generally share their boundaries with those of regional government.

SHAs provide the bridge between the Department of Health and local NHS services: brokering solutions to local problems and holding local health services to account.

Under the revised arrangements they are expected to focus on the following functions:
- performance managing the NHS local public health function and working closely with the Department's regional directors of public health in the government offices of the regions
- ensuring successful delivery through:
  — performance management of PCTs
  — strategic planning and the oversight of major investment and reconfigurations
  — supporting research, innovation, education and training and ensuring its integration with service commissioning
  — tertiary level commissioning when this cannot be undertaken by PCTs
  — overseeing and managing the system in association with the regulators
- ensuring robust and integrated emergency planning
- taking their NHS trusts to foundation status.

Primary care trusts

A primary care trust (PCT) is a freestanding NHS body which commissions and provides healthcare for its local population, and which is performance

The changing structure and management of the NHS — 1

managed by the strategic health authority. PCTs have their own budgets, employ staff and develop integrated services for patients.

The first primary care trusts in England were created in April 2000 and succeeded primary care groups (PCGs). In 2005 there were over 300 in England but in July 2005 Sir Nigel Crisp, chief executive of the NHS, published *Commissioning a patient-led NHS*. This document called for major structural changes to primary care trusts and strategic health authorities and faster, universal adoption of practice-based commissioning. It required merged PCTs to be in place by October 2006 and for changes to service provision by PCTs to be complete by December 2008.

The idea is that fewer larger PCTs (about 120–160) will be more effective at commissioning health services. Initially the Department of Health wanted to separate the commissioning role completely from the provision of services, with PCTs farming out their provider services to other organisations. But in a reversal Health Secretary Patricia Hewitt said it would be up to individual PCTs whether or not they continued to provide services. To maintain close contact with individual health professionals, the new larger PCTs are expected to use a system of localities.

The concepts behind primary care groups and trusts grew out of commissioning and fundholding. GP fundholding was introduced in the 1990s and showed that individual practices had the ability to be effective purchasers of care for their patients. At the same time, commissioning groups developed and here the focus was on the whole local population rather than one practice. Meanwhile, GP fundholders were forming multifunds and the government was establishing

total purchasing projects — all of which were beginning to look relatively similar.

Functions of primary care trusts

Primary care trusts have three main functions:

- *Health improvement* — this enables local health professionals to extend their remit from traditional areas of healthcare to all services and aspects of the community related to health. The kingpin of policy is the local delivery plan (LDP), which has input from local primary care trusts, NHS trusts, local authorities and the strategic health authority. The chair of each primary care trust is a co-signatory to the LDP.
- *Primary and community health service development* — this involves two main aspects:
  a) primary care professionals have a role in deciding what resources are available for primary care and how they are used. The development of primary care services is costed in the primary care investment plan. This sets out the agreed plans for investment in primary care services, staff, premises and information management and technology as part of a three-year investment cycle.
  b) clinical governance — the focus is on improving clinical standards overall but the remit extends from dealing with poor clinical practice to encouraging best practice and continuing professional development. All GPs are expected to undergo a yearly appraisal.
- *Commissioning hospital and community services* — the majority of commissioning has been at the level of the PCT, including most specialised services. PCTs commission through long-term service agreements. These are based on integrated care pathways, which focus on

conditions or client groups rather than organisations.

Commissioning in PCTs should support evidence-based practice and implementation of national guidelines. National service frameworks are likely to guide many service agreements.

It is clearly vital that primary care professionals have ownership of commissioning decisions as they are in the frontline delivering the service. In support of this view, from April 2005, GP practices in England have had the option of taking over the role of commissioning some or most of the services needed by their patients. PCTs apportion the global sum for commissioning activity to individual practices as appropriate. Up to 100 per cent of any savings made by managing referrals more efficiently can be ploughed back into services for patients within practices. In *Commissioning a patient-led NHS* the Department of Health said it expected PCTs to have arrangements for universal coverage of practice-based commissioning by December 2006. Practice-based commissioning needs to occur within the local PCT commissioning framework. In January 2006, The Department of Health issued *Practice-based commissioning: achieving universal coverage* to assist with implementation.

The unified budget for each PCT includes elements that were previously divided into three funding streams: hospital and community health services, prescribing and cash-limited medical service funds. The budget offers an important means of transferring resources without the artificial boundaries that existed before.

PCTs, and now GP practices, commission a broad range of services including hospital, community, dental provision, nursing, ambulance services, and facilities for expectant or nursing mothers.

PCTs sign up to an annual accountability agreement and a primary care investment plan with strategic health authorities. They have responsibility for the management, development and integration of all primary care services including medical dental, pharmaceutical and optical.

They have taken on responsibility for all family health services practitioner contractor services allowing a coherent view of the development of all NHS services in the area. PCTs now maintain lists of primary care professionals who perform primary care services for patients. A practitioner must be on such a list to perform services for NHS patients. Also from 1 January 2005 PCTs have been legally obliged to commission out-of-hours primary care services which meet national quality requirements. Providers must report to PCTs on compliance with the requirements.

Different structures across the UK

Though there are many similarities between the English system and others in the UK, there are also marked differences. Given their three respective assemblies, there is no central force to homogenise the different systems.

In Wales, the local health boards (LHBs) have a significant democratic mandate and involve a wide range of primary care professionals.

In Scotland, the management of acute and primary care services has been brought together under unified NHS boards. During 2004 community health partnerships were developed across Scotland to allow primary care professionals to become more involved in planning and delivery.

The primary care trust hierarchy

Primary care trusts have a complex hierarchy reflecting the need to have an

The changing structure and management of the NHS — 1

effective mix of managerial skills and health professional input.

The primary care trust board is the governing body of the organisation and is dominated by lay members (five in all, and the PCT chair cannot be a practising health professional). They are joined by the chief executive, finance director, director of public health and three health professional members (including the professional executive committee chair, the director of clinical governance and at least one nurse)

The chair of the board is responsible through the strategic health authority to the Health Secretary for the efficient running of the board. The chair is responsible for leading the board and for ensuring that it successfully discharges its overall responsibility for the organisation as a whole.

The PCT professional executive committee (PEC) is the engine room of the organisation. It comprises a professional majority of GPs, nurses, allied health professionals and public health and social services input. The PEC chair is a health professional elected from members of the committee and is in contract to the chair of the primary care trust board. Members of the PEC are nominated by election through their peer group and short-listed by a panel against a list of competences for the professional executive committee member role.

Additionally there is the primary care trust management team, some of whose members sit both on the PCT board and the PEC.

The chief executive is responsible to the chair of the PCT board, which is itself responsible for strategic direction of the PCT. He or she is responsible to the PEC chair for operational matters but in terms of accountability, the chief executive is the accountable officer for the primary care trust. Thus the chief executive is also accountable through the strategic health authority to the accounting officer of the Department of Health for the funds entrusted to the PCT.

The chief executive and the PEC are responsible for the day-to-day management of the PCT including developing and initiating service policies, investment plans, priorities and projects to be delivered by the PCT.

Financial considerations

It is the duty of a PCT to remain within the resource and cash limit and to keep the PCT in financial balance. From October 2002 revenue allocations for the NHS were made direct to PCTs rather than via strategic health authorities, and some 80 per cent of NHS revenue funds is channelled through PCTs.

In early 2005 the Department of Health allocated £64.3bn to PCTs for 2006/07 and £70.4bn for 2007/08. The allocations are designed to improve access to services for patients further, with waiting times for operations down to a planned maximum 18 weeks by 2008. All PCTs are receiving an average increase in their revenue of at least 8.1 per cent a year over the two years. The cash allocations are also intended to fund the public health White Paper initiatives, such as community matrons and school nurses. Those in the greatest need, such as the 88 designated spearhead PCTs, have been allocated extra money.

Primary care trust non-executives

As members of the PCT board, non-executives are corporately responsible for fulfilling the organisation's healthcare responsibilities. They have a number of obligations and responsibilities that are comparable to board members of other NHS organisations —

setting the strategy, monitoring progress and ensuring probity. They also need to be people's champions, giving the local community a major input into the PCT board. Non-executives also are involved in supporting more specialist work in areas such as the development of clinical governance and commissioning.

Non-executive directors are nominated by the NHS Appointments Commission.

The tasks that should be common to all non-executive board members are to:

- provide leadership and ensure strategic direction in accordance with government policy and the needs of the local community
- focus on results and outcomes and ensure that executives deliver objectives
- ensure that local and specialist services are run for the people using them
- make a reality of the values of equity, accessibility and responsiveness
- take a leading role in developing partnership with the local community, user and carer group, patients' forums, local authorities, voluntary and other organisations
- promote quality in all aspects of service and ensure that clinical governance is developed
- safeguard the rights of the people using the service and working within the service by active participation in the complaints process, equal opportunities, staff support, the appointment of senior staff and staff appeals
- provide an independent scrutiny of management, ensuring that the management process serves patient care and that excellence in management is achieved
- ensure effective financial stewardship through financial planning and strategy, financial control and value for money
- promote public service values.

Primary care trusts as learning organisations

The primary care trust should be a learning organisation for all those involved. Each PCT should have clear mechanisms for assessing everybody's learning needs and take responsibility, wherever possible within a multiprofessional framework, for providing the right resources to meet those needs.

A series of **teaching PCTs** have been developed in disadvantaged and under-doctored areas, but every PCT needs to be both teaching and learning.

Through the use of education and research activities, a teaching PCT is able to provide different career options for GPs and other healthcare professionals. Such arrangements assist the recruitment and retention of essential staff in areas that are under-resourced.

The final number of teaching PCTs has not been set in stone, but it is envisaged that there will be between 25 and 30 across the country. Three teaching PCTs were established in April 2001 as test-bed sites in Sunderland, Salford and Bradford. A further eight were established in April 2002, 11 more from April 2003, seven in July 2003, and a further two sites in August 2003.

Further information

Primary care trusts. www.dh.gov.uk/PolicyAndGuidance/OrganisationPolicy/PrimaryCare/PrimaryCareTrusts

Teaching PCTs. www.dh.gov.uk/PolicyAndGuidance/OrganisationPolicy/PrimaryCare/TeachingPrimaryCareTrusts

Evidence based commissioning for PCTs: a directory. DH, March 2003.

Commissioning a patient-led NHS. DH, July 2005.

The changing structure and management of the NHS — 1

Personal medical services

By December 2003, over 40 per cent of general practitioners in England were said to be working through personal medical services (PMS) schemes, covering many thousands of patients. The approach to providing services, which is also being piloted for NHS dentistry (personal dental services) and in local pharmaceutical services, became a permanent option in April 2004.

In the case of PMS, it has permitted the development of new ways of delivering primary care under local contracts. GPs may be salaried, and by agreeing to provide PMS under part I rather than part II of the NHS Act 1977 they cease to be independent contractors. The schemes also pave the way for pre-registration house officers to spend time training in GP practices.

Examples of some of the aims of the schemes include:
• increasing the range and availability of services and developing links with social services, also improving equity in access to those services
• developing a special focus on services for groups such as children, older people, mentally ill people, ethnic minorities, or the homeless
• developing greater clinical effectiveness of treatment
• providing more flexible working opportunities for GPs and members of primary care teams.

Some of the schemes aim to be one-stop shops for local primary and community health services. PMS has been targeted at areas which experience high levels of illness and where there are often problems in recruiting GPs.

Primary care trusts are able to provide personal medical services or to contract with PMS providers giving a flexibility in tackling particular local problems in primary care.

Alternative provider medical services (APMS) offer opportunities for restructuring of services. PCTs can enter APMS contracts with any individual or organisation that meets the provider conditions. This includes the independent and voluntary sectors, not-for-profit organisations, and NHS trusts and foundation trusts.

Guidance issued in December 2003 indicated that specialist PMS was being developed. PMS schemes have previously been required to be responsible for delivery of a full range of general medical services equivalent services with at least one GP involved. Neither of these stipulations apply in the case of specialist PMS. It is envisaged that the following would be well served by specialist PMS services:
• care for vulnerable groups
• extending the range of services delivered in primary care
• delivering out-of-hours services.

The nature of PMS working challenges the traditional model of primary care and may mean that the concept of one nationally negotiated contract of employment for all GPs is gradually eroded.

To set up a PMS project the person or group to provide the services (typically a GP practice, group of practices or a nurse) negotiates a PMS agreement with the primary care trust.

Providers agree to supply tailor-made primary care services to the local population for an agreed level of funding. The scheme itself decides how to spend the money on staff and service delivery. Under PMS, the range of services to be provided is specified in the locally negotiated agreement. A total sum is paid annually (often in 12

Wellard's NHS Handbook 2006/07

monthly instalments) for those services.

Several of the PMS pilots were led by nurses and patient satisfaction with such services was found to be high. Typically they provide a point of access, continuity and stability in a deprived area.

Personal medical services. www.dh.gov.uk/PolicyAndGuidance/ OrganisationPolicy/PrimaryCare/ PrimaryCareContracting/PMS

PMS national helpline: 0845 9000008

Department of Health. *Sustaining innovation through new PMS arrangements.* December 2003.

Department of Health. *Alternative provider medical services (APMS) guidance.* April 2004.

NHS walk-in centres

NHS walk-in centres provide high-quality, quick and convenient treatment to help relieve pressure on GPs and hospital emergency departments. They are a complementary service, playing a major role in helping patients make better use of the NHS. The centres offer free consultations, available without appointment, and provide treatment for minor injuries and illnesses, general health information, self-treatment advice, information about out-of-hours GP/dental services and local pharmacy services.

For the past few years funding support has continued for the centres because of the contribution they are making to achieving national 24/48 hour primary care access targets

and to reducing pressures in hospital emergency departments for minor injury treatment.

By December 2005, there were 67 NHS walk-in centres open in England. A further 22 sites are under development which will bring the total to 89. This includes seven centres which are being procured from the independent sector near to busy rail stations to meet the needs of commuters. The first of these opened near Manchester Piccadilly station in November 2005. They will be open for 12 hours a day and make it easier for commuters to fit seeing a GP or nurse around their daily lives.

The centres are situated in major towns and cities, including centres in supermarkets or retail areas and alongside hospital A&E departments. They operate during the day and at weekends, in times and places that people find convenient. The average number of daily visits at each site is 110. Total activity has grown to more than two million visits a year.

Walk-in centres are nurse-led, though the skill mix may include GPs, other health professionals and social services staff. Centres are managed by an NHS body or GP co-operative and endorsed by the local primary care trust, GP co-op and the wider health economy.

Walk-in centres link with and complement GP surgeries, acting as patient filters. The centres, in conjunction with NHS Direct, are freeing up more GP time. They develop IT links between themselves and GPs, and other primary care services to further promote continuity of care. The work of the centres is consistent with local delivery plans and they liaise with other NHS providers to ensure consistency in working arrangements, referrals, protocols and

The changing structure and management of the NHS — 1

patient registration arrangements.

A 2002 Bristol University report, commissioned by the Department of Health, showed that:

- 74 per cent of consultations were managed entirely in walk-in centres
- 45 per cent would have contacted their GP if the centre had not been available
- 26 per cent would have gone to their local hospital emergency department
- the majority of healthcare professionals felt the centres improved access to healthcare.

Walk-in centres. www.nhs.uk/england/noAppointmentNeeded/walkinCentres

University of Bristol. *National evaluation of NHS walk-in centres*. 2000. www.epi.bris.ac.uk/wic

Care trusts

The government has been determined to overcome some of the unhelpful divisions between health and social care so as to improve the quality of care provided to patients and users. A care trust is an NHS organisation to which local authorities can delegate health-related functions, in order to provide integrated health and social care to the local community.

Care trusts were announced in the NHS Plan in July 2000. They are seen as important vehicles for modernising both health and social care and for helping to ensure integrated services that are focused on the needs of patients and users.

They are being established where it can be shown that they will improve services. They do not have to be coterminous with NHS or local authority boundaries.

Many primary care trusts are able to perform the majority of the functions of a care trust and PCTs are being allowed to progress to care trusts in their own time and on the understanding that the model will only be actively encouraged when it can be shown to provide added benefit.

Care trusts provide and commission health and social care services often for specific client groups such as older people, mentally ill people and children. The trusts offer a real opportunity for integrating complex packages of care for a wide range of older people. They enable the care pathway from acute services, through intermediate care to sustained care at home, to be followed in a coherent way.

People, with mental health problems need integrated health and social care and care trusts are an important vehicle for providing this, particularly in urban areas.

The first care trusts were set up in April 2002 in Bradford, Camden and Islington in London, Manchester and Northumberland, with a strong focus on providing mental health services. Witham, Braintree and Halstead care trust began work in October 2002 with an emphasis on older people's services. In April 2003, Sandwell and Sheffield care trusts were created, both providing mental health services, and in October 2003 Bexley care trust was created to provide older people's services.

Some groups of children have complex needs and the integration of services is vital to improving the care they receive. This is particularly important for children with disabilities, special needs and children and adolescents with mental health problems.

Again the care trust model is suitable for meeting such challenges. Thirty-five sites are pathfinders of children's trusts in a three year pilot.

Children's trusts are the government's preferred model for achieving local integration. They integrate local education, social care and some health services for children and young people. Children's trusts can also include elements such as youth offending teams and Sure Start local programmes. They may also bring in other local partners such as housing and voluntary organisations.

The *Every child matters* Green Paper anticipated that by 2006 most local authorities would have a children's trust. They will normally be led from a local authority and they must have three core features:

• clear short and long term objectives covering the five Green Paper outcome areas of: enjoying and achieving, staying safe, being healthy, making a positive contribution, and economic wellbeing
• a director of children's services in overall charge of delivering these outcomes and responsible for services within the trust and coordination of services outside the organisation
• a single planning and commissioning function supported by pooled budgets.

Similar arguments are being applied for client groups such as adults with learning disabilities and people with physical disabilities.

Though NHS and local council partnerships already exist under Health Act flexibilities, care trusts are creating improved integration. The enabling legislation for care trusts is the Health and Social Care Act 2001. They consolidate a single strategic approach, with a set of aims and targets which allows for financial flexibility and efficiency.

Councils only delegate powers to care trusts, not transfer them. The council remains ultimately accountable and also has significant influence in the supervision and management of the care trust itself. The care trust's board includes a member from social services. Boards must also reflect the different streams of accountability that exist in the NHS and local government. Governance arrangements allow local people to be represented and set out the role, function and responsibility of the trust board. Care trusts must be accountable to service users and have representation from patients' forums.

Detailed local discussion is required to determine the level of resources to be transferred to a care trust. The basis for reaching agreement about resources — for example, how to manage overspends and underspends, the year-on-year agreement about the level of resourcing and the treatment of capital assets and expenditure — must also be decided. When a local authority delegates functions to a care trust, it is on the basis that any charging regime for those services will continue and any policy change will be made by the local authority. All NHS services provided through a care trust remain free at the point of use.

A care trust can be formed following an application from a primary care trust, a council or specialist NHS trust to the Health Secretary.

Care trusts. www.dh.gov.uk/
PolicyAndGuidance/OrganisationPolicy/
IntegratedCare/CareTrusts

Department of Health. *Children's trusts.*
January 2003.

The changing structure and management of the NHS — 1

NHS trusts

When NHS trusts were first created in 1991 as self-governing units, they provided hospital, community, mental health or ambulance services on behalf of the Health Secretary. They had their own board of directors and were free to organise their affairs, subject only to the legal framework within which they operated and the contracts they negotiated with healthcare purchasers.

They were given freedom to:
• acquire, own and dispose assets
• make cases for capital development
• create their own management structures
• employ their own staff, determine staffing structures, and set their own terms and conditions of employment
• treat private patients
• generate income (subject to this not interfering with other obligations).

These freedoms have continued down the years and those being offered to prospective foundation trusts do not greatly exceed the existing provisions.

In order to achieve NHS trust status NHS hospitals, community units, mental health services and so on, had to introduce new management structures, including a board of executive and non-executive directors led by a chair, produce sound business plans and financial forecasts and robust accounting systems to support the contracting process. Strategies for the provision of services also had to be developed in which the quality of the service and the views of patients were important.

NHS trusts were therefore able to operate flexibly, develop their services and take risks in promoting and establishing new services.

On the financial side:
• all trusts earn their income
• trusts have been able to borrow funds, within annual approved limits
• they can retain depreciation and any surpluses after meeting financial obligations and can use this money to repay loans, invest or for capital spending
• trusts must make a 3.5 per cent return on their assets and break even
• their accounts must be presented in a prescribed way.

The dilemma for trusts has been how to produce the continuing year-on-year efficiency savings in real terms expected of them, and at the same time to contain increasing cost pressures such as staff agency costs, drug expenditure and the European working time directive.

Management has had to acquire the skills of evaluation and for contracting services. Clinicians have been encouraged to form a partnership with mangers in the organisation, to improve the control and development of services.

Trusts have become more aware of their accountability to the general public and to their purchasers for the cost, quality and delivery of services and have publicly to prove this accountability in an annual report.

In addition to their existing financial duties, trusts were required by the Health Act 1999 to safeguard and improve the quality of care. This was associated with the comprehensive introduction of clinical governance systems throughout the health service. At the beginning of 2002 a legal obligation to involve and consult patients and the public was added by virtue of section 11 of the Health and Social Care Act 2001.

Another change occurring in the early 2000s in response to the NHS Plan was the replacement of the former internal market between purchasers and providers of healthcare with the duty of acting in partnership. Through vehicles such as local delivery plans, NHS trusts work collaboratively within a local health economy. At the same time, NHS trusts have been expected to deliver the quality of their service in line with national performance targets and frameworks.

Acute hospital trusts obtain most of their revenue through service agreements with primary care trusts (PCTs) for the provision of healthcare. PCTs have been encouraged to develop long-term commissioning relationships with provider hospitals and draw up three-year service delivery plans based on estimates of patients' overall needs.

However the tradition of a district general hospital comprehensively providing most of the secondary healthcare needs of the catchment population is changing. With primary care trusts holding the purse strings far more care can be provided outside the hospital both in primary care itself and in innovative settings such as intermediate care services. Recent changes concerning NHS financial flows and the payment by results regime (chapter 11), granting patients greater choice over where they are treated, and the diversification of the health service provider market, with for instance the introduction of independent sector treatment centres, are bringing further challenges.

Foundation trusts

Under the Health and Social Care (Community Health and Standards) Act which became law in November 2003, NHS foundation trusts are being established as free-standing legal entities, free from direction by the Secretary of State for Health. They are independent public interest organisations, modelled on co-operative societies and mutual organisations.

Foundation trusts are controlled locally and have as their members local people who have been patients, members of staff and those representing organisations such as PCTs. The trusts' members elect a board of governors. The governors appoint the trust's chairman and non-executive directors and oversee the organisation's management board which is responsible for day-to-day management.

The freedoms for NHS foundation hospitals include to:
• retain the proceeds from land sales to invest in new services for patients
• decide what they can afford to borrow for investment in services, and the ability to make their own decisions about capital investment
• use the flexibilities of the new pay system to modernise the NHS workforce, including developing additional rewards for those staff who are contributing most.

Foundation trusts operate according to a licence, issued and monitored by Monitor, an independent regulator, to guarantee NHS standards and values.

A core element of foundation trust policy is the borrowing regime that allows the trusts to access capital within a framework of safeguards designed to mitigate institutional failure. Access to capital is based on the trust's ability to service debt and the level of borrowing is governed by the prudential borrowing code set by the regulator.

Those NHS trusts which have a three-star rating (a two-star rating from November 2005) have been eligible to apply. To protect foundation trusts from any future threat of privatisation there

The changing structure and management of the NHS — 1

Monitor, the regulator of NHS foundation trusts

Monitor is responsible for authorising, monitoring and regulating NHS foundation trusts, but does not have a role in routine performance management. The regulator is independent of the Health Secretary and is accountable to Parliament. The regulator was established in January 2004 under the Health and Social Care (Community Health and Standards) Act 2003, as an independent corporate body. One of its first tasks was to review for suitability the first wave of NHS trusts wishing to become foundation trusts.

The terms of the formal authorisation issued by the regulator set out the conditions under which a foundation trust is required to operate and covers such things as:

- a description of the goods and services related to the provision of healthcare which the foundation trust is authorised to provide
- a list of assets, such as buildings, land or equipment which are designated by the regulator as protected because they are needed for the NHS services which the foundation trust is required to provide
- limits on the amount of income which the trust is allowed to earn from private charges
- limits on the amount of money the trust is allowed to borrow
- the financial and statistical information the foundation trust is required to provide.

The regulator monitors the activity of established foundation trusts to ensure that they comply with the requirements of the terms of their authorisation.

Inspection of a trust's performance against healthcare standards is carried out by the Healthcare Commission. The commission sends Monitor copies of inspection reports relating to NHS foundation trusts. In the event of failings in healthcare standards, or other aspects of a foundation trust's activities, which amount to a significant breach in the terms of authorisation, Monitor has powers to intervene in the running of the trust.

In the event of the financial failure of a foundation trust, the regulator initiates a failure regime, which ensures that essential NHS services continue to be provided. Under secondary legislation, the regime is based on well-established insolvency procedures for companies with modifications applied to allow for the protection of essential services and assets.

The board of Monitor consists of up to five members appointed by the Health Secretary. It is chaired by Bill Moyes, and is supported by an office team, numbering around 25 people.

Monitor, 4 Matthew Parker Street, London SW1H 9NL. Tel: 020 7340 2400. www.regulator-nhsft.gov.uk

is a legal lock on their assets. These remain within public ownership. The government hopes that the governance arrangements for foundation trusts should allow patients and the public to play a more effective part in the running of the NHS locally. Local people elect their representatives to serve on the trust's board of governors.

NHS foundation trusts are part of the NHS, and subject to NHS systems of inspection. They treat NHS patients according to NHS principles and standards. Service contracts between primary care trusts and foundation trusts for the provision of healthcare services are legally binding. Foundation trusts adopted the NHS payment by results system from April 2004 ahead of the rest of the service.

By February 2006 there were 32 NHS foundation trusts:

Authorised April 2004

Basildon and Thurrock University Hospitals NHS Foundation Trust

Bradford Teaching Hospitals NHS Foundation Trust

Countess of Chester Hospital NHS Foundation Trust

Doncaster and Bassetlaw Hospitals NHS Foundation Trust

Homerton University Hospital NHS Foundation Trust

Moorfields Eye Hospital NHS Foundation Trust

Peterborough and Stamford Hospitals NHS Foundation Trust

Royal Devon and Exeter NHS Foundation Trust

The Royal Marsden NHS Foundation Trust

Stockport NHS Foundation Trust

Authorised July 2004

Cambridge University Hospitals NHS Foundation Trust

City Hospitals Sunderland NHS Foundation Trust

Gloucestershire Hospitals NHS Foundation Trust

Derby Hospitals NHS Foundation Trust

Guy's and St. Thomas's NHS Foundation Trust

Papworth Hospital NHS Foundation Trust

Queen Victoria Hospital NHS Foundation Trust

Sheffield Teaching Hospitals NHS Foundation Trust

University College London Hospitals NHS Foundation Trust

University Hospital Birmingham NHS Foundation Trust

Authorised January 2005

Barnsley Hospital NHS Foundation Trust

Chesterfield Royal Hospital NHS Foundation Trust

Gateshead Health NHS Foundation Trust

Harrogate and District NHS Foundation Trust

South Tyneside NHS Foundation Trust

Authorised April 2005

Frimley Park Hospital NHS Foundation Trust

Heart of England NHS Foundation Trust.

Lancashire Teaching Hospitals NHS Foundation Trust

Liverpool Women's NHS Foundation Trust

The Royal Bournemouth & Christchurch Hospitals NHS Foundation Trust

The Royal National Hospital for Rheumatic Diseases NHS Foundation Trust

Authorised June 2005

Rotherham NHS Foundation Trust.

In January 2005 the Department of Health announced that a further 32 trusts had submitted preliminary applications for foundations status, including for the first time eight mental health trusts. Authorisations for this group are expected to commence from spring 2006. The Department has said that by 2008 it expects all NHS trusts to have become foundation trusts. In November 2005 it published a set of financial diagnostic checks to test whether potential applicants were ready for foundation status

A review of the foundation trust policy, conducted by the Healthcare Commission, was published in July 2005.

Foundation trusts. www.dh.gov.uk/ PolicyAndGuidance/OrganisationPolicy/ SecondaryCare/NHSFoundationTrust

Foundation Trust Network. www.foundationtrustnetwork.org

The Healthcare Commission's review of NHS Foundation trusts. July 2005.

The changing structure and management of the NHS — 1

Specialised services

Since April 2002 PCTs have been responsible for securing health services for their local populations, including the commissioning of specialised services. Specialised services comprise those which are not normally provided within all hospitals, such as cleft lip and palate, renal and specialist cancer services. They are defined in the specialised services national definitions set, and are provided in relatively few specialist centres to catchment populations of more than a million people. PCTs are expected to work together to ensure that specialised services are commissioned effectively. They are included in long-term service agreements, planned through a series of national advisory groups and provided by nominated specialist providers.

Very highly specialised services are commissioned centrally by the Department of Health under the auspices of the national specialist commissioning advisory group.

DH guidance, issued in March 2003, refers to the continuing role of regional specialised commissioning groups (RSCGs) or their equivalent, and provides examples of good practice in collaborative commissioning of specialised services.

In April 2002, the membership of RSCGs changed to reflect the fact that PCTs had become responsible for commissioning the services. Collaborative commissioning arrangements need to encompass two groupings of specialised services: those with planning populations of 3–6 million (level 2) and those with planning populations of around 1–2 million (level 1).

Examples of specialised services with planning populations around 1–2 million:
- cancer services
- cardiac surgery services
- liver services
- neonatal intensive care services
- neurosurgery services
- renal replacement therapy services.

Examples of specialised services with planning populations around 3–6 million:
- AIDS and HIV treatment services
- blood and marrow transplantation services
- burn (severe) care services
- cleft lip and palate services
- deep brain stimulation for (severe) Parkinson's disease
- genetic services
- haemophilia services
- medium and high secure psychiatric services
- paediatric intensive care services
- pulmonary hypertension services
- rare cancer services
- spinal injury services.

Where a specialised service has a planning population greater than six million (that is, there are fewer than eight specialist centres in the country for that particular specialised service) the level 2 groups should consider joint working arrangements.

To ensure a coherent approach to commissioning and workforce planning at local level, specialised services need to be incorporated in PCTs' local delivery plans and workforce programmes.

Specialised services definition. www.dh.gov.uk/PolicyAndGuidance/ HealthAndSocialCareTopics/ SpecialisedServicesDefinition

The changing structure and management of the NHS — 1

What are local delivery plans?

Local delivery plans are three-year programmes to improve the health status and healthcare of a local population. They have to reflect national priorities.

Local delivery plans cover:
• the most important health needs of the population
• the main healthcare requirements of local people
• the range and location of services and the investment required.

Primary care trusts draw up a local plan at their level and in so doing they work with NHS trusts, other members of the local health economy, such as local authorities. The strategic health health authority's local delivery plan is based on those of its constituent PCTs.

PCTs commission services in service agreements in the context of the three-year delivery plan, which is reviewed frequently with updates being made as appropriate. Specific targets expected to be achieved are included in the financial plan, which comes from the delivery plan and shows how resources will be deployed.

Treatment centres

A series of treatment centres (TCs) are being created in an initiative to increase rapidly the number of planned surgical operations performed. By separating elective surgery from emergency work productivity can be improved. The centres, operated by both the NHS and the independent sector, are also providing scheduled diagnostic and treatment services.

The first independent sector TC opened in Daventry, Northamptonshire, in October 2003, and two mobile centres, which move around England performing an additional 41,600 cataract operations over five years, were announced in January 2004.

Treatment centres can be run by NHS trusts, primary care trusts or by an independent provider. They may be stand alone new builds, refurbished sites or virtual treatment centres — defined services within an existing hospital building, using care pathways to ensure process efficiency and improve the patient's overall experience of care.

There are 44 NHS-run treatment centres fully open across England and another two are in development. Over 240,000 patients had been treated in NHS centres since the start of the programme in April 2003. There are also 14 independent sector run schemes and three sites providing interim services.

The House of Commons Health Committee

The Health Committee is one of 16 cross-party committees of the House of Commons overseeing individual government departments. The committees conduct inquiries, during the course of which they collect both written and oral evidence. They have the power to require the submission of written evidence and documents, to send for and examine witnesses. Their findings and recommendations are submitted to the House as printed reports.

The Health Committee has a maximum of eleven members. They are appointed by the House and, unless discharged, remain in post until the next dissolution of Parliament. The committee is supported in its work by a team of staff and by part-time special-

The changing structure and management of the NHS — 1

ists, usually experts in the field of academia or professions relevant to the committee inquiries.

A new committee was formed after the May 2005 general election and it is currently chaired by Labour MP Kevin Barron. The committee is appointed to examine, on behalf of the House of Commons, the 'expenditure, administration and policy of the Department of Health (and any associated public bodies)'. Its constitution and powers are set out in House of Commons Standing Order no. 152. Within this remit it has complete discretion to decide which area to investigate. The committee's oral evidence sessions are usually open to the public and are often televised. Deliberative meetings are held in private.

When the inquiry ends, a report is agreed and then published by the Stationery Office. The report is usually published in two volumes: the findings of the committee and the background (memoranda and oral) evidence. The government is committed to responding to such reports within two months of publication.

As well as making recommendations to the government the committee acts to promote public debate, examine officials and other witnesses about the implications of policy, analyse policy and facilitate the placing of information in the public domain.

Recent Health Committee reports have covered:
• changes to primary care trusts
• smoking in public places
• NHS continuing care
• the use of new medical technologies within the NHS
• the influence of the pharmaceutical industry.

The Health Committee, 7 Millbank,

London SW1P 3JA. Tel: 020 7219 5466. E-mail: healthcom@parliament.uk www.parliament.uk/ parliamentary_committees/ health_committee.cfm

Arm's length bodies

Under the terms of the Department of Health's arm's length bodies (ALBs) review, a number of new ALBs are being set up between 2005 and 2008. The new bodies are:
• **NHS Institute for Innovation and Improvement**
The NHS Institute is working at national level to integrate, promote and support innovation, learning, leadership and improvement in the NHS. Its focus is on achieving practical outcomes that help the health service deliver better quality and more effective patient care.
• **Health and Social Care Information Centre**
Became fully operational in April 2005 and drew functions and staff from the NHS Information Authority and the Department of Health statistics division. It coordinates information requests across the health and social care system, sets data standards and carries out data collections and analysis as required.
• **Human Tissue Authority (HTA)**
The HTA is responsible for implementing the Human Tissue Act. It regulates activities such as anatomical and post-mortem examinations, transplantations and the storage of human material for education, training and research. It will merge with the Human Fertilisation and Embryology Authority to form the Regulatory Authority for Fertility and Tissue (RAFT) in April 2008.
• **NHS Business Services Authority**
The Business Service Authority is taking on the functions of the Dental Practice

Board, NHS Pensions Agency and Prescriptions Pricing Authority from April 2006, and provisionally also those of the Counter Fraud and Security Management Service and the NHS Logistics Authority. It will be the main processing facility and centre of excellence for payment, reimbursement, remuneration and reconciliation for NHS patients, employees and affiliated parties.

• **NHS Blood and Transplant**
The authority replaced the National Blood Authority and UK Transplant in October 2005. It promotes the donation of blood and organs, coordinates the 24-hour organ matching and allocation service, and arranges and keeps track of the collection, preparation and distribution of blood.

• **Regulatory Authority for Fertility and Tissue (RAFT)**
The authority will replace the Human Fertilisation and Embryology Authority and the Human Tissue Authority in April 2008.

Non contract activity

The introduction of the payment by results regime has resulted in a change to the way healthcare activity taking place out of the area is funded. Guidance replacing the out of area treatment arrangements with non contract activity (NCA) was issued in April 2005. When healthcare services are provided to a patient when they are away from their home area, the home commissioner is now invoiced directly by the NHS trust providing the service.

Acts of Parliament

The Health Act 1999
The infrastructure upon which the government restructured the NHS in England was set out in the Health Act, which received royal assent in June 1999. The Act implemented the measures set out in the government White Paper: *The new NHS*. It also covered the variations in NHS reforms contained in the separate White Papers for Scotland and Wales.

The Act abolished GP fundholding and the concept of the internal market. It reformed primary care, permitted the creation of independent primary care trusts (in England) and enabled the executive control of new clinical governance arrangements.

The Act's main provisions were:
• the abolition GP fundholding and the implementation of primary care trusts
• local healthcare driven by health improvement programmes
• powers to remove barriers between the NHS, social services and wider local government, through flexibility over fund transfer and operational arrangements
• high security hospitals may be constituted as NHS trusts
• the creation of the Commission for Health Improvement (CHI) as a statutory body
• a statutory duty on all NHS trusts to improve the quality of care
• reserve powers to support the pharmaceutical price regulation scheme, by which the price of drugs charged to the NHS is monitored and controlled
• new powers for the NHS tribunal to disqualify doctors and other health practitioners who commit fraudulent acts or who act in ways that are

The changing structure and management of the NHS — 1

detrimental to the health service.

New powers to enable the Secretary of State for Health to monitor professional competence were introduced, attenuating the self-regulating authority of the General Medical Council and other such bodies. This provision enabled the government to alter in council, rather than through primary legislation, aspects of education and training, fitness to practice, registration and discipline.

The Act also allowed the introduction of the following patient services:
- walk-in high street health centres
- increased use of day surgery in health centres
- health checks and advice sessions in new clinics
- varied healthcare services available at one site
- wider health partnerships — for example GPs to team up with dentists, optometrists and pharmacists — providing a range of health services from one complex.

The Health and Social Care Act 2001

The Health and Social Care Act became law in May 2001. The Act delivered aspects of the NHS Plan and the government's response to the Royal Commission on Long Term Care.

It primarily changed:
- the funding and organisation of the NHS, including family health services, in England and Wales
- partnership arrangements between NHS providers and local authorities, by the introduction of care trusts
- long-term care provision
- the prescribing rights of healthcare providers
- the provision of pharmaceutical services
- the use of patient information.

To implement those parts of the NHS Plan that required primary legislation the Act made changes to both the framework and financing of the NHS in England and Wales. New public and private partnerships in the NHS were also allowed for.

NHS trusts and primary care trusts might remunerate and set terms and conditions of employment for employees as they thought fit, subject to regulations and directions by the Health Secretary.

Local authorities were to form overview and scrutiny committees, to scrutinise the NHS and represent local views on the development of health services. NHS organisations had a duty to have arrangements for involving patients and the public in decision-making about the operation of the NHS, and independent advocacy services would be established across the country.

The requirement that remuneration paid to a GP must not, except exceptionally, consist of a salary which has no reference to the number of patients to whom a GP has undertaken to provide general medical services was removed. New arrangements governed the regulation of family health service (FHS) practitioners. Health authorities were required to maintain lists covering all practitioners providing FHSs, including deputies and locums for their area, and only those included in such lists would be able to deliver services. A new body, the Family Health Services Appeals Authority, was established to deal with appeals by practitioners against health authority decisions. The NHS Tribunal would be abolished. The Medical Practices Committee, which was concerned with the distribution of general practices, was also being abolished.

Powers allowed primary care trusts and NHS trusts to apply to form care

Wellard's NHS Handbook 2006/07

trusts, which would build on existing health and local authority powers to create partnerships and provide integrated care. There was also provision for failing services to be directed to form an alternative form of partnership arrangement.

The funding and provision of long-term care in England and Wales was changed, with the provision by local authorities of nursing care taken away. Local authorities would be responsible for arranging and meeting the care needs of people who had had long-term care funded through preserved rights to certain state benefits. Care provided by a registered nurse for people in nursing homes would be free.

Provision was made for the extension of prescribing rights to health professionals other than doctors, dentists and certain specified nurses, health visitors and midwives who already had such rights.

Health authorities had to arrange for the supply of drugs, medicines and listed appliances for patients by medical and other practitioners under the NHS. Specifically, the relevant authority was empowered (under patient group directions) to specify the categories of person whose prescriptions would be dispensed, and any conditions in accordance with which they must prescribe. Arrangements for the provision of additional pharmaceutical services by remote means were also made, mainly to provide a way to control the development of internet, mail order, home delivery and other arrangements, which might involve dispensing across health authority boundaries.

Arrangements were introduced, by which community pharmacy and related services might be provided on a pilot basis — known as local pharmaceutical

services — and how these services would be financed, set up, monitored and reviewed.

The Health Secretary might require or permit patient information to be shared for medical purposes where he or she considers that this is in the interests of improving patient care or in the public interest.

The NHS Reform and Health Care Professions Act 2002

The main elements of the NHS Reform and Health Care Professions Act 2002 are:

- the establishment of strategic health authorities
- the redistribution of functions between strategic health authorities and primary care trusts, conferring on PCTs many of the roles of the former health authorities
- PCTs to recognise local representative committees — local medical committees, local dental committees, local optical committees and local pharmaceutical committees. The committees can be recognised either solely for the PCT's own area or recognised by more than one PCT for their joint areas
- PCTs to receive direct funding for providing and commissioning services from the Department of Health
- the duty of quality enlarged to secure improvement not only in healthcare but also in the environment in which that healthcare is provided
- altered functions for the Commission for Health Improvement (Healthcare Commission) extending its powers to overseeing private sector bodies providing healthcare to NHS patients
- the abolition of community health councils, and patients' forums to be established in their place for each NHS trust and PCT
- the establishment of the Commission

The changing structure and management of the NHS — 1

for Patient and Public Involvement in Health
• the creation of the Council for the Regulation of Healthcare Professionals (Council for Healthcare Regulatory Excellence) to promote the principle of good self regulation and the public's interest
• improved co-operation to maintain the health of prisoners.

The Community Care (Delayed Discharges etc) Act 2003

The Community Care (Delayed Discharges etc) Act, which received royal assent in April 2003, introduces a system of reimbursement for delayed hospital discharges and removes local authorities' ability to charge for community equipment and intermediate care. The main provisions are:

Delayed discharge payments
• For individuals who are the responsibility of social services, the Act introduces a financial incentive for local authorities to provide any community care services or carer's services that are needed for the individual's safe transfer to a more appropriate setting.
• The Act initially applies only to acute hospital care, but contains the power to be extended to other types of NHS care such as intermediate care. It does not apply to mental healthcare.
• NHS bodies are required to notify the relevant local authority of individuals

whom they believe are likely to need community care services upon discharge from hospital and work with them to assess a patient's needs.
• The local authority then has a minimum number of days (two days) to put together a discharge plan in consultation with the relevant NHS bodies and determine which services it will provide to an individual or their carer upon discharge. Sundays and public holidays are excluded from the two-day period.
• The local authority is required to make a payment (£100) to the relevant NHS body where it has not succeeded in putting together a discharge plan for an individual within the specified number of days or where a patient's discharge has been delayed because the local authority has not been ready to provide services to the patient or their carer at the specified time of discharge, whichever of these is later.
• The charging provision was introduced in January 2004.

Local authority community care services
• The Act also removes local authorities' power to charge for certain community care services. The community care services prescribed in regulations to be made free of charge are intermediate care and certain community equipment services.

The NHS workforce — 2

The human resources agenda

Some 1.3m staff work for the NHS across the UK and are its most important asset. NHS trusts spend 70 per cent of their revenue on staff costs. A service with this many highly skilled and qualified staff requires a strong focus on the management of human resources (HR).

The government wants the health service to be one of the best employers in the country, with quality of care for staff and patients going hand in hand. This was spelt out in 1998 in *Working together: securing a quality workforce for the NHS*. Three aims for human resources in the NHS in England were set out:

- to ensure a quality workforce, with the right numbers having the right skills and diversity and organised in the right way
- to demonstrate improvement in the quality of working life for staff
- to fulfil the management capacity and capability to deliver this agenda.

The NHS Plan builds on this with specific commitments to recruit new staff:

- 7,500 more consultants
- 2,000 more general practitioners
- 20,000 more nurses
- over 6,500 more allied health professionals.

Human resources in the NHS Plan

Human resources in the NHS Plan was published in July 2002 as the new HR strategy for the NHS and to promote good practice in NHS organisations with the intention of encouraging its universal adoption. It outlines how the NHS should become the employer of choice and offer a model career to staff. It brings together the numerous NHS workforce initiatives needed to make the NHS Plan a reality. The document recognises that good management of staff will lead directly to improvements for patients.

To meet the challenging objectives of achieving a major expansion in staff numbers and a major redesign of jobs, *HR in the NHS Plan* is built on four pillars:

- making the NHS a model employer
- ensuring the NHS provides a model career through offering a skills escalator
- improving staff morale
- building people management skills.

Delivering improved patient access and choice, shorter waiting times, and improved standards of care needs more staff working in different ways. Increasing the number of NHS staff is key to improving patient care. It is important to ensure that staff who have been trained move quickly into permanent jobs.

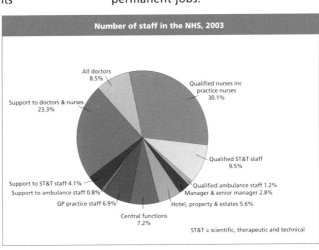

Number of staff in the NHS, 2003

- All doctors 8.5%
- Qualified nurses inc practice nurses 30.1%
- Support to doctors & nurses 23.3%
- Qualified ST&T staff 9.5%
- Qualified ambulance staff 1.2%
- Manager & senior manager 2.8%
- Hotel, property & estates 5.6%
- Central functions 7.2%
- GP practice staff 6.9%
- Support to ambulance staff 0.8%
- Support to ST&T staff 4.1%

ST&T = scientific, therapeutic and technical

39

NHS staff (England), full time equivalents,
30 September 2004

Total employed staff (inc GP & practice staff)	1,071,203
Total employed staff (HCHS only)	968,435
Total non-medical staff (inc GP practice staff)	961,979
Total non-medical staff (HCHS only)	889,973
Professionally qualified clinical staff	549,836
All doctors	109,224
GPs	30,762
HCHS medical & dental staff (excl locums)	78,462
of which: Consultants (including directors of public health)	28,141
Total qualified nursing staff	315,440
Qualified nursing, midwifery & health visitor staff	301,877
GP practice nurses	13,563
Total qualified scientific, therapeutic & technical staff	108,585
Qualified allied health professions	48,338
Other qualified scientific, therapeutic & technical staff	60,246
Qualified ambulance staff	16,587
Support to clinical staff	284,394
Support to doctors & nursing staff	231,652
Support to scientific, therapeutic & technical staff	44,089
Support to ambulance staff	8,653
NHS infrastructure support	178,098
Central functions	85,498
Hotel, property & estates	56,593
Manager & senior manager	36,007
Other non-medical staff or those with unknown classification	432
Other GP practice staff	58,443

Notes:
HCHS = hospital &community health services
Nursing & midwifery figures exclude students on training courses leading to a
first qualification as a nurse or midwife
Source: Department of Health

Modernising the way services are delivered means redesigning jobs around the needs of patients. The NHS Plan sets out a different approach of plotting the patient journey and identifying all tasks, diagnostic procedures, interventions and types of care to be delivered. This analysis is used to describe a number of jobs in terms of their necessary qualifications, skills and knowledge.

The changing workforce programme is central to this work and is helping NHS organisations develop new staff roles.

Making the NHS a model employer

The model NHS employer embraces a composite of best policies, practices and facilities. *HR in the NHS Plan* paints a picture of NHS organisations progressing to the ideal through a series of accredited phases.

Building on *Improving working lives* (IWL), the NHS needs to be able to offer:
• better working conditions
• model employment practices
• the ability to balance life in and outside work
• job security
• lifelong learning
• fair pay
• staff involvement
• good communications.

Above all, the management style of the model employer needs to be facilitative and involving, seeking to help each individual make the most of themselves.

Development programmes for all staff need to support these changes. A start has been made through:
• *Positively diverse* — to build and manage a diverse workforce
• the NHS childcare strategy

• NHS Professionals in recruitment
• flexible careers and retirement schemes
• *Working together, learning together* — the lifelong learning network
• the NHS taskforce on staff involvement.

To encourage best practice to be spread across the NHS, the Improving Working Lives accreditation system is being expanded so that NHS organisations can gain IWL Practice Plus status as model employers.

The skills escalator

The skills escalator describes a career as a succession of stages, each with its own pay band and learning requirements. Staff are assisted constantly to renew and extend skills and knowledge through lifelong learning, enabling them to move up the escalator. Meanwhile roles and workload are passed down the escalator, giving greater job satisfaction and generating efficiency gains.

The skills escalator is also about attracting a wider range of people to work within the NHS by offering a greater variety of step-on and step-off points.

Pay modernisation

Pay modernisation is critical to expanding the NHS workforce and redesigning job roles. Former myriad pay scales and grades grouped staff in ways which were increasingly irrelevant to the way the NHS needs to work.

The three major pay modernisations are: *Agenda for change* covering non-medical staff, the consultants contract and the general medical services contract for GPs. In all three cases one of the main purposes is to ensure that the relevant pay systems can enable and assist rather than restrict job and service

The NHS workforce — 2

redesign at local level.

Agenda for change has been introduced for most staff over two years. The system combines national standards with local flexibility for employers. It is based on the principle of equal pay for equal work and rewards staff who develop into new roles. A limited number of pay bands are used and jobs are matched to these using evaluation. The work of the Whitley Councils has been taken over and the remit of the pay review bodies has been modified.

Agenda for change represents the most substantial pay reform ever undertaken in the NHS.

Modernising learning and development

Education and training programmes are being redesigned to ensure more flexible and accessible learning, transferable skills and career pathways. Learning programmes need to be commissioned which reflect new roles, support patient-focused care and service change. To do this NHS organisations need to have in place:

- a regularly monitored, robust learning and development strategy
- local champions and arrangements with staff and trade union representatives for protected learning time
- arrangements for learning to be increasingly accessible in the work place.

Additional investment is benefiting many thousands of staff through access to NHS learning accounts and national vocational qualifications.

Modernisation of professional regulation

Patients and the public need to know that staff treating them are fully qualified and skilled for the work they do. The reform programme covering education, registration, training and continuing professional development, and revalidation of health professionals, is based on ensuring regulatory bodies are more accountable, consistent, open and responsive to change.

The Council for Healthcare Regulatory Excellence has been established to coordinate the role of existing regulatory bodies. New bodies have also been set up to regulate nursing and allied health professionals.

Modernising workforce planning

Strategic health authorities and local health communities have prepared capacity plans for 2008 that will underpin important aspects of the *NHS improvement plan*. These were signed off in 2004 and supported the development of broader local delivery plans in 2005.

Workforce planning is now led by local organisations, supported by the Department of Health and NHS Employers. The Department will:

- provide national assumptions which can be adapted to local circumstances
- ensure that integrated plans are produced that will deliver national objectives
- provide national support, for example, by assisting with international recruitment.

Local plans prepared by primary care trusts, in conjunction with local providers and social services, need to be aggregated by strategic health authorities for DH sign off.

Improving staff morale

Almost all staff in the NHS work very hard and many do so well beyond the call of duty. All the measures outlined in *Human resources in the NHS Plan* are intended to contribute to improving the morale of staff in the NHS. NHS organisations, professional bodies and individual staff also need to express publicly all that is good about the NHS and to spread a sense of optimism about the improvements being made.

Supporting human resources development

An annual NHS human resources conference, regular face-to-face HR briefings and a national HR advisory group have been improving communication between the Department of Health, the wider HR community and other stakeholders. Specific HR programmes have also been under way to engage chief executives, chairs and other board members.

The SHRINE (strategic human resource intelligence) network supports the development of formal and informal links between HR managers to share good practice and collaborate on local and regional initiatives.

The pay system

A new pay system applying to all directly employed NHS staff, except doctors and dentists and the most senior managers, has been introduced in England. The government's intentions were set out in *Agenda for change* published in 1999. All NHS trusts in England have been expected to implement the proposals from December 2004. The target date for completion of the process was 31 December 2005. Roll out of the system across the UK has also been taking place.

Basic pay is being decided through the NHS job evaluation scheme. There are two pay spines (one for nurses and other health professions, the second for other staff) each with eight pay bands and a particular job is placed in the correct pay band through evaluation. Individuals are expected to develop within their posts and as they do so they will normally progress up one pay point a year until they reach the top of the band.

A personal development plan describes how the learning for each member of staff is supported each year. One set of terms and conditions applies to all staff groups, including the number of hours worked and days of annual leave. There are supplements for working outside normal hours and extra pay for staff who work in high cost areas. Additional pay may also be provided where recruitment and retention of staff is especially difficult.

The Whitley councils have been abolished. The remit of the review body for nurses, midwives and health visitors and the allied health professions has been expanded to include a wider number of qualified health professionals and their support staff.

A third pay spine is for doctors and dentists and recommendations concerning their pay continues to be made by the doctors and dentists review body.

Details can be found on the Department of Health website which include:
- full details of the *Agenda for change* agreement
- a handbook explaining the NHS job evaluation scheme
- information on the knowledge and skills framework and the terms and conditions of service handbook.

The NHS workforce — 2

The European working time directive

The European working time directive (EWTD) has applied to all health and social care staff with the exception of doctors in training. Staff are only exempt from regulations if they sign a waiver. However, the continuation of the waiver is being reviewed by the European Commission.

The extension of the EWTD to doctors in training in August 2004 presented a major challenge to the health service. Traditionally, doctors in training have provided much of the out-of-hours medical cover. Progress has been made in reducing hours through the New Deal but the EWTD imposes more stringent requirements:

- it is a legal requirement
- there are more stringent rest requirements
- there will be a phased reduction in maximum hours worked from 58 in 2004 to 48 in 2009
- the SiMAP judgement of the European Court of Justice means that if doctors are on call and required to be on hospital premises they are deemed to be working.

Implementing the directive requires innovative approaches to how services are staffed and provided. Solutions include:

- developing new health practitioner roles
- hospital at night teams
- fewer tiers of cover linked with new working patterns.

The annual NHS national staff survey

The national staff survey was launched in 2003 with the purpose of collecting staff views about working in their local NHS organisation. All 572 NHS trusts in England took part and results were published by the Healthcare Commission. The survey enabled each organisation, for the first time, to benchmark itself against similar NHS organisations, on a range of measures of staff satisfaction and opinion.

NHS Professionals

NHS Professionals was created in November 2000 as an in-house staff agency so as to reduce the NHS's dependency on commercial recruitment agencies. The move is intended to ensure better value for money and at the same time offers staff who sign up to it benefits such as holiday pay, ongoing pension contributions and training.

The agency is working across local healthcare economies and covers doctors, nurses and other staff. For doctors it includes the flexible careers scheme.

NHS Professionals became a special health authority at the beginning of 2004 and provides a national service to the NHS, helping trusts to best manage their temporary staffing needs. It is responsible for:

- the strategic oversight of temporary labour markets
- management of agency framework contracts
- setting standards and the policy framework for NHS temporary staffing
- the operational management of NHS Professionals service in partnership with the local NHS.

In parallel, the NHS Purchasing and Supplies Agency has been developing regional and national contracts for the provision of temporary staff by commercial agencies.

National recruitment line:
0845 60 60 345

www.nhsprofessionals.nhs.uk

Trusts are able to use the survey results to inform improvements in working conditions and practices at a local level, and to provide information for monitoring *Improving working lives.*

A national framework to support local workforce strategy

In December 2005, the Department of Health published *A national service framework to support local workforce strategy development — a guide for HR directors in the NHS and social care.* It suggests a framework within which governing bodies and boards supported by HR directors and managers across health and social care can develop their local strategies.

The document introduces 10 high impact human resource changes, identified by the Department of Health and HR professionals, which show

The NHS pension scheme

The NHS pension scheme is designed specifically for NHS employees, providing retirement, illness, redundancy, voluntary early retirement and family benefits. As the health service employs well over one million people (one in five public sector workers and one in 20 of all people employed in the UK), the NHS scheme represents a significant investment fund. There are some 1.6 million pension scheme members and pensioners.

During the operation of the scheme, employee contributions may be enhanced by making additional voluntary contributions, either by investing in a money-purchase arrangement for extra pension or buying added years of scheme membership. Benefits are generally payable for life and inflation proofed with final entitlement based upon years of membership and final salary. Membership of the scheme costs employees 6 per cent of pensionable pay (5 per cent for manual workers); yet the real cost approximates to 3.5 per cent because of the operation of tax relief on contributions and a lower level of national insurance contributions.

Overall, both employer and government contributions to the scheme mean that benefits are worth over 20 per cent of pensionable pay. The scheme is underwritten by the government, having the support of the NHS trades unions and professional bodies.

NHS Employers is leading a review of the pension scheme in conjunction with the Department of Health, the NHS Pensions Agency and the National Assembly for Wales. The review came about due to:
• pressure to modernise the scheme
• Inland Revenue proposals on changes to the tax regime for pensions
• government policy on moving public sector schemes over time to a normal pension age of 65.

In January 2005, a consultation document was produced for the review. The new pension arrangements are expected to be confirmed by ministers in 2006.

On 1 April 2004 the NHS Pensions Agency became a special health authority with a corporate board with a lay majority.

NHS Pensions Agency, Hesketh House, 200 Broadway, Fleetwood, Lancs FY7 8LG. Tel: 01253 774774. www.nhspa.gov.uk

The NHS workforce — 2

bottom line impact in terms of patient care and efficiency. These are:

1. Support and lead effective change management
2. Effective recruitment, good induction and supportive management
3. Develop shared service models and effective use of IT
4. Manage temporary staffing costs as a major source of efficiency
5. Promoting staff health and managing sickness absence
6. Job and service re-design
7. Appraisal policy development and implementation
8. Staff involvement, partnership working and good employee relations
9. Championing good people management practices
10. Effective training and development.

Further information

Human resources and training
www.dh.gov.uk/PolicyAndGuidance/HumanResourcesAndTraining

Professional regulation in the NHS.
www.dh.gov.uk/PolicyAndGuidance/HumanResourcesAndTraining/ModernisingProfessionalRegulation

The European working time directive.
www.dh.gov.uk/PolicyAndGuidance/HumanResourcesAndTraining/WorkingDifferently/EuropeanWorkingTimeDirective

Working together: securing a quality workforce for the NHS. DH, 1998.

Report of the taskforce on staff involvement. DH, 1999.

A health service of all our talents: developing the NHS workforce. DH, 2000.
Human resources in the NHS Plan.

DH, July 2002.

Improving working lives. DH, 2002.

Agenda for change: a modernised pay system for the NHS. DH, November 2002.

Equality and diversity in the NHS — progress and priorities. DH, human resources directorate. October 2003.

Delivering HR in the NHS Plan 2004. DH, May 2004.

Delivering the NHS improvement plan: the workforce contribution. DH, November 2004.

A national framework to support local workforce strategy development — a guide for HR directors in the NHS and social care. DH, December 2005.

Commissioning a patient-led NHS human resources framework for SHAs and PCTs. DH, December 2005.

NHS Employers

NHS Employers was set up in November 2004 as part of the Department of Health's change management programme. It is run by the NHS Confederation and aims to be the authoritative voice for the NHS on employment and human resources issues. It has taken over much of the human resources agenda for the NHS in England that has been devolved by the Department of Health, including national negotiations, and providing employers with information and support.

It draws together NHS employer views on how to implement NHS employment policy frameworks and represents those views nationally. It supports the implementation of *Agenda for change* and the revised GP and consultant contracts. It is also leading on workforce areas such as, improving working lives, the NHS pension scheme review, recruitment, retention and return to the NHS, equality and diversity and European issues.

To create the organisation, some 50 posts were transferred from the Department of Health. The posts covered national pay policy, disciplinary frameworks, recruitment campaigns and human resources communications.

NHS Employers has an assembly of 200 people to steer policy and provide representatives for panels, task forces and projects. A policy board of 22 people, drawn from the assembly, has detailed responsibility. The organisation's director is Steve Barnett.

NHS Employers, 29 Bressenden Place, London SW1E 5DD. Tel: 020 7074 3200. www.nhsemployers.org

NHS Employers, 2 Brewery Wharf, Kendell Street, Leeds LS10 1JR. Tel: 0113 306 3000. www.nhsemployers.org

The NHS Institute for Innovation and Improvement

The NHS Institute for Innovation and Improvement was established in July 2005 as a special health authority for England. It is located at the University of Warwick and incorporates some of the functions of the Modernisation Agency, NHS Leadership Centre and NHSU. The institute also incorporates the National Innovation Centre.

It had a budget of £80m for 2005/06 and up to 170 staff. It is not a provider of large-scale training programmes but rather focuses on new ideas, technologies, and practices to improve services to patients.

The institute:
• works closely with clinicians, NHS organisations, patients, the public, academia and industry to identify best practice
• develops the NHS's capability for service transformation, technology and product innovation, leadership development and learning
• supports the rapid adoption and spread of new ideas by providing guidance on practical change ideas and ways to facilitate local, safe implementation
• promotes a culture of innovation and life-long learning for all NHS staff.

Potential areas of innovation that the NHS Institute will deliver include developing more personalised care for people with long-term conditions, the testing of new procurement models, and ensuring further value from the NHS annual £4bn training programme for the widest possible range of staff.

The institute will also host responsibility for the Centre for Excellence in Patient and Public Involvement, managing it by contract. The centre will support the delivery of patient and public involvement (PPI) and be a collective of innovation in PPI leadership, learning and development.

The NHS Institute for Innovation and Improvement, University of Warwick Campus, Coventry CV4 7AL. Tel: 0800 555 550. www.institute.nhs.uk

Managers

Political parties, whether in government or in opposition, have been known to indulge in manager bashing of the simplistic 'white coats good, grey suits bad' variety. But when ministers

The NHS workforce — 2

have set the agenda and objectives and have decided on the structures and systems of the NHS, it is the managers who must deliver them. Doctors, nurses and other clinical and operational staff provide the service to individual patients, but it is the managers who turn the ministers' wishes and the government's policies into reality.

To achieve this, the NHS manager must be a communicator and persuader, an eternal optimist with unquenchable energy and a facilitator who can manage across any number of organisational boundaries.

Effective management in each organisation is undoubtedly important, but far more crucial is the ability to make the connections between different contributors — health and social services, primary care trusts and NHS trusts — and weave together those different contributions into a strong fabric which delivers the required results.

In the early decades of the NHS, the traditional structure for running hospitals was the matron, the medical superintendent and the hospital secretary. NHS management has travelled a considerable distance since then, but the doctor-nurse-manager combination is still, at its best, an unbeatable team, particularly in hospitals and community health settings.

Following the Griffiths NHS management inquiry, from 1984 appointments were made at each tier of management which firmly placed one person in charge of the organisation. Many of the general managers were former administrators while some were drawn from the medical, nursing and finance professions. For the first time, recruitment from outside the NHS was encouraged.

The reforms of 1991 brought new structures and cultures. The creation of

NHS trusts meant that the number of chief executives and management teams more than quadrupled and the culture was one of competition, separation and quasi-market rules.

The roles and responsibilities of managers

Within a strategic health authority, health board, NHS trust or primary care trust, the board clearly has the formal and inescapable responsibility for providing direction and making decisions. Equally undeniable, however, is the role of the chief executive in providing leadership for the organisation and, above all, setting the tone in terms of culture, style and values, which is then reflected by its managers.

Within any NHS organisation, it is the responsibility of the managers — particularly the chief executive — to deliver the oft-quoted dual responsibility of ensuring both that the organisation is doing the right things but also ensuring that it is doing things right. Internally, managers need to develop staff and the organisation as a whole; looking outside, they need to read the political straws in the wind and develop and manage the many complex external relationships.

The disciplines of corporate governance (chapter 1) have been increasingly clearly emphasised in recent years. To this has been added the concept of clinical governance, enunciated for the first time in *The new NHS* White Paper, which introduced the same emphasis on clinical governance (page 48) as had previously been established for corporate governance.

NHS managers come from a wide range of backgrounds. One group is recruited through the national management training scheme, established in 1955. The scheme, with a number of changes of title and emphasis, is still bringing in around 70 graduates or mature postgraduate entrants a year to the NHS for a two-year training programme. Alongside these are many others who move up from administrative posts or from clinical or other professions. Across the NHS, chief executives have come from medical, finance or nursing backgrounds as well as professions allied to medicine, social services, the civil service and outside the health service.

Managers within the NHS undertake a variety of education and training programmes, ranging from postgraduate diplomas to MBAs. For middle managers and those from clinical professions, a particular niche has been filled by distance learning programmes, the most notable of which is MESOL (Management Education Scheme by Open Learning). The continuing professional development of NHS managers has been approached in a somewhat ad hoc manner for some years, but greater coordination and consistency is being brought to this important area through the NHS leadership development programme.

Medical staff

The NHS Plan called for an increase in the number of hospital consultants and general practitioners in England. By December 2004 there were an extra 9,389 consultants and 3,752 more GPs, compared to October 1997. The number of medical students in England has risen by 50 per cent since 1997 from 5,050 to 7,662. There are 2,250 more medical school places and four new medical schools opened their doors in 2002/03.

The main groups of doctors provid-ing clinical care in the NHS are general practitioners, consultants and junior hospital doctors.

The general practitioner

For the majority of the population the general practitioner is the first, the continuing and perhaps the only contact with the NHS. Patients register with a practice for primary care services and this enables GPs to build up a rapport with an individual patient and their family. GPs attend their patients in their consulting rooms and at home, and sometimes in a clinic or hospital. Over 90 per cent of all episodes of illness are managed wholly in general practice.

Initial decisions are made about each problem presented. The aim is to make an early diagnosis; with physical, psychological and social factors being taken into account in the treatment that is devised. GPs also undertake the continuing management of their patients with long-term, recurrent or terminal illnesses.

In the UK, unlike other countries, patients do not normally have direct access to a hospital consultant but they are referred by their GP. After a patient has attended hospital the consultant keeps the GP informed of any findings and often it is the GP who gives treatments and prescribes on the recommendation of the consultant.

From April 2002 GPs in England have been members of primary care trusts (PCTs). GPs in Scotland have been able to join community health partnerships (CHPs) and in Wales they have become members of local health groups (LHGs). Within PCTs, CHPs and LHGs, GPs work in primary healthcare teams with practice nurses, district nurses, health visitors, community midwives, community matrons, practice receptionists and

The NHS workforce — 2

managers. Increasingly, other health professionals are associated with GP practices, such as pharmacists, counsellors, social workers, chiropodists, community psychiatric nurses and speech therapists.

Clinics for the care of asthma, diabetes, hypertension and other chronic disorders have become widespread in general practice, and hospital consultants may provide support to the GPs running such clinics.

Partnerships. Over the past few years, there has been a trend towards multi-partner practices. The single-handed practitioner is increasingly less common (in 2003 only 8 per cent of GP principals practised single-handed).

There are about 11,000 practices in the UK, of which some 9,265 are in England and Wales.

Table. Total number of unrestricted GP principals and average list sizes (2003)

	GPs	Patients
• England	28,568	1,802
• Wales	1,783	1,695
• Scotland	3,801	1,380
• N Ireland	1,069	1,632
• Total UK	35,221	1,746

Source: *OHE Compendium of health statistics, 2004/05*

Table. Percentage distribution of unrestricted GP principals by size of practice, UK

	1975	1985	1995	2003
Single-handed	17	12	10	8
Two doctors	21	16	13	11
Three doctors	25	21	16	13
Four doctors	18	19	18	16
Five doctors	10	15	17	16
Six + doctors	9	17	26	35

Source: *OHE Compendium of health statistics, 2004/05*

Practice organisation. Methods of working have changed and the range of services available from practices have increased in recent years. As a result the total number of practice staff has risen. In 2003, there were 12,000 whole-time-equivalent practice nurses working in England.

Locally GPs have traditionally made decisions collectively through the local medical committee and these work within the context of PCTs. Nationally, there is the General Practitioners Committee (GPC) of the BMA, which is composed of members elected to represent groups of local medical committees. The GPC deals with the employers' organisation NHS Employers on matters affecting terms and conditions of service and presents evidence to the Doctors' and Dentists' Review Body on levels of remuneration.

The educational and professional side of the GP's work has been developed by the Royal College of General Practitioners. Membership of the college is attained by examination, and the MRCGP diploma is registrable with the General Medical Council (GMC).

Training practices have to satisfy strict criteria of selection to take on GP registrars (trainees). The three-year postgraduate vocational training scheme is compulsory. It includes two years in selected hospital posts and a further 12 months is spent in general practice under the guidance of a GP trainer. Over 60 per cent of GP registrars are women.

In 2004, 40 per cent of all GPs in England were women, compared to some 27 per cent in 1991.

With the creation of personal medical services (PMS) schemes some GPs now work as salaried employes of the NHS rather than as independent contractors. PMS allows for more flexible working and the government has achieved its NHS Plan target of having more than a third of GPs working in such schemes.

General practitioners with special interests. Some GPs are developing advanced skills so as to provide a variety of extended services that have traditionally usually been provided in secondary care. Such GPs need to undertake appropriate training and accreditation and are then known as general practitioners with special interests (GPSIs). They are able to take patient referrals from GPs in other practices. There are over 1,345 such specialists in post in England.

GPSIs are seen as a way of achieving more targets in primary care while at the same time enhancing the professional status of the GPs involved. Funding of the work of GPSIs is the the responsibility of the local primary care organisation. Hospital consultants are usually involved in planning such arrangements.

GPSIs are likely to specialise in areas such as: care for older people, care for the homeless and other people who find access to traditional services difficult, coronary heart disease, diabetes, dermatology, ear, nose and throat (ENT), genetics, mental health (including substance misuse), musculoskeletal medicine, other procedures suitable for a community setting (cystoscopy, endoscopy, echocardiology, vasectomy, etc), palliative care and cancer, and women and child health (including sexual health). There is also a generic model for those GPs wishing to specialise in service development and new models of care.

The GP and hospitals. Many GPs undertake clinical assistant sessions in local hospitals either in general subjects or in specialties in which they have a particular interest. This benefits the hospital and the patients of the practice.

Hospital consultants

Over 26,000 hospital consultants covering some 50 specialties are employed in the NHS in Great Britain. In 2003 in England, 25 per cent of consultants were women.

Nationally negotiated terms and conditions of service and the job plan drawn up between the employer and the consultant govern the contractual relationship most consultants have with the service. Responsibility for the management of consultants' contracts is largely in the hands of NHS trusts. A revised consultant contract was implemented in April 2004 (box).

Senior medical staff of university medical schools can hold honorary (unpaid) contracts with NHS trusts. These enable them to treat NHS patients and provide a useful interchange between medical schools and the NHS.

Consultants undertake full responsibility for the clinical care of patients. Most act as the head of a team, or firm, of junior doctors. The team may include doctors in the grades of specialist registrar and senior house officer, as well as clinical assistants, hospital practitioners (who are GPs) and associate specialists and staff grade doctors (who are in permanently established sub-consultant grades). The consultant is responsible for these staff, for overseeing their work and ensuring that they do not undertake responsibilities beyond their competence.

There is a new emphasis on a consultant-led rather than consultant-based health service, with more out-of-hours commitments being shouldered by younger consultants.

The consultant entry scheme gives

The NHS workforce — 2

NHS trusts the opportunity to fill consultant vacancies on a fixed term basis.

Medical organisation. NHS trusts have a statutory responsibility to appoint a medical director. Many clinical services are also managed by clinical directorates, often with a consultant as the director. In different directorates there are significant variations in the extent of the clinical director's management responsibilities for budgets and staff. The clinical directors will usually be members of the hospital's management board, which works with the executive directors on operational policy. All consultants in the hospital will be members of the medical staff committee which meets to deal with professional issues and put forward medical advice to managers.

Hospital career structure

For many years there has been a debate about the imbalance between the number of junior and senior posts in hospital medicine. Reductions in junior doctors' hours of work, brought about by the 1991 'new deal' arrangements and by the subsequent European working time directive (EWTD), have put medical staffing structures under pressure.

From August 2004, there was a reduction to an overall average working week of 58 hours for doctors in training. Future years should see further reductions.

Hospital doctors in training

Hospital doctors in training (or junior doctors) work under the supervision of consultants, receive training and hold short-term contracts. They are responsible for their own actions, but while they are under instruction, some responsibility also rests with the consultant(s) overseeing their training.

Junior doctors can receive training in any clinical setting which has been approved for the purpose by a medical royal college or faculty. It is required that there be an educational component in their weekly programme and that they be involved in clinical audit. The grades of hospital doctors in training are described below.

The foundation programme. When medical students pass a qualifying examination in medicine they are entitled to provisional registration with the General Medical Council. From August 2004 newly qualified doctors have been undertaking a two-year foundation programme (which includes the previous pre-registration year) covering core clinical skills including patient safety, high standards of clinical governance and communication, and time management skills. This leads to specialist training programmes and general practice training programmes, that is a set series of jobs giving a range of experience and skills needed to compete training. The measures are set out in *Modernising medical careers*.

During **foundation year one (F1)** newly qualified doctors work in approved hospital posts as housemen/women. They must hold resident posts in both medicine and surgery, usually of six months' duration. Successful completion of the first year will fulfil the criteria for full registration with the GMC.

The programme for **foundation year two (F2)** consolidates emergency medical skills and gives exposure to different clinical specialties, allowing doctors to decide on career paths earlier in their working lives than previously.

At the end of the second year, the doctor should be competent to accept professional accountability for patient safety through clinical governance and be ready to start a programme of further specialist training.

Specialist registrar. The final phase of training for doctors occurs during their years at this grade. The Department of Health is considering whether some consultant training should be shortened to four years

The consultants' contract

In October 2003 a majority of senior hospital doctors in England voted for implementation of a revised consultant's contract and the contract has also been implemented in other parts of the UK. In England individual doctors were asked to give a formal commitment to the new arrangements and agree a job plan within three months. In return they were received a pay increase backdated to April 2003.

The main change in the revised contract is that it is time sensitive. Doctors agree a schedule of programmed activities (PAs) over four hour periods that are necessary to fulfil their duties. Typically over a week, 7.5 PAs are allocated to direct clinical work and 2.5 PAs to other professional activities. But consultants may agree to do extra PAs.

A new system of mandatory job planning applies to all consultants. This includes stipulating clinical duties, out-of-hours commitments and service objectives. Job planning is linked to annual appraisals. Consultants are expected to offer the first portion of their spare time to the NHS before doing private practice. Supplements are received for on-call work.

Consultants may also receive clinical excellence awards recognising their contribution over and above what is normally expected of the job.

instead of the current five year qualifying period in a drive to speed up the expansion of the medical workforce.

The Postgraduate Medical Education and Training Board awards certificates of completion of training (CCTs). A specialist register of fully qualified doctors is being kept by the General Medical Council.

Research. All doctors are encouraged to undertake research during the training years. Some junior doctors work in limited tenure posts with honorary status in the NHS.

Staff grade. For doctors who do not wish or are not able to become a consultant, a non-training staff grade exists.

Pay and conditions. The pay of doctors in training is linked to seniority with annual increments in a banding system. There are significant increases in pay for those junior doctors working the longest hours in the most intensive posts.

Doctors and the quality of care

The standards of clinical care provided by doctors are crucial to the drive to improve quality in the NHS. In *Support-*

Table. Medical and dental staff employed in NHS hospitals, 2002

	Number	Staff per 100,000 population
England & Wales	69,694	133
Scotland	8,429	167
N Ireland	2,411	142
UK	80,534	136

Notes. All figures relate to whole-time-equivalents, excluding staff working in community health services

Source: *OHE Compendium of health statistics, 2004/05*

The NHS workforce — 2

ing doctors, protecting patients, published in 1999, the chief medical officer for England Professor Liam Donaldson proposed that NHS doctors working in England should take part in an external clinical audit and face annual appraisals. This has been implemented across the NHS.

Also in 1999, the General Medical Council proposed a system of revalidation for doctors linked with registration. This, it believed, was one way of assuring the public that senior doctors were continuing to perform effectively.

Clinical excellence awards

Clinical excellence awards reward the exceptional contribution of NHS consultants, over and above that normally expected in a job, to the values and goals of the NHS and to patient care. The scheme is overseen by the national advisory committee on clinical excellence awards.

The former discretionary points and distinction awards have been replaced with the single, more graduated scheme comprising both local and national elements.

Doctors in management

All doctors are involved in management, from GPs managing their own practice and being involved in primary care trusts, to consultants and junior doctors managing their teams in hospitals.

In the 1980s hospitals developed a clinical directorate structure, with some form of hospital board as the single decision-making body for the organisation. The 1990 NHS reforms further accelerated this movement with the establishment of trusts and the statutory position of a medical director on every trust board. The medical director has specific management responsibili-

ties as well as being a full member of the corporate body.

In response to these developments a group of doctors founded the British Association of Medical Managers (BAMM) in 1991, which fosters management education for doctors.

Although combining clinical and managerial responsibilities in a medical career presents challenges, the need for doctors' involvement in NHS management is not in question.

Further information

Health Departments. *Modernising medical careers.* February 2002.

Department of Health. *Medical schools: delivering the doctors of the future.* March 2004.

General Medical Council. *The new doctor.* 2005.

Clinical excellence awards. www.advisorybodies.doh.gov.uk/accea

The General Medical Council

The role of the General Medical Council (GMC) is to protect the public by maintaining a register of doctors who are competent and fit to practise medicine. The regulatory body publishes a booklet for doctors and managers entitled *Good medical practice*, which codifies what the public and the medical profession agree is expected of every doctor and is the basis for the curriculum in UK medical schools. Among doctors' duties, the guidance states that they should:
- make the care of the patient their first concern
- respect the rights of patients to be fully involved in decisions about their care

Wellard's NHS Handbook 2006/07

The general practitioner contract

In February 2003 agreement was reached between the NHS Confederation and the British Medical Association on a new employment contract for GPs providing general medical services (GMS). Following a vote of acceptance by GPs, it was implemented from April 2004.

The contract aims to reward GPs for higher quality care, improve their working lives and ensure patients benefit from a wider range of services in the community.

Family doctors are being rewarded according to the quality of care they provide. The contract agreement is being accompanied by investment across the UK of over £8bn over three years.

The contract marks a radical departure by funding practices rather than individual GPs. Each practice is given a global sum to cover their staffing and running costs, based on an allocation formula which reflects the needs of local people. There is a guarantee that all patients will receive the full range of services, alongside greater choice for some services and faster access. There is additional money for practices which provide some services within the community rather than hospital.

A new categorisation of services helps GPs to manage their workload by enabling practices to transfer responsibility for providing some services, mainly to other practices or to their primary care organisation. The contract provides GPs with greater flexibility to determine the range of services they wish to provide locally, including the opportunity to opt out of extra services and out-of-hours cover.

The contract aims to facilitate the modernisation of practice infrastructure including premises and IT, support the development of best human resource management practice and help GPs achieve a better work/life balance.

In summary, the contract aims to:
- widen the range of services in primary care
- enable primary care organisations and practices to design services to meet local needs
- create new roles for nurses and other health professionals
- improve the attractiveness of primary care as a career choice for doctors
- improve the quality of services
- allocate funding more fairly
- trigger a major overhaul of GP surgeries.

There are three levels of services that practices can choose to offer under the contract:
- every practice must provide essential services
- most practices are likely to offer additional services, for example, contraceptive services, child health surveillance and some minor surgery.
- some practices may decide to make enhanced services available, for example, improved access, anti-coagulant monitoring and intrapartum care.

The quality and outcomes framework (QoF) financially rewards practices for delivering a wider range of services. Clinical and quality areas of primary care (for example, mental health, length of consultation) have

been assigned points. There are four domains to score points in, each of which contain a range of areas described by key indicators:
• clinical
• organisational
• patient experience
• additional services.
Practices agree with PCTs the indicators they expect to deliver on.

In April 2006 further modifications were made to the contract.

There are national terms and conditions for GPs within each of the four UK countries. At the same time there is flexibility in how some of these terms and conditions are implemented locally by primary care organisations.

General medical services contract. www.dh.gov.uk/PolicyAndGuidance/ HumanResourcesAndTraining/ ModernisingPay/GPContracts

Investing in general practice. The new general medical services contract. www.nhsconfed.org/ gmscontract

Investing in general practice — revisions to the GMS contract for 2006–07 in England, stage 1. NHS Employers Briefing, December 2005.

• keep professional knowledge and skills up-to-date
• report on a colleague whom they believe may not be fit to practise.

In 1997 procedures were introduced to deal with serious concerns about doctors' performance.

The GMC was reformed in 2002 through a parliamentary order. This has been designed to ensure that the GMC is smaller and able to work more quickly in the public interest. It has greater lay representation than before, and, for the first time, is able to link registration with performance through the introduction of revalidation.

In the proposed revalidation process, every practising doctor will submit evidence to the GMC, collected over a five-year period, which must show that their practice is up-to-date and of a high standard. Provided they meet set standards, they will retain their licence to practise. In time, only those doctors holding a licence to practise will be able to exercise any of the privileges currently associated with registration, such as prescribing.

Appraisal is a professional process introduced by the Department of Health in England for doctors working in the NHS. The aim is to give doctors regular feedback on past performance and continuing progress and to identify development needs. Annual appraisals provide a regular, structured system for recording progress towards revalidation.

The Council for Healthcare Regulatory Excellence works with the health professional regulatory bodies, such as the General Medical Council, to build and manage a strong system of self-regulation. It was set up in April 2003 to improve the consistency and accountability to Parliament of the regulators' work and covers all of the United Kingdom.

General Medical Council, Regent's Place, 350 Euston Road, London NW1 3JN. Tel: 0845 357 3456. www.gmc-uk.org

Council for Healthcare Regulatory Excellence, 1st Floor, 11 Strand, London WC2N 5HR. Tel: 020 7389 8030. www.chre.org.uk

Wellard's NHS Handbook 2006/07

Occupational health smart cards and the electronic staff record

By March 2004 some 35,000 doctors in training throughout the NHS in England had been issued with personalised photo-bearing smart cards. Card preparation and distribution is centred on postgraduate deanery areas. The initiative is sponsored by the Department of Health and managed by NHS Employers.

The occupational health smart card (OHSC) records details of pre-employment checks, General Medical Council registration numbers, contractual details, together with occupational health and immunisation records for medical staff. This is designed to save administrative time and enable doctors when they move jobs to start work without delay.

The data is stored securely within the card and can be readily updated. The scheme is being extended to other medical grades and to locum doctors where they will benefit from the portability of the smart card as they move from trust to trust. Doctors in Wales are also being issued with cards. The cards can continue to be used when a doctor takes up a consultant or other career grade post.

Dealing with poorly performing doctors — the National Clinical Assessment Service

The National Clinical Assessment Service (NCAS) is a division of the National Patient Safety Agency designed to help primary care trusts, NHS trusts and other NHS organisations in England, Wales and Northern Ireland streamline procedures for dealing with poorly performing doctors.

To help doctors and dentists in difficulty, NCAS provides advice, takes referrals and carries out targeted assessments where necessary. Once an assessment has been carried out by medical and lay assessors, NCAS advises the NHS employer on the appropriate course of action. It aims to provide faster, fairer results, as well as ending lengthy, expensive suspensions, multiple investigations of the same problem, variable local approaches and delay.

The chief medical officer recommends that all NHS organisations that are considering suspending a doctor should consult the NCAS first. Where there are doubts or concerns about a doctor's performance a senior person at the PCT or NHS trust may refer the doctor to the NCAS.

The focus is on problem solving, and where a problem with the doctor's performance is found, on answering the question 'what practical steps need to be taken so that this doctor can return to practice without risk to patients?'

To complement the work of the NCAS, the Department of Health issued a health service circular in December 2003. *Maintaining high professional standards in the modern NHS: a framework for the initial handling of concerns about doctors and dentists in the NHS* covers action to be taken, including quick and effective investigation, when concern about an employed doctor or dentist first arises, and the action to consider to protect the public such as restrictions on their practice or excluding them from work. This advice was supplemented by further guidance on new disciplinary procedures issued in February 2005. A new national framework came into force on 1 June 2005. The procedures abolish the right of a

The NHS workforce — 2

consultant to appeal to the Health Secretary, and end the distinction between personal and professional misconduct. As a consequence, NHS doctors and dentists are disciplined for misconduct under the same procedures as other NHS staff.

The Scottish Executive Health Department has also acted on poorly performing doctors. Its report *Prevention better than cure* sets out a framework of action. The report recommends that NHS organisations should encourage an atmosphere of openness and support and that all medical staff should have a continuous career portfolio, copies of which should be held by the individual and the appropriate deanery. It also puts forward a mentoring scheme for training grade doctors.

Further information

NCAS, 1st Floor, Market Towers, 1 Nine Elms Lane, London SW8 5NQ. Tel: 020 7084 3851. E-mail: ncas@ncas.npsa.nhs.uk www.ncaa.nhs.uk

NCAS, Wales Office, Sophia House, 28 Cathedral Road, Cardiff CF11 9LF. Tel: 029 2063 6120. E-mail: ncas@ncas.npsa.nhs.uk

Department of Health. *Assuring the quality of medical practice. Implementing 'Supporting doctors, protecting patients'*. January 2001.

Scottish Executive Health Department. *Prevention better than cure — ensuring safer patients and better doctors*. 2001. www.scotland.gov.uk/library3/health/ddit-00.asp

HSC 2003/012. *Maintaining high professional standards in the modern NHS*.

National Audit Office. *The management of suspensions of clinical staff in NHS hospital and ambulance trusts in England*. TSO, 2003.

Department of Health. *Maintaining high professional standards in the modern NHS. Doctors' and dentists' disciplinary framework*. February 2005.

Nursing staff

There are around 500,000 nurses, midwives and health visitors available to work in the United Kingdom. Nurses specialise in a variety of areas including learning disabilities, adult nursing, mental health and children's nursing. They are employed in management roles or can become leaders in their clinical field, for example cancer nursing or the management of care for older people with long-term conditions.

Nurses today work in a wide range of sectors. They are employed in NHS hospital and community settings and also in nursing and residential homes, independent clinics and hospitals, and independent hospices and nursing agencies. Nurses are also employed by other public sector services such as the prison service, the defence medical service, the police service, in higher education and by local authorities. The NHS remains the largest employer of nurses with between three and four times as many nurses as in all other forms of nursing employment. However, the number of nurses working in the independent sector has almost doubled in the past ten years.

The majority of nurses are women; only 9 per cent of qualified nurses are men. The age of working nurses has increased with the proportion of NHS nurses under the age of 35 dropping from 40 per cent in 1996 to 33 per cent in 2000. Nearly a third of NHS nurses (29 per cent) are now over 44 years old. The nursing profession will lose many of its most experienced practitioners through retirement over the next few years.

Regulation

The Nursing and Midwifery Council (NMC) is the statutory regulatory body for nursing, midwifery and health visiting. It:
• maintains a register of qualified nurses
• sets standards for the conduct, practice and education of nurses
• provides professional advice on standards
• considers allegations of misconduct or unfitness to practise due to ill health.

The council links nurse registration with evidence of continuing professional development.

Education

Ten years ago nurse education moved from hospitals to universities with the introduction of Project 2000. Today nursing students study for either diplomas or degrees. Both diploma and degree courses are based on an equal mix of theory and practice and lead to qualification as a registered nurse.

Most nursing students study for higher education diplomas. There are around 62,000 nursing and midwifery students currently in training in the UK and approximately 15 per cent of nursing students follow degree courses which are heavily oversubscribed — though this diploma/degree balance differs in the four countries of the UK. In Wales the universities are offering an increasing number of pre-registration nursing degree course places, with the aim of all pre-registration nursing courses eventually being at degree level.

Nursing students are exempt from tuition fees. Maintenance funding differs between diploma and degree students. While diploma students receive a non means-tested bursary worth around £5,000, students on degree programmes receive a means-tested bursary that can be supplemented with a student loan.

Nurses' roles

Nurses are extending their roles, learning new skills and taking on additional responsibilities. NHS modernisation, with its commitment to creating services shaped around the needs of patients, casts nurses in a central role. Initiatives like NHS Direct, the telephone consultation service, are intended to improve access to health services and increasingly empower people to become partners in their own healthcare through the provision of reliable information and advice.

The way nurses' roles are extended is identified in the NHS Plan for England which promotes ten ways in which nurses are widening their range of clinical practice. These roles are to:
• order diagnostic investigations such as pathology tests and X-rays
• make and receive referrals direct, say, to a therapist or a pain consultant
• admit and discharge patients for specified conditions and within agreed protocols
• manage patient caseloads, say, for diabetes or rheumatology
• run clinics, say, for ophthalmology or dermatology
• prescribe medicines and treatments
• carry out a wide range of resuscitation procedures including defibrillation
• perform minor surgery and outpatient procedures
• triage patients using the latest IT to the most appropriate

The NHS workforce — 2

health professional
• take a lead in the way local health services are organised and in the way that they are run.

All these roles are currently being undertaken by nurses in some parts of the UK and the challenge is to make these extended roles become mainstream throughout the health service. Suitably qualified nurse practitioners work with increased autonomy in a number of clinical areas, and since 2000 the NHS has appointed nurse, midwife and health visitor consultants.

The Royal College of Nursing is particularly concerned that attention should also be paid to the essentials of care, such as dignity, privacy, hygiene and nutrition. These are fundamental and affect patients' perceptions of the quality of care they receive and often their clinical outcomes. With the appointment of clinical matrons in acute hospitals, much emphasis has been placed on the major role they can have in making sure that patients get quality care. They have been tasked with ensuring that healthcare associated infections are kept to a minimum and that cleaning standards are maintained at the highest level.

NHS modernisation and the health service reforms have led to nurses in the community working in new ways. Nurses are running their own practices. Nurses are increasingly getting involved with commissioning and planning for the healthcare needs of their local communities.

Department of Health guidance on the care of patients with long-term conditions in 2005 initiated the appointment of some 3,000 community matrons in England to improve case management, and to concentrate on reduced hospitalisation and improved outcomes for such patients.

Healthcare assistants

As nurses take on more responsibilities, healthcare assistants will continue to play an integral role in healthcare delivery as the providers of nursing care under the overall supervision of a registered nurse. Surveys of both patients and registered nurses indicate that healthcare assistants are considered to be good carers.

During the 1990s the number of healthcare assistants grew in both the NHS and independent sectors. Data for the NHS in England indicates that between 1988 and 1998 the registered nursing workforce remained relatively stable while the non-registered nursing workforce grew from 93,000 to 105,000. Similar changes took place in other parts of the UK, though in Scotland the non-registered nursing workforce slightly decreased.

Recruitment and retention

The delivery of high quality patient care depends on the skills and experience of nurses but there are simply not enough skilled nurses in the workforce. The NHS Plan for England recognised that staff shortages were 'the biggest constraint the NHS faces today' and set targets for the nursing workforce.

NHS trusts have increasingly had to turn to overseas recruitment and using agencies to ease this nurse shortage crisis. The government is also taking action including running high profile advertising campaigns to encourage people to enter the profession or to return to nursing. Better pay is believed to be the single most important factor that would encourage nurses to stay in the profession. Improving nurses' working lives is also a significant factor in addressing recruitment and retention. Introducing employee friendly ways of working, providing support for training and development and the implementation of clear policies to tackle discrimination and harassment all serve to make nursing a more attractive career.

For nursing, the future looks positive in terms of the opportunities which are opening up for the profession and the contribution nurses are making, and will continue to make, to the drive to improve the quality of patient care. But nursing's potential — and that of NHS modernisation — will only be fulfilled through the creation and maintenance of a strong and motivated nursing workforce.

Further reading

Chief nursing officer. www.dh.gov.uk/AboutUs/HeadsOfProfession/ChiefNursingOfficer

Department of Health. *Making a difference.* July 1999.

HSC 1999/217. *Nurse, midwife and health visitor consultants.*

HSC 1999/218. *Improving working lives in the NHS.*

Department of Health. *The essence of care.* February 2001.

Department of Health. *Modern matrons — improving the patient experience.* April 2003.

Department of Health. *Liberating the talents. Helping primary care trusts and nurses to deliver the NHS Plan.* November 2002.

Department of Health. *Practitioners with special interests in primary care. Implementing a scheme for nurses with special interests in primary care.* April 2003.

Department of Health. *Freedom to practise: dispelling the myths.* November 2003.

Department of Health. *Supporting people with long term conditions. Liberating the talents of nurses who care for people with long term conditions.* February 2005.

Dentists

There are some 20,300 dentists working in the general dental services in the UK (or 34 per 100,000 population). In addition dentists work in community and hospital dental services.

Professionals complementary to dentists work to treatment plans devised by supervising dentists. Appliances such as dentures, crowns and bridges and orthodontic appliances are constructed by a dental technician working in a dental laboratory.

General dental practitioners are free to accept or reject any potential patient and to practise where they wish. Under the dental contract, the remuneration of dentists by the NHS includes payment for preventive care as well as restorative treatments. NHS patients accepted by their dentist are offered continuing care, emergency cover, and guaranteed free replacement of similar dental treatments if they fail within a year.

Dentists also receive payments for individual child treatments on top of capitation fees paid for continuous care for children over a period of time. The standard period of continuing care for both adults and children is 15 months.

By November 2005 dentists had received personalised information from the Dental Practices Board which included details of how much they would be entitled to under the revised

The NHS workforce — 2

dental contract, which became operational from April 2006, and the level of service they would be expected to provide in return. This information was then used by primary care trusts to agree local contracts with practitioners.

The new contract aims to encourage dentists to stay in the NHS, gives them the security of an annual NHS income and the opportunity to spend more time on preventive work. Patient charges are simpler and many patients no longer need regular six-monthly check-ups. As PCTs have local control of resources for dentistry, they can immediately commission new services to replace capacity where a dentists leaves the NHS.

Over 30 per cent of dentists had been working in personal dental services pilots and in April 2006 the opportunity arose for these to become permanent arrangements.

Capitation payments in England for children under six years are raised in deprived areas by an additional 25 per cent.

The community dental service is generally located within NHS trusts. There are 1,750 community service dentists in the UK. In 2004 the document *Creating the future* was put out for consultation by the Department of Health. This outlines proposals to reform the roles, education and career structures of salaried primary care dentists.

Within hospital dentistry there are 2,790 dentists practising in the UK. There are four main specialties in hospitals: oral and maxillofacial surgery, orthodontics, paediatric dentistry and restorative dentistry. These services are provided within NHS trust hospitals according to the needs of the local population.

Optometrists (opticians)

A comprehensive, professional optical service is available in the UK only from optical practitioners registered with the General Optical Council or General Medical Council. There are three types.

Ophthalmic medical practitioners are doctors who specialise in eyes and eye care. They are qualified to test sight and prescribe spectacles and other appliances. There are some 820 such practitioners providing services in the UK.

Optometrists (also known as ophthalmic opticians) are qualified to test sight and to prescribe and dispense spectacles and other optical appliances. Some community-based optometrists monitor patients with existing eye diseases. They undertake a degree course, followed by a year's supervised practice and a further examination before registration. Some 8,650 are registered in the UK.

Dispensing opticians are qualified to dispense and supply spectacles, but they must be specifically certified to fit contact lenses. Success in the examination of the Association of British Dispensing Opticians after a two-year course and a year of practice under supervision leads to registration. There are some 4,500 dispensing opticians registered in the UK.

Professional & support staff

The NHS is the second largest organisation in the world and a massive network of groups of staff are required to help provide and maintain its services. On the health professional and technical side, there are the allied health professions (AHP) (box 1), medical laboratory staff and other smaller groups (box 2).

Wellard's NHS Handbook 2006/07

Non-medical staff are categorised as administrative and clerical, maintenance, domestic and ancillary.

The allied health professions

Regulation to ensure that the public is protected from bogus practitioners has been an important issue facing this sector.

In April 2002 the Health Professions Council (HPC) was established. It is regulating over 150,000 members of 13 professions. These are: arts therapists, biomedical scientists, chiropodists and podiatrists, clinical scientists, dietitians, occupational therapists, operating department practitioners, orthoptists, paramedics, physiotherapists, prosthetists and orthotists, radiographers and speech and language therapists.

The purpose of the council is to protect the public and ensure fitness to practise of members of the allied health professions (AHPs). It sets professional standards of education and training, practice and conduct, keeps a register of those who meet the standards and takes remedial action where those standards are not met. It has powers to require registrants to demonstrate their continuing competence. From April 2005, the registers have only been open to those with approved training who are deemed fit to practise.

In moves to improve the effectiveness and productivity of the NHS, the roles of a number of the health professionals are being extended.

In March 2004, the Department of Health also issued proposals for the regulation of healthcare assistants, therapy assistants, all sectors of the healthcare scientist workforce, assistant practitioners, and those undertaking similar roles across a wide range of healthcare settings. A second consultation paper proposed the regulation herbal medicine and acupuncture practitioners.

In 2005 the Department of Health was consulting on bringing applied psychologists under the HPC umbrella.

Health Professions Council, Park House, 184 Kennington Park Road, London SE11 4BU. Tel: 020 7582 0866. www.hpc-uk.org

Department of Health. *Enhancing public protection: proposals for the statutory regulation of healthcare support staff in England and Wales.* March 2004.

Care practitioners

In November 2004 the NHS Modernisation Agency reported on the developing role of emergency care practitioners. They meet the urgent care needs of emergency patients and complement the existing practitioners and clinical

Box 1. Number of allied health profession registrants (November 2005)	
Profession	**Registrants**
Arts therapists	2,190
Biomedical scientists	21,618
Clinical scientists	3,629
Dietitians	6,184
Occupational therapists	24,630
Operating department practitioners	8,271
Orthoptists	1,209
Paramedics	11,572
Physiotherapists	39,602
Podiatrists/chiropodists	12,357
Prosthetists and orthotists	752
Radiographers	23,577
Speech and language therapists	10,046
Total:	**165,637**

Source: Health Professions Council

The NHS workforce — 2

teams and bring them together.

In March 2005, a consultation document set out a proposed education and training programme for healthcare professionals wishing to become surgical care practitioners (SCPs). Such practitioners perform straightforward surgical procedures as well as caring for patients before and after surgery. They have a first level qualification in, for example, nursing, physiotherapy or operating department practice, and work under the supervision of a consultant surgeon.

Similarly, in November 2005, the grade of medical care practitioner (MCP) was proposed by the Department of Health. They are expected to be science graduates or first level health professionals who undertake a two-year course. They will be supervised by a hospital consultant or GP, but they will be allowed to practice without a qualified doctor being in attendance. There are likely to be some 2,000 MCPs recruited in England.

Administrative and clerical staff

There are some 169,000 administrative and clerical staff (whole-time equivalents) working in the UK, of which 131,850 work in England. They perform a wide range of clerical functions, from typing letters to maintaining an array of budgets on computer spreadsheets to ensuring the large quantity of documentation connected with the day-to-day running of the NHS is kept in order. Many are required to have in-depth knowledge of computer software and coding systems — for clinical records, accounting systems and databases, for example — to carry out their role effectively.

Medical secretarial work, more specialised than basic secretarial support, provides an important back-up

---

Some of the allied health professions

Art , music or drama therapists encourage people to express their feelings and emotions through art, such as painting and drawing, music or drama.

Biomedical scientists (medical laboratory technicians) carry out investigations to provide scientific evidence to support the decision-making of clinicians. Their major areas of specialisation are clinical chemistry, haematology, blood transfusion, cellular pathology, medical microbiology and immunology.

Chiropractors treat disorders of the joints, especially spinal injuries.

Clinical scientists oversee specialist tests for diagnosing and managing disease. They advise doctors on using tests and interpreting data and they also carry out research to understand diseases and devise therapies.

Dietitians apply the science of nutrition to promoting health and treating disease.

Occupational therapists treat physical and psychiatric conditions using specific activities. They work in three main areas: physical disability; mental health problems and learning difficulties.

Operating department practitioners participate in the assessment of the patient prior to surgery and provide individualised care.

Orthoptists diagnose and treat defects of vision, eye position and abnormalities of eye movement.

Osteopaths treat disorders of the skeleton by manipulation and massage.

Paramedics provide specialist care and treatment to patients who are either acutely ill or injured. They can administer a range of drugs and carry out certain surgical techniques.

Physiotherapists help to rehabilitate those who have suffered loss of physical function as a result of illness, injury (sports-related, for example) or old age.

Podiatrists (or chiropodists) provide a comprehensive foot health service. Podiatrists may work in private practice as well in the NHS.

Prosthetists and orthotists supply artificial limbs, other parts and mechanical aids.

Radiographers produce images utilising X-rays, radioisotopes, ultrasound and magnetic fields. These images are used in diagnosis and monitoring the progress of treatment.

Speech and language therapists assess, treat and help to prevent speech, language and swallowing difficulties.

service to doctors. Staff working in NHS finance departments maintain vital administrative functions such as payroll, audit and management accounts.

In England, two thirds of staff working in hospitals and community health services are direct care staff, and one third are management and support. Almost 80 per cent of the non-medical workforce (WTEs) are female, and over 6 per cent are from minority ethnic groups.

Maintenance staff

The NHS has a large number of buildings and plant that require constant supervision to ensure they provide a safe and secure environment for staff and patients. Staff and patients depend on essential services, such as water and electrical supplies, and heating and piped gas systems, being in good order. Engineers, electricians, plumbers and building operatives all play their part.

Domestic and ancillary staff

About 100,000 staff fall into the domestic and ancillary categories. Hospital hotel services departments oversee catering, linen, portering and domestic work. Facilities management has a wider brief, covering general estates work. Private contractors as well as in-house teams run many hotel services in hospitals.

The NHS provides over 300m meals and snacks each year to patients, staff and the public at a net annual cost of over £500m. A typical NHS trust may spend 2–3 per cent of its budget on catering, employing chefs, kitchen assistants and other staff to maintain the service. Hospitals need to be able to provide varied menus, catering for all tastes, cultures and appetites. Some meals are prepared to meet special or modified diets requested by a dietitian on behalf of a patient.

Domestic staff aim to ensure that the highest standards of hygiene — crucial in the clinical environment — are maintained. They also serve meals and drinks to patients, manage residential accommodation and provide a general housekeeping service. Increasingly, ward housekeepers have been appointed.

Hospital porters transport patients and materials around the hospital and maintain stocks of medical gases, among other general duties. They are

The NHS workforce — 2

often the first point of contact for patients attending hospital.

Linen services and laundry staff ensure that there is a constant supply of fresh linen — hospitals in England and Wales require around 20m freshly laundered items each week. They provide clean sheets for patients, sterile clothing for staff and uniforms for nurses.

Ancillary staff perform a wide range of vital duties including operating the hospital switchboard, working in hospital shops, hairdressing and providing transport.

Box 2. Professional & technical staff: some of the smaller groups

Anatomical pathology technician
Animal technician
Artificial kidney assistant
Audiological scientist
Audio-visual technician
Biomedical scientist
Cardiographer
Cardiology physiologist
Clinical biochemist
Clinical cytogeneticist
Clinical embryologist
Clinical engineer
Clinical measurement technician
Clinical microbiologist
Clinical perfusionist
Clinical scientist
Contact lens technician
Critical care technologist
Cytogenics and molecular genetics assistant
Cytology screener
Dental hygienist
Dental surgery assistant
Dental technician
Dental therapist
Electrolysist

Electronics technician
Emergency care practitioner
Gastroenterology technologist
Glaucoma technician
Hearing therapist
Hearing/vision screener
Heart/lung technician
Laboratory aide
Medical artist
Medical chartist
Medical illustrator
Medical laboratory assistant
Medical photographer
Medical physics technician
Medical physics technologist
Molecular geneticist
Neurophysiologist
Nuclear medicine technologist
Operating department practitioner
Pharmacy technician
Phlebotomist
Physiological measurement technician
Post-mortem technician
Quality assurance scientist
Quality control technician
Radiotherapy technologist
Radium technician
Rehabilitation engineer
Respiratory function technician
Respiratory physiologist
Prosthetics technician engineer
Renal dialysis technologist
Surgical care practitioner
Surgical instrument curator
Surgical/orthopaedic appliance technician
Technologist in equipment management
Vascular technologist

 Managers in partnership

In June 2005, Managers in Partnership (MiP), a new trade union for NHS managers was launched with more than

4,000 foundation members. It aims to build on the strengths of UNISON and the FDA.

MiP is representing and providing a policy voice for NHS managers and is working with government, the Department of Health, NHS Employers and other professional bodies. The chief executive is Jon Restell.

Managers in Partnership, 2 Caxton Street, London SW1H 0QH. Tel: 0845 6011144. www.miphealth.org.uk

Electronic recruitment

An online recruitment service for the NHS was launched in December 2003. It allows candidates to view job adverts and apply for positions electronically. Over 520 NHS organisations in England use the site (www.jobs.nhs.uk). Similar recruitment sites are in place in the NHS in Wales and Scotland.

Department of Health figures suggest that as many as a quarter of a million people find new jobs in the NHS each year and the service is making substantial savings in recruitment costs. The website means that there is one place at which people can find and apply for jobs across the NHS.

The project is linked to the NHS careers service, and will link into the electronic staff record (ESR) as the national access point for electronic applications into the ESR system.

Health and safety

Healthcare premises can present hazards to patients, visitors and staff alike and it is important that any risks are minimised. The health and safety responsibilities of NHS managers should therefore be seen in the overall context of a comprehensive risk management programme (chapter 5). This chapter sets out the legal obligations of the NHS in the health and safety sphere. It describes good practice and how best to achieve it.

There has to be a commitment to good health and safety practice within the organisation, irrespective of its size. This responsibility is outlined in the Health and Safety at Work Act 1974, which states:

'It shall be the duty of every employer to ensure, so far as is reasonably practicable, the health, safety and welfare at work of all his employees.'

The Management of Health and Safety at Work Regulations 1999 identify the employer's key duties as:
- assessing the risk to health and safety of employees and to everyone else who may be affected by the work activity. This is so that the necessary preventive and protective steps can be identified. Appropriate records should be kept of assessments undertaken. The purpose of a risk assessment required by these regulations is to assist an organisation to identify the requirements imposed upon it by both new and existing safety law
- making arrangements for putting into practice the preventive and protective measures that follow from risk assessment. They should cover planning, organisation, control, monitoring and review. Such measures should be recorded
- co-operating and coordinating with other employers, where they share premises or workplaces.

There are also certain duties placed upon employees to:
- make full and proper use of any arrangements established by the employer for health and safety at work
- report to the employer details of any

The NHS workforce — 2

work situation which might represent a serious and imminent danger.

Effective health and safety, however, is not only about doing what the law requires, it is also about recognising that accidents and illness are costly to the individual member of staff and that they impact upon the quality of the services provided and the financial success of the organisation concerned.

Work undertaken by the Health & Safety Executive (HSE) accident prevention advisory unit confirmed that the cost of accidents in an NHS hospital amounts to at least 5 per cent of its annual running costs. But the analysis did not set out the effect on patients of increased waiting times or cancelled procedures due to these incidents.

Policy. Organisations can contribute to improved performance by the development of a clear and concise written safety policy which recognises that good health and safety can enhance business performance and minimise loss. The organisation should also recognise that the only effective approach to injury, illness and loss prevention is one based on the systematic identification and control of risk.

The policy should influence all activities, including the selection of people, equipment and materials and the way that work is undertaken.

The ultimate responsibility for health and safety lies with the chief executive of each NHS organisation, who must ensure that all staff are aware of the safety policy and that it is implemented and monitored regularly to ensure its effectiveness. In addition, a competent person with the appropriate educational qualifications and experience should be available to provide health and safety assistance to each organisation.

The policy should cover staff, patients, visitors and others in contact with the services identified. This should include contractors, employees provided by employment businesses and employees and other employers on the same site. Temporary and fixed-contract employees should also be included.

Directorate or departmental policies should also be produced. They should specify duties and responsibilities, and give details of the arrangements in place for identifying hazards and assessing risks.

Organising. The creation of a culture which allows health and safety policies to be put into effective practice is important. This culture should be sustained by effective communications and should encourage the co-operation of all employees and safety representatives. The competence of staff at all levels should be ensured through effective recruitment, placement and transfer procedures.

The HSE accident prevention advisory unit places great emphasis on competence-based training and inspectors seek evidence that it is being carried out where needed.

The range of existing legislation which requires adequate safety training is substantial. The general duty under Section 2(2)(c) of the Health and Safety at Work Act 1994 requires each employer to provide, so far as is reasonably practicable, adequate training for all employees. In addition, the Management of Health and Safety at Work Regulations 1999 contains an all-embracing requirement relating to capabilities and training in regulation 13. Whereas in the past, some organisations may have assumed that safety training requirements were directed at employees who were personally engaged in hazardous work, the latest regulations make no distinction between managers and other employees. As the approved code of practice states, training is an important way of achieving competence and helps to convert information into safe working practices. It contributes to the organisation's health and safety culture and is needed at all levels, including top management.

Well-trained managers will lead by example, demonstrate their commitment and provide clear direction. They will also understand the benefits of good co-operation and communication with staff and their representatives. It is essential that staff are involved in the planning and reviewing of performance, the writing of procedures and problem solving.

Planning. A planned and systematic approach should be adopted to policy implementation. Plans should identify clear objectives and targets within specified timescales. They should be measurable, achievable and realistic. Such plans may need to reflect the targets set in corporate contracts and business plans.

Hazards should be identified and risks to staff and others assessed. Performance standards should be set for plant, equipment, substances, procedures, people and products.

Priorities should be established according to risk and resources subsequently allocated. Procedures should be established which can be followed in the event of 'serious or imminent danger' to persons at work.

Measuring performance. Actual performance should be measured against predetermined plans and standards. Monitoring should be carried out both actively, by looking at the extent of compliance with legislation or the achievement of objectives and reactively, by monitoring accidents, illness and other incidents.

An organisation needs to know how well it is performing, against certain standards. Good quality information is needed relating to staff accidents and in particular for areas of major concern such as lifting and handling, sharps and needlesticks, falls and violence to staff. With such information, trends can be identified and remedial action taken, including organisational policy changes and, where appropriate, initiatives commenced to reduce the number of incidents.

Auditing and reviewing performance. The use of auditing and performance review allows an organisation to see if its policy, organisation and systems are achieving the right results. Auditing allows directors and managers to weigh up their organisation's performance in relation to both their own predetermined standards and those of other, possibly competing, organisations.

Monitoring provides the information to enable review activities to take place. Auditing complements monitoring activities by assessing whether policy, organisation and systems are achieving the right result. The reliability and effectiveness of internal systems can be tested in this way.

Conclusion

Effective health and safety management demands comprehensive policies which fulfil the spirit and the letter of the law and which are considered in all business practice and decision-making.

Organisations achieving success in health and safety create and sustain a culture which secures the motivation and involvement of all members of staff and the control of risks. Such organisations minimise risks in an operation by drawing up plans and setting performance standards, with the aim of elimi-

The NHS workforce — 2

nating and controlling risks.

They measure their performance against predetermined plans and standards, the implementation and effectiveness of which they assess as a basis for taking appropriate remedial action. They aim to evaluate performance to maximise learning and to ensure that appropriate action is taken to improve the control of specific risks. They also undertake evaluations to improve overall health and safety performance and to develop further their health and safety policies.

Further reading

EL[95]89. *Health at work in the NHS.*
EL[96]44. *Health and safety management in the NHS.*

House of Commons. Committee of Public Accounts. *Health and safety in NHS acute hospital trusts in England. Second report.* TSO, December 1997.

HSC Health Services Advisory Committee. *Management of health and safety in the health services.* HMSO, 1994.

HSG[97]6. *Health and safety management in the NHS.*

National Audit Office. *Health and safety in NHS acute hospital trusts in England. Report by the Comptroller and Auditor General.* TSO, 1996.

HSC Health Services Advisory Committee. *The safe disposal of clinical waste.* TSO, 1999.

Current health and safety issues

There are various issues which are currently of particular concern in the NHS or where developments are taking place:

Lifting and handling. All staff employed by NHS trusts should receive appropriate lifting and handling training which takes account of the nature of their duties and responsibilities. Risk assessments should be undertaken for any duties which require lifting and handling and appropriate refresher training identified as part of this process. As far as is practicable trusts should provide appropriate equipment to lift patients and move goods in order to minimise the possibility of staff injuring themselves.

Sharps and needlesticks. The BMA code of practice on the safe use and disposal of sharps gives advice on the hazards, assessment and management of risk and the policies and procedures required for those involved with the use and disposal of sharps.

Stress. It has been recognised that the cost of stress to industry continues to increase and that employers should be addressing the cause of workplace stress as well as treating the symptoms. NHS employers should be aware of the HSE guidance *Stress at work — a guide for employers* (HS(G)116).

Violence to staff. The risks of violence to staff in health premises continue to increase. Trusts should be aware of the NHS zero tolerance campaign.

Legionella precautions. Risk assessments should be carried out and a strategy put in place for the management of legionella risks.

Health & Safety Executive management audits. The HSE has placed increasing emphasis on trusts adopting a structured approach to health and safety management based on risk assessment. Visits by the HSE to trusts have concentrated on the effective management of health and safety.

Patient falls from windows. The HSE issued a reminder to NHS trust managers and owners of registered nursing homes about the risk of patients falling out of windows. Guidance on window openings and construction was issued by NHS Estates in 1989. It stated that 'a restricted opening of not more than 100mm (4in) is recommended for general use in areas where windows are within easy reach of patients'.

Risk of hanging. Following the publication of NHS Estates Hazard Notice HN(98)04 regarding the risk of hanging from ligature points such as bed curtain rails and shower curtain rails, a target to reduce the number of suicides by mental health inpatients has been set by the chief medical officer. New mental health facilities should have collapsible rails fitted and action should be taken to change any existing rails to the collapsible type.

Immunity status — hepatitis B. A register should be maintained to ensure that the immunity status of all staff who undertake exposure-prone procedures is known.

Latex sensitisation. Local policies and procedures should be in place which address the purchase and use of medical gloves and the management of staff and patients sensitised to latex in line with the Medical Devices Agency Device Bulletin DB9601 *Latex sensitisation in the healthcare setting* and Safety Notice SN 9825.

Risks of scalding. Managers should be aware of the risk of scalding to vulnerable groups of patients when bathing. Thermostatic mixer valves should be installed in areas where patients could be at risk when bathing. An effective programme should be in place to ensure their maintenance and a system for monitoring water temperatures should be established. Guidance on safe bathing water temperatures is contained in the NHS Estates guidance note *Safe hot water and surface temperatures*.

Waste anaesthetic gases. HSE information sheet for the health service No. 7 outlines good practice for those involved with waste anaesthetic gases, to enable them to comply with the Control of Substances Hazardous to Health Regulations. Such persons should also be aware of the continuing review of occupational exposure standards for the four anaesthetic gases (halothane, isoflurane, enflurane and nitrous oxide).

Waste disposal. The Health Services Advisory Committee's guidance on the safe disposal of clinical waste has been republished (*The safe disposal of clinical waste*. ISBN 0 7176 2492 7). The guidance provides advice on how to comply with both health and safety and environmental law.

3 — Implementing NHS strategy

This chapter outlines the NHS Plans for England, Wales and Scotland. It provides a checklist on implementation in England. It also describes more recent strategy documents including the Department of Health's priorities and planning framework for 2003/06–2007/08 and the out of hospital care White Paper.

The NHS Plan for England

The NHS Plan for England, published in July 2000, represents a blueprint for the radical reform of the NHS over ten years and sets out how extra money announced in the comprehensive spending reviews is to be allocated and spent.

Funding healthcare

The NHS will continue to be funded from the tax system and be free at the point of use.

Investing in NHS facilities

Clean hospitals

A nationwide clean-up campaign involves every hospital having a regular inspection of cleanliness. National standards for cleanliness form part of the NHS performance assessment framework.

Better hospital food

A 24-hour NHS catering service with a new NHS menu is to be developed.

Investing in NHS staff

More training places

There will be a year-on-year increase in training places:

- 5,500 more nurses, midwives and health visitors being trained
- 4,450 more therapists and other key professional staff being trained
- 1,000 more specialist registrars
- 450 more doctors training for general practice

- a further 1,000 new medical school places.

Improved pay for NHS staff

A market forces supplement to top up the pay of staff in areas of labour market shortages is proposed. There is to be help with accommodation costs for nurses and other staff and an expansion of childcare facilities.

Improving working lives

A performance framework for human

NHS Plan — main targets

Beds
- 2,100 extra NHS beds in general and acute wards
- 5,000 extra intermediate care beds — in community hospitals, designated hospital wards, new facilities and private nursing homes
- 1,700 extra non-residential intermediate care places
- a 30 per cent rise in adult critical care beds over three years

Staff
- 7,500 more consultants
- 2,000 more GPs
- 20,000 more nurses
- 6,750 more allied health professionals

Facilities
- 100 new hospitals to be built by 2010
- 500 one-stop primary care centres
- over 3,000 GP premises modernised
- 250 scanners
- modern IT systems in every hospital and GP surgery

resources is to be incorporated into the performance assessment framework. All NHS employers are to be assessed against performance targets and an *Improving working lives* (IWL) standard.

International recruitment
The Department of Health is to work to recruit suitably qualified staff from abroad where they are not creating local shortages.

Training and development
£145m allocated for training and development for all staff.

Changed systems for the NHS
The Department of Health is to monitor performance, put in place a proper system of inspection, provide back-up to assist modernisation and correct failure. The Department will champion the interests of patients.

Setting priorities and developing standards
The DH is, with leading clinicians, managers and staff, to set national standards. These standards are to take two forms:
• national service frameworks (NSFs)
• output from the National Institute for (Health and) Clinical Excellence (NICE).

Information on performance standards
• The performance assessment framework is to apply to all NHS trusts and primary care trusts.
• Responsibility for the annual publication of the results of the performance assessment framework is to transfer to the Commission for Health Improvement (now the Healthcare Commission), working with the Audit Commission.
• Every GP practice and PCT has to have

systems in place to monitor referral rates from every GP practice.
• Revised efficiency targets will be based on service levels achieved by the best trusts.

Incentives and earned autonomy
NHS organisations were to be classified according to the performance assessment framework:
• red* organisations — fail to meet a number of the core national targets
• yellow organisations — meet all or most national core targets, but are not in the top 25 per cent of organisations on the performance assessment framework
• green organisations — meet all core national targets and score in the top 25 per cent.

The green-light NHS organisations are to be rewarded with greater autonomy and national recognition.

(* Red, yellow and green classifications subsequently became the star rating system of zero to three stars. In 2005 the Healthcare Commission began to monitor the performance on NHS organisations against new criteria set out in *Standards for better health* and instituted an annual health check for them.)

Inspection
CHI (now the Healthcare Commission) will inspect each NHS organisation every four years.

Financial incentives
A national health performance fund for each health authority area rewards progress against agreed objectives.

Intervention
Failing organisations are to be subject

3 — Implementing NHS strategy

to a rising scale of intervention reflecting the seriousness of their problems.

Non-executive directors
The NHS Appointments Commission makes all appointments to NHS boards. It comprises a chair and commissioners, each with a regional role.

Service reconfiguration
The National Independent Panel (later to become the Independent Reconfiguration Panel) is to advise on contested major service configuration changes and is to be made up of one-third citizens and patients, one-third health professionals and one-third managers.

Scrutiny of the NHS
Local government is to scrutinise the NHS locally. Chief executives of NHS organisations are to be required to attend the local authority scrutiny all-party committee.

The power to refer major planned changes in local services to the Health Secretary will transfer from community health councils (CHCs) to the local all-party scrutiny committees. These committees are to be able to refer contested major service reconfigurations to the Independent Reconfiguration Panel.

Changes between health and social services
Social services will be delivered in new settings such as GP surgeries and staff will work alongside GPs and other primary and community health teams as part of a local care network.

Intermediate care
An extra £900m investment is to provide for intermediate care and related services for older people.

Incentives for joint working
Local authorities, health authorities and PCTs are to receive incentive payments to encourage joint working.

Care trusts
Care trusts are to commission and deliver primary and community healthcare as well as social care for older people and other client groups. Social services is to be delivered under delegated authority from local councils. Care trusts will be established where there is a joint agreement at local level that this model offers the best way to deliver better care services.

Changes for NHS doctors
Personal medical services
A third of GPs are to be working to personal medical services (PMS) contracts.

Single-handed practices
New contractual quality standards will be introduced for single-handed practices.

Hospital doctors
Specialist registrar posts are to be centrally funded. There is to be a greater role for consultants in shaping health services:
- hospital consultants will be part of the task forces and modernisation boards
- new forms of commissioning will draw on the expertise of hospital consultants
- radical forms of clinically-led care will be piloted.

The consultant contract has been renegotiated.

Medical education
The senior house officer grade provides broader educational experience and a reduction in workload. A medical

education standards board (now known as the Postgraduate Medical Education and Training Board) is to be established to provide a coherent approach to postgraduate medical education, replacing the existing separate bodies.

Changes for nurses, midwives, therapists and other NHS staff
Breaking down barriers between staff
Qualified nurses, midwives and therapists are being empowered to undertake a broader range of clinical tasks, including prescribing drugs, working under protocols. Midwives are working with doctors and nurses in developing maternity and child health services and Sure Start projects. Pharmacists have been invited to apply to become local pharmaceutical services that pilot alternative contracts.

Training and development for staff
£140m allocated to support training and development for all staff, including an individual learning account of £150 a year or training to NVQ Level 2 and 3 for non-professional staff.

Modernising education and training
A pre-condition of delivering patient care is to be the ability to communicate with patients. A new common foundation programme will enable students and staff to switch careers and training paths more easily.

Leadership
Every hospital has to have senior sisters and charge nurses who are easily identifiable to patients and who are accountable for a group of wards. Service modernisation sessions will be introduced to enable managers and clinicians to apply lessons that have been learned elsewhere in the NHS. Support and training for clinical and medical directors will be undertaken.

Changes for patients
Information to empower patients
• The expert patient programme is to be extended. NICE is to publish patient-friendly versions of its clinical guidelines. Patients are to be helped to navigate through health information with the development of new media.
• Letters between clinicians about a patient's care are to be copied to the patient as of right.

Strengthening patient choice
• A wider range of information is to be published about each GP practice.
• Every patient will be able to book hospital appointments and elective admissions.

Protection for patients
The National Clinical Assessment Authority (later the National Clinical Assessment Service) is to provide rapid and expert assessment of an individual doctor's performance, recommending relevant action to the employer. The NHS Tribunal is to be abolished, and the power to suspend or remove GPs from a primary care list devolved to primary care trusts. The right of consultants to appeal against dismissal to the Health Secretary is to end.

The UK Council for the Regulation of Healthcare Professionals (later the Council for Healthcare Regulatory Excellence) is to coordinate the work of the regulatory bodies.

A patient advocacy service
A patient advice and liaison service (PALS) will be established in every trust.

3 — Implementing NHS strategy

Rights of redress
When a patient's operation is cancelled by the hospital on the day of surgery for non-clinical reasons, the hospital will have to offer another binding date within a maximum of 28 days or fund the patient's treatment at the time and hospital of the patient's choice.

Patients' views
NHS trusts and PCTs should ask patients and carers for their views on the service they receive. Every NHS organisation, as well as care homes, has to publish an annual account of these views and the action taken as a result. Financial rewards for trusts are to be linked to the results of the annual national patients survey. A patients' forum is to be established in every NHS trust and PCT to provide input into the running of services.

Patients represented throughout the NHS
The Commission for Health Improvement (now the Healthcare Commission) is to include citizen and lay inspectors on its review teams and older people are to be represented on its inspection teams to ensure older people's interests are fully taken into account. A citizens council is to be established to advise NICE on its clinical assessments.

Community health councils were abolished in September 2003.

The relationship between the NHS and private sector
There is a national framework for partnership between the private and voluntary sector and the NHS. New arrangements set out in a concordat cover private and voluntary providers.

NHSplus
NHSplus has been established as a national agency to deliver occupational health services to public and private sector employers. These services build on local services provided by hospitals and PCTs.

Cutting waiting times for treatment
Primary care
Patients are to have greater access to authoritative information about how to care for themselves and their families.
• NHS Direct and GP out-of-hours services are to be integrated. A phone call to NHS Direct is to be a one-stop gateway to out-of-hours healthcare.
• Every PCT is to have schemes to help people receive more assistance from pharmacists.
• Patients are to be able to see a primary care professional within 24 hours and a GP within 48.
• Patients are to be able to have more tests and treatment in primary care centres rather than hospital.
• Consultants are to deliver more outpatient consultations in primary care and community settings.
• Up to 1,000 specialist GPs are to take referrals from fellow GPs for conditions in specialties such as ophthalmology, orthopaedics, dermatology and ear, nose and throat conditions.

Hospital care
No one should wait more than four hours in A&E from arrival to admission, transfer or discharge.

Maximum waiting times
• waiting lists for hospital appointments and admission are to be replaced with booking systems
• the maximum waiting time for a routine outpatient appointment is to be three months
• the maximum wait for inpatient

treatment is to be six months. Urgent cases are to be treated in accordance with clinical need.

Improving health and reducing inequality

Reducing inequalities in access to NHS services

The medical practices committee is to be abolished and a medical education standards board (the Postgraduate Medical Education and Training Board) introduced to track the number and distribution of doctors in primary care.

A single resource allocation formula covering all NHS spending is to be introduced. Action on tackling health inequalities is to be measured and managed through the NHS performance assessment framework.

Children

There will be:
- an expansion of Sure Start projects covering a third of children under four living in poverty
- the creation of a children's fund worth £450m over three years
- reform of the welfare foods programme
- full implementation of the teenage pregnancy strategy
- effective screening programmes for women and children
- a sexual health and HIV strategy.

Reducing smoking

The NHS is to provide comprehensive smoking cessation services; nicotine replacement therapy (NRT) available on prescription, complementing smoking cessation treatment. NICE is to advise GPs on the most appropriate and cost-effective prescribing regimes for NRT and buproprion. The Committee on Safety of Medicines is to consider whether NRT should be on general sale.

Improving diet and nutrition

Action will include:
- a national school fruit scheme for every child in nursery or infant school under the age of six, entitling them to a free piece of fruit each school day
- a five-a-day programme to increase fruit and vegetable consumption
- work to increase provision and access to fruit and vegetables
- initiatives to improve the overall balance of diet
- action to tackle obesity and physical inactivity
- a hospital nutrition policy.

Tackling drugs and alcohol-related crime

A national treatment agency accountable to the DH will be set up.

Partnerships to tackle inequality

Partnership between health and local services will be a key strategic role for health authorities.
- The NHS will help develop local strategic partnerships, strengthening links between health, education, employment and other causes of social exclusion. In the meantime effective health action zones will continue.
- There are to be integrated, public health groups across NHS regional offices (now strategic health authorities) and government offices of the regions.
- A healthy communities collaborative is to spread best practice.

Clinical priorities

Cancer

A national cancer plan published. Existing screening programmes are to be extended and new programmes for other cancers introduced.
- The breast screening programme is to

3 — Implementing NHS strategy

be extended to women aged 65–70. The service is to be upgraded.
• The cervical cancer screening programme is to be upgraded by introducing new technologies.

An NHS cancer research network is to be implemented. NICE is to issue guidance on how best to organise urological, haemotological, and head and neck cancer services and supportive/ palliative care.

Coronary heart disease

Investment is to be channelled into expanding the workforce, especially consultants. The number of cardiologists is to increase to 685. Rapid access chest pain clinics are to be established to assess all patients with new onset chest pain which their GP thinks might be due to angina.

Mental health

One thousand graduate primary care mental health workers are to be employed to help GPs manage and treat common mental health problems. An additional 500 community mental health staff are to be employed to work with GPs and primary care teams, NHS Direct, and in A&E departments.

Fifty early intervention teams are to be established to provide treatment and active support in the community to young people and their families. All young people who experience a first episode of psychosis are to receive the early and intensive support they need.

Over three years 335 crisis resolution teams are to be established. All people in contact with specialist mental health services are to be able to access crisis resolution services.

There are to be women-only day centres in every health authority.

Seven hundred more staff are to be recruited to increase the breaks avail-

able for carers, and to strengthen carer support networks.

Implementation checklist

Some of the actions achieved to implement the NHS Plan include:
• pre-booked outpatient appointments and inpatient admissions
• clean hospitals — general environment and cleanliness improved
• hospital food — significant catering improvements underway
• staff
 — progress in recruiting more staff and increasing training places
 — market forces supplement implemented
 — progress on implementing *Improving working lives*
 — modernisation of the NHS pay system implemented
• national service framework programme continues to unfold
• increased output of technology appraisals and guidelines from the National Institute for Health and Clinical Excellence
• Commission for Health Improvement becomes the Healthcare Commission
• NHS Appointments Commission established
• independent reconfiguration panel in place
• extensive work to develop intermediate care
• care trusts pilots underway
• over 40 per cent of GPs opting for personal medical services employment
• 89 walk-in centres open or planned
• 90 per cent of patients who wish to do so are able to see a primary care professional within one working day and a GP within two working days
• expert patient programme extended
• National Clinical Assessment Service created
• Postgraduate Medical Education and

Training Board set up
- patient advice and liaison services created and patient and public involvement forums set up
- PCTs publish patient prospectuses
- local government overview and scrutiny committees established
- concordat with private sector up and running
- clinical matrons and consultant nurses in post
- expansion of NHS Direct
- significant progress on reducing access times
- smoking cessation programmes developed
- national fruit scheme for children and five-a-day campaign underway
- progress in the clinical priority areas of care of older people, cancer, coronary heart disease and mental health.

National planning framework

National standards, local action: health and social care standards and planning framework 2005/06–2007/08, published in July 2004, sets out new targets and healthcare standards for then NHS in England, detailing what patients can expect from NHS providers.

While the standards aim to safeguard and raise quality across the board, the national targets will accelerate improvements in a small number of national priority areas.

The reduced number of national targets include:
- achieving year-on-year reductions in MRSA levels and future reductions in other healthcare associated infections
- an 18 week maximum waiting target from start time to treatment by 2008
- helping people to manage their long-term conditions so they spend less

time in hospital
- improving the health of black and ethnic minority communities.

Since many of the NHS Plan targets are being achieved before targets dates the document offers a new set of standards — and a new focus — where needed.

The NHS improvement plan

The NHS improvement plan. Putting people at the heart of public services set out in June 2004 the priorities for the NHS between then and 2008. It supports the continuing commitment to a 10-year process of reform outlined in the NHS Plan.

In particular, it records than in return for the rise in investment the health service will offer the following:
- patients will be admitted for treatment within a maximum of 18 weeks from referral by their GP, and those with urgent conditions will be treated much faster
- patients will be able to choose between a range of providers, including NHS foundation trusts and treatment centres
- patients will be able to be treated at any facility that meets NHS standards, within the national maximum price that the NHS pays for the treatment they need
- patients will have access to a wider range of services in primary care, including access to services nearer their workplace
- electronic prescribing will improve the efficiency and quality of prescribing
- people with complex long-term conditions will be supported locally by a new type of clinical specialist, to be known as community matrons
- major investment in services closer to home will ensure better support for patients who have long-term condi-

3 — Implementing NHS strategy

tions, enabling them to minimise the impact of these on their lives
• the NHS will develop into a *health* service rather than one that focuses primarily on sickness and will, in partnership, make further in-roads into levels of smoking, obesity and the other major causes of disease. There will be a sustained drive to reduce inequalities in health

• there will be incentives for healthcare providers to offer care that is efficient, responsive, of a high standard and respects people's dignity.

In March 2005, NHS chief executive Sir Nigel Crisp gave more detail on how the implementation plan would be delivered (in *Creating a patient-led NHS*). Major themes of the document are:

Ten high impact changes

The NHS Modernisation Agency, through its work with hundreds of NHS clinical teams, identified ten high impact changes that organisations in health and social care could adopt to make significant, measurable improvements in the way they delivered care. The changes drew on the learning from its work and build on the successes already achieved. They are rooted in the day-to-day experience and achievements of thousands of frontline clinical teams right across the NHS. The changes are evidence based. They have been field tested and evaluated in real life NHS settings and developed and adapted to have the best chance of success.

If the principles were adopted systematically by the whole NHS, said the agency:
• the experience of patients would be greatly enhanced by more appropriate and timely care
• hundreds of thousands of clinician hours, hospital bed days and appointments in primary and secondary care would be saved
• clinical quality and clinical outcomes would be tangibly improved
• it would be easier to attract and retain staff and there would be more enjoyment and pride at work.

Change No 1: Treat day surgery as the norm for elective surgery
Change No 2: Improve access to key diagnostic tests
Change No 3: Manage variation in patient discharge
Change No 4: Manage variation in patient admission
Change No 5: Avoid unnecessary follow-ups
Change No 6: Increase the reliability of performing therapeutic interventions through a care bundle approach
Change No 7: Apply a systematic approach to care for people with long-term conditions
Change No 8: Improve patient access by reducing the number of queues
Change No 9: Optimise patient flow using process templates
Change No 10: Redesign and extend role

NHS Modernisation Agency. *Ten high impact changes for service improvement and delivery.* September 2004.

- a patient-led service
- what services will look like
- securing services
- changing the way the NHS works.

Sir Nigel commented: 'The past five years have been about building capacity and capability. The next will be about improving quality, making sure that we give the very best value for money and use the new capacity and capability to build a truly patient led service.'

Commissioning a patient-led NHS

Sir Nigel Crisp produced another strategic document in July 2005. Although short it is having a fundamental influence on the future organisational shape of the NHS. *Commissioning a patient-led NHS* calls for £250m savings in overhead costs and a merger of primary care trusts and of strategic health authorities. Sir Nigel also called for universal coverage of practice-based commissioning. He expected PCTs to have provision for this in place by December 2006. The Department's view is that by creating larger PCTs their commissioning function will be strengthened.

PCT boundary changes will be completed by October 2006 and there will be some 120–160 of the new PCTs covering England. The number of SHAs is likely to come down from 28 to about 11. One objective is to have PCT boundaries coterminous with those of local authorities where possible, so as to facilitate liaison concerning social services.

Out of hospital care

After one of the biggest (and most expensive) public consultation exercises in the UK on out of hospital services, *Our health, our care, our say: a new direction for community services* was published at the end of January 2006. The main thrust of the White Paper is for the NHS to provide safe, high quality services in the community closer to the patient's home. This has been an enduring theme of governments for at least 20 years. Another long-standing ambition embraced by the document is a greater emphasis on prevention.

It introduces a new NHS life check for people to assess their lifestyle risks. The assessment tool will be available online or in hard copy, and this will be supplemented with specific health and social care advice.

The White Paper aims to bring more support to maintain mental health and emotional wellbeing. There is a promise to make it easier for people to get information when they need to choose a GP practice. In social care, there will be an increase in the take-up of direct payments to individuals who need services.

There is an emphasis on reducing inequalities and increasing the quantity and quality of primary care in underserved deprived areas. There will be more support for people will long-term care needs and more investment in the expert patient programme.

A key assumption is that primary and community care services purchased by the NHS will grow faster than secondary care in acute hospitals. Associated with this will be a new generation of community hospitals and polyclinics with strong ties to social care.

An overview and next steps

Towards the end of 2005 the Department of Health was being criticised for devising a string of reforms to the NHS which did not necessarily coalesce. Perhaps to counter this view, in December 2005 the Department published

3 — Implementing NHS strategy

Health reform in England: update and next steps.

This aims to explain how the strategic reforms are intended to be mutually reinforcing.

The four connected streams of work it sets out are:

- more choice and a much stronger voice for patients (demand-side reforms)
- more diverse providers, with more freedom to innovate and improve services (supply-side reforms)
- money following the patients, rewarding the best and most efficient, giving others the incentive to improve (transactional reforms)
- system management and decision-making to support quality, safety, fairness, equity and value for money (system management reforms).

Further information

The NHS Plan: a plan for action, a plan for reform. DH, July 2000.

The NHS improvement plan. Putting people at the heart of public services. DH, June 2004.

National standards, local action. Health and social care standards and planning framework 2005/06–2007/08. DH, July 2004.

Creating a patient-led NHS. Delivering the NHS improvement plan. DH, March 2005.

Crisp, Sir Nigel. *Commissioning a patient-led NHS.* DH, July 2005.

Health reform in England: update and next steps. DH, December 2005.
Our health, our care, our say: a new direction for community services. DH, January 2006.

The NHS Plan in Scotland

The national plan for the NHS in Scotland — *Our national health: a plan for action, a plan for change* (December 2000) has radically altered the way the NHS is organised in Scotland.

Under the plan, in the 12 mainland health board areas a single unified NHS board replaced the former board structures of health boards and NHS trusts and the structural reforms have been taken further.

There is a single local health plan replacing the health improvement programme and trust implementation plans. Conditions specific standards cover the four major cancers, secondary prevention of myocardial infarction, and the treatment of schizophrenia, for delivery locally. A national coronary heart disease register is being developed. There is a pledge to remove postcode prescribing.

Investment priorities have included:
- a £100m health improvement fund between 2000 and 2004
- hospital building and modernising primary care facilities
- 24-hour primary care cover
- workforce
- IT
- equipment.

Some £15m has been invested in national demonstration projects on:
- preventing heart disease
- improving sexual health
- improving children's health.

Further major reforms of the NHS in Scotland were announced in May 2005. In what has become known as the Kerr report, after its lead author Professor David Kerr, recommendations are made for a greater emphasis on long-term conditions and preventive care. The document creates a framework for change over 20 years and proposes a locally responsive NHS rather than a hospital-centred approach. It also calls for a move to team-based care. A tiered model of out-of-hours emergency care is proposed.

Our national health: a plan for action, a plan for change. 2000. www.show.scot.nhs.uk/sehd/onh/onh-00.htm

NHS Scotland. *A national framework for service change in the NHS in Scotland: building a health service fit for the future* (Kerr report). May 2005. www.show.scot.nhs.uk/sehd/nationalframework/Reports.htm

NHS Scotland. *Delivering for health.* November 2005. www.scotland.gov.uk/Publications/2005/11/02102635/26356

The NHS Plan in Wales

The Welsh plan — *Improving health in Wales: a plan for the NHS with its partners* (January 2001), sets out a programme of action to simplify the structure of the Welsh NHS while making it more accountable to the public.

Local health groups have been replaced by local health boards. Health authorities were abolished from April 2003 with the National Assembly providing direction and oversight.

Action is being taken to target improvements in care for cancer, coronary heart disease, diabetes, mental illness, learning disabilities, oral health, health promotion for children and older people.

All NHS organisations are expected to develop and deliver action plans for public involvement in the health service, working more closely with local government and the voluntary/independent

sectors. New patterns of service are being developed to support rehabilitation and independence.

Designed for life, published in May 2005, builds on the 2001 document and aims to promote the health and wellbeing of people in Wales through partnerships of NHS staff, service users and the public in a ten-year programme. The strategy emphasises the importance of patients having prompt access to their primary care team, who will be central to the delivery of chronic disease management.

Improving health in Wales: a plan for the NHS with its partners. www.wales.gov.uk/healthplanonline

Welsh Assembly Government. *Designed for life: creating world class health and social care for Wales in the 21st century.* May 2005.

83

4 — Involving patients

The NHS should put patients at the centre of everything it does. To embed this approach within the NHS requires a change in attitude among staff and a new approach to mechanisms for patient and public involvement (PPI). The NHS Plan set out arrangements to establish a new system of involvement for England which has replaced community health councils (CHCs) in England as part of the modernisation programme. The system is also designed to respond to the Bristol Royal Infirmary Inquiry report, which recommended representation of patient interests on the inside of the NHS and at every level.

The Commission for Patient and Public Involvement in Health

The Commission for Patient and Public Involvement in Health (CPPIH) was established in January 2003 to oversee the patient and public involvement (PPI) system.

The CPPIH is an independent, non-departmental public body that:
• sets up, funds, staffs and performance manages PPI forums
• appoints members to forums
• sets quality standards for, and issues guidance to PPI forums
• reports to the Health Secretary about how the system is working
• makes reports to other national bodies
• carries out national reviews of services from the patient's perspective.

As a result of the Department of Health's review of arms' length bodies, the CPPIH is due to be abolished in August 2006.

Patient and public involvement forums

Following the abolition of community health councils in September 2003, 572

Improving access — a strategic view

Increased capacity
• More staff
• More facilities
• Faster diagnosis

For elective care:
• Treatment centres
• Overseas teams
• Overseas treatment
• Independent sector

For emergency and primary care:
• Walk-in centres
• Out-of-hours services
• NHS Direct

Service redesign
• New roles, eg nurse consultants and practitioners with a special interest
• Faster diagnosis
• Intermediate care
• Demand management
• Day surgery

Faster and more convenient care for patients
• **Primary care:** Patients get to see a GP within two days or another primary care professional within one day
• **A+E:** Patients wait no more than four hours from arrival to admission, transfer or discharge
• **Outpatient care:** Patients wait no more than three months for an appointment
• **Inpatient care:** Patients wait no more than six months to be admitted

Booked appointments

Choice
Patients can choose where they go for elective care

patient and public involvement (PPI) forums have been taking the lead role in providing an independent voice for patients and the public.

Local voluntary and community not-for-profit bodies act as support organisations to at least two PPI forums. They provide premises for, and staff to support, their forums. The forum support organisations are managed on a geographical basis by nine regional centres.

Each forum comprises up to 20 volunteers, recruited locally and trained appropriately.

In each NHS trust and PCT, the forums:
- provide advice and information to patients and their carers about services
- monitor and review the trust's service from the perspective of the patient
- seek the views of patients (especially minorities and those who are not usually heard)
- inspect premises where services are delivered
- refer matters of concern to the strategic health authority, local authority overview and scrutiny committees (OSCs) or Commission for Patient and Public Involvement in Health (CPPIH)
- produce an annual report which is submitted to the local trust, the Health Secretary and CPPIH
- monitor the effectiveness of patient advice and liaison services (PALS) and independent complaints advocacy services (ICAS).

The forums are also reviewing care provided by the private sector and treatment centres for NHS patients. Care and children's trusts are similarly monitored. PPI forums are being set up for foundation trusts.

The forums work together to share experiences and address common issues.

In March 2005, the Department of Health announced a consultation on strengthening forums by merging them, so that there would be one forum per PCT. It would require all PPI forums to have chairs appointed by the NHS Appointments Commission. There would be fewer, larger contracts with the independent sector to provide staff support to forums. A resource centre would also be developed to provide advice and guidance to forums.

Patient advice and liaison services

The NHS Plan signalled the creation of patient advice and liaison services (PALS) within NHS trusts and primary care trusts. PALS aim to ensure that members of the public have the information and advice they need when using NHS services. Help is available to patients and their carers, friends and family. To provide support PALS teams liaise with staff, managers, health organisations and support groups to solve problems. As a last resort they can help patients make formal complaints.

PALS staff are employed by the trusts and should have direct access to chief executives. By reacting and passing on patient feedback PALS can contribute to improving NHS services.

Independent complaints advocacy services

The Health and Social Care Act 2001 called for independent advocacy services to be provided by the NHS for people who wish to complain formally about their care or treatment. To meet this need independent complaints advocacy services (ICAS) are located in every NHS trust and PCT area.

The service provides independent advice, support and advocacy for people wishing to make a formal complaint about their NHS care or treatment. ICAS

4 — Involving patients

work with people to help them think through what outcome they want, choose the best route and help them through these procedures, whether through complaint or reconciliation. ICAS also help people navigate the complaints procedure.

A statutory duty on the NHS to consult patients

Section 11 of the Health and Social Care Act 2001 places a duty on NHS trusts, primary care trusts and strategic health authorities to make arrangements to involve and consult patients and the public in service planning and operation, and in the development of proposals for changes. This statutory duty means consulting and involving:

- not just when a major change is proposed, but in ongoing service planning
- not just in the consideration of a proposal, but in the development of that proposal
- in decisions about general service delivery, not just major changes.

The duty to involve and consult came into force on 1 January 2003 and guidance on strengthening accountability was issued in February 2003.

Improving the patient's experience

In October 2004, the Department of Health published *Getting over the wall*, which is designed to help the NHS shift the focus of its patient and public involvement work from activity — process — to outputs and outcomes. It argues that only when patient and public involvement is part of everyday practice will patients have a greater say in the way the NHS is planned and developed, and their experiences improve. The report provides a number of examples of progress that NHS

organisations have made in this area.

Patient prospectuses

Each year primary care trusts have been asked to produce a patient prospectus entitled *Your guide to local health services,* as part of improving communications locally with the public.

The provision of clear information about available services is an essential element of the DH's approach to improving the patient experience, as it is one of the five areas patients say matter most to them.

Research by MORI has shown that members of the public have found the prospectuses useful and they have helped to change behaviour by offering patients more choice about where they might access advice and treatment.

Director for patients and the public

In April 2003 the Department of Health appointed Harry Cayton to the post of director for patients and the public. His role is to:

- champion the voice of patients and carers and the public throughout the NHS and in the Department
- support staff to be responsive to the needs of, and work in partnership, with patients and carers
- act as a national spokesperson in promoting and explaining patient-focused policy.

Patient choice

Delivering the NHS Plan describes how explicit patient choice should be progressively introduced across the NHS. The nhs.uk website provides regularly updated information on waiting for all major treatments at all providers.

Since July 2002 patients in England waiting six months for heart surgery have been able opt for earlier treatment at an alternative hospital. Over half of patients have taken up this option. A similar scheme for cataract patients in London began in October 2002.

At the start of a nationwide roll out of choice across the NHS, further schemes were announced in February 2003. Choice has been extended to patients, mainly older people, needing cataract operations in the south of England where waiting times have been the longest. As a result waiting times were cut to three months by 2005. From April 2005, patients become eligible to choose an alternative provider of bypass surgery, angioplasty and valve surgery at the point of referral by their cardiologist following angiography.

To broaden the scope of the patient choice initiative the Department of Health held a national consultation exercise in the autumn of 2003, to look at ways in which the delivery of health and social care could offer more choice.

All of this activity has been leading up to the target of being able to offer all patients requiring surgery a choice of four to five providers at the point of referral by December 2005.

Building on the best. Choice, responsiveness and equity in the NHS set out, in December 2003, how NHS services should become more responsive to patients, by offering more choice across the spectrum of healthcare. The aim was to extend choice beyond elective care into services such as chronic conditions, primary care and maternity services. Harry Cayton, director for patients and the public, led the work.

Priority was given to the following actions:
• to give people a bigger say in how they are treated — patients may record their own information securely

on the internet in their own Health Space. In time this will link to their electronic medical record so they can make their preferences known to the clinical team
• to increase choice of access to a wider range of services, such as diagnostic tests, in primary care, encouraging innovative new providers and extending more flexible ways for people to access care
• to increase choice of where, when and how to get medicines, by making repeat prescribing simpler, freeing up restrictions on the location of new pharmacies, expanding the range of medicines pharmacies can provide without a prescription, promoting minor ailments schemes where pharmacies can help patients manage conditions like coughs, hay fever and stomach upsets without involving their GP and increasing the range of healthcare professionals who can prescribe
• to enable people to book appointments at a time that suits them, from a choice of hospitals
• to widen choice of treatment and care, starting with greater choice in maternity services and greater choice over care at the end of life.
• to ensure people have the right information, at the right time, with the support they need to use it so that this becomes central to how people are cared for. New technology will be embraced such as digital TV, and a programme of kitemarking information from a variety of sources will be developed so that patients know what to rely on.

Better information

The 2004 report *Better information, better choices, better health* is a three-year programme of action, at both

4 — Involving patients

national and local level, designed to improve equitable access to the quality information people need and want to exercise choices about their personal health and healthcare.

To help patients make an informed choice of hospital, the website www.nhs.uk/england is being enhanced to provide a range of information identified as important to patients when making this choice. The website currently presents information on:

- prospective waiting times
- access information (such as parking and transport)
- patient experience and quality (taken from the Healthcare Commission performance ratings)

Work is underway to ensure that the information held on the website is accessible to everyone, with plans including more appropriate use of symbols and pictures in addition to other media. The information is also available in printable versions so that it can be given directly to patients. By 2008, patients will be able to choose any healthcare facility for their treatment that meets NHS standards and prices. National level information on healthcare providers will become more important in a free choice environment as more patients choose non-local hospitals for their treatment. As people become used to such choice and as waiting times fall, they will demand more information on the quality of services and will be more likely to base their decisions on this information.

Choose and book

Choose and book is a national service that will, for the first time, combine electronic booking and a choice of time, date and place. The aim was that by the end of 2005 it would be available to all patients in England requiring elective

care (over 10 million each year). However, there were delays in establishing the necessary computer links.

When the system is up and running, patients should be able to choose a convenient place, date and time for their initial appointment from one of four or five hospitals (or other healthcare provider facilities) commissioned by their PCT. Once the patient has chosen their provider of care they have the options of:

- booking their appointment electronically at their GP practice
- booking their appointment through the choose and book local patient advisory service
- booking their appointment on the internet.

The patient will access the electronic booking system using their unique booking number, which is specific to the referral made by the GP, and a password chosen by the patient.

Because of the computer problems, the system went ahead at the end of 2005 using manual systems.

National patient survey programme

Asking patients what they think about the care and treatment they have received is an important step towards improving the quality of care, and to ensuring that local health services are meeting patients' needs. A useful way of doing this is by carrying out surveys of patients who have recently used the health service.

The Healthcare Commission (www.healthcarecommission.org.uk) is responsible for the national programme of surveys of patients. These are designed to provide detailed feedback to NHS organisations about the experience of patients and their views of their care, to provide information that the commission can use to assess the performance of healthcare providers, and to monitor the experience of patients at a national level. Results are collated by the NHS survey advice centre at the Picker Institute Europe. The centre website (www.nhssurveys.org) gives further information about the survey timetable and action required by trusts.

The expert patient programme

There is growing acceptance that patients with long-term chronic conditions, and their carers, often have a wealth of knowledge and experience about the management of their particular illness — they can become experts in their own right.

In the expert patient programme, the government is working with patients, voluntary groups and health professionals to enable people living with chronic conditions to play a greater role in managing their health. The user-led model of self management has been shown to work effectively. It can lead to better outcomes, can serve to enhance the relationship between patients and their healthcare professionals by ensuring that dialogue is more informed, and help to reduce inappropriate use of services.

User-led self management training programmes are being introduced for patients with chronic diseases. A pilot phase between 2002 and 2004 evaluated local programmes and the work is being spread across the NHS during 2004 to 2007. A six-week course for anyone living with a long-term health condition covers topics such as: dealing with pain and tiredness, exercise, communicating with family, friends and health professionals, and planning for the future. Over 21,000 people have attended an expert patient course.

Copying letters to patients

The NHS Plan and Bristol Inquiry report recommended the practice of copying to the patient letters written between clinician's about their individual care. This initiative is being taken forward and in April 2003 good practice guidelines were issued by the Department of Health. Pilot programmes were also funded in 2002/03 to test some concepts before their wider implementation.

There is widespread support that the partnership between doctors and their patients should be improved and strengthened, and that providing better and timely information to patients is an essential element of this. Copying letters to patients is one strand in the different ways needed to improve communications between patients and professionals in the NHS.

The general principle is that all letters that help to improve a patient's understanding of their health and the care they are receiving should be copied to them as of right. Where the patient is not legally responsible for their own care (for instance a young child, or a child in care), letters should be copied to the person with legal responsibility, for instance a parent or guardian. There may be reasons why the general policy of copying letters to patients should not be followed. These include where:
• the patient does not want a copy
• the clinician feels that it may cause harm to the patient or for other reasons
• the letter includes information about a third party who has not given consent
• special safeguards for confidentiality may be needed.

The pilot projects showed that introducing systems for sharing letters yielded overall improvements in a number of areas.

4 — Involving patients

Further information

Choose and book.
www.chooseandbook.nhs.uk

Copying letters to patients.
www.dh.gov.uk/PolicyAndGuidance/
OrganisationPolicy/
PublicAndPatientInvolvement/
CopyingLettersToPatients

Expert patients programme.
www.expertpatients.nhs.uk

Patient advice and liaison services.
www.pals.nhs.uk

Patient choice. www.dh.gov.uk/
PolicyAndGuidance/PatientChoice

Patient consent. www.dh.gov.uk/
PolicyAndGuidance/
HealthAndSocialCareTopics/Consent

Patient UK. www.patient.co.uk

Department of Health. *The expert patient: a new approach to chronic disease management for the 21st century.* September 2001.

Department of Health. *Supporting the implementation of patient advice and liaison services. A resource pack.* January 2002.

Department of Health. *Strengthening accountability: involving patients and the public.* February 2003.

Department of Health. *Copying letters to patients. Good practice guidelines.* April 2003.

Department of Health. *Building on the best. Choice, responsiveness and equity in the NHS.* December 2003.

Department of Health. *Choice at six months: implementation guide.* March 2004.

Department of Health. *The NHS improvement plan: putting people at the heart of public services.* June 2004.

Department of Health. *Choose and book — patient's choice of hospital and booked appointment.* August 2004.

Department of Health. *Getting over the wall. How the NHS is improving the patient's experience.* October 2004.

Department of Health. *Implementing choice at referral for cataracts.* November 2004.

Department of Health. *Better information, better choices, better health. Putting information at the centre of health.* December 2004.

Department of Health. *Creating a patient-led NHS: delivering the NHS improvement plan.* March 2005.

Department of Health. *Choice at six months: good practice.* May 2005.

Commission for Patient and Public Involvement in Health, 7th Floor, 120 Edmund Street, Birmingham B3 2ES. Tel: 0121 222 4500. www.cppih.org

'Caring about carers — a national strategy'

Around 5.7m people in Great Britain care for an ill or disabled friend or relative. Over three quarters of a million of these provide care for more than 50 hours a week, most of it voluntary and unpaid. Many of those being cared for require 24-hour supervision. One in six households contains a carer.

It is estimated that the cost of replacing this army of health and social care support workers with equivalent paid employees is £8bn a year, with some care agencies putting the figure at over £30bn. The Stroke Association published research in 1998 showing that carers provide around 200m hours of voluntary care to stroke sufferers each year, at a saving to the government of £1.5bn. Despite this, there is evidence to show that carers' needs are not met well. Many, for example, find it impossible to take a break due to lack of practical support. Three-fifths of all carers receive no regular visitor support services.

Although in many parts of the country carers receive good support from local authorities, research suggests this has often been inadequate and inconsistent across Britain. Minority ethnic carers and carers of mentally ill people are particularly at risk of poor support.

In recent years there has been an increasing national recognition of the scale of the issue, culminating in the government's national carers strategy, published in 1999. In 1989 the White Paper *Caring for people* called on local statutory agencies to make support for carers a key responsibility. Two laws, the NHS and Community Care Act 1990 and the Carers (Recognition and Services) Act 1995, have both boosted the carers' cause.

The carers' strategy, *Caring about carers*, promised £140m over three years, specifically to enhance the provision of breaks. The package of measures also included:

- legislation to allow local authorities to address carers' needs
- entitling carers to a second pension
- proposals to allow carers to receive extra social payments
- reducing council tax for more disabled people being cared for
- support for neighbourhood services, including carers' centres
- helping carers to return to work
- new census questions to tackle incomplete information about carers
- support for young carers, including help at school.

In February 2005, the Department of Health said that the total awarded to local councils for the carers grant since it was introduced in 1999 amounted to £635m. A fund of £185m went to councils for 2005/06.

In England quality standards for local carer support have been given government approval. The national carers strategy is being taken forward in Scotland by the Scottish Executive, and the Wales Carers Strategy is being implemented in the principality.

The Carers and Disabled Children Act 2000

The Carers and Disabled Children Act 2000 enables carers to receive services in their own right. The Act implemented part of the government's strategy for carers and enables local authorities to supply certain services direct to the carer, either because the user has refused help from the LA or because it is better for the service to be provided in this way. The LA decides,

4 — Involving patients

following assessment, the services provided to the carer.

Local authorities may make direct payments to parent carers of disabled children, giving more flexibility and control over the support required, and also make direct payments to disabled 16 and 17 year olds, who fall outside the remit of other community care legislation.

The Carers (Equal Opportunities) Act 2004

The Carers (Equal Opportunities) Act 2004 received royal assent in July 2004. The Act aims to ensure that carers are able to take up opportunities which those without caring responsibilities take for granted.

It will:

- ensure that carers know that they are entitled to an assessment of their needs
- place a duty on councils to consider a carer's outside interests (work, study or leisure) when carrying out an assessment
- promote better joint working between councils and the health service to ensure support for carers is delivered in a coherent manner.

As a result of the Act, existing legislation, namely the Carers and Disabled Children Act 2000 and Carers Recognition and Service Act 1995, will be amended.

Carers website

A website for carers can be accessed at www.carers.gov.uk. It gives information on progress in implementing the national strategy.

Further information

Carers UK. www.carersuk.org

Department of Health. *Caring about carers: a national strategy for carers.* February 1999.

Local authority circular: LASSL[99]2. *Caring about carers: a national strategy for carers.*

The Long-Term Medical Conditions Alliance

The Long-Term Medical Conditions Alliance (LMCA) brings together a network of over 100 national voluntary organisations. It works to promote understanding of the needs of people managing their lives with chronic illness. It also plays a communication role and helps information about central policies spread out to individual (often small) organisations, and in turn communicates back up the ladder of responsibility the views of individual members and their supporters or carers.

The LMCA has promoted research to inform and develop policies for commissioning services for people with long-term healthcare needs. It has been given National Lottery funding to work with some of its member organisations to improve their capacity to use their members' experiences to inform policy-making and health and social care provision.

Long-Term Medical Conditions Alliance, 202 Hatton Square, 16 Baldwins Gardens, London EC1N 7RJ. Tel: 020 7813 3637. www.lmca.org.uk

5 — The advance of clinical governance

Overview

An important principle set out in the NHS Plan is 'the NHS will work continuously to improve quality services and to minimise errors'. The commitment is to ensure that services are driven by a cycle of continuous quality improvement and that through commitment to learning from mistakes a culture of greater openness about problems is developed.

The processes of clinical governance and of enhancing the quality of care provided by the health service have since become embedded in NHS organisations. This chapter looks at the components that go to make up the quality agenda encompassed by clinical governance and related issues, such as risk management, complaints, clinical negligence, the competence of health professionals, continuous professional development, NHS research and development and information sources for evidence-based healthcare.

The model for delivering improved quality set out in the 1998 Department of Health strategy *A first class service: quality in the new NHS* holds good (figure). It encompasses clear standards of service, dependable local delivery and monitored standards, with an overarching emphasis on patient and public involvement. Each of the elements of the model are described in the succeeding sections of the chapter.

Under standards of service are elements such as the programmes of work set out in the national service frameworks and National Institute of Health and Clinical Excellence guidance.

At the heart of delivering improved quality should be clinical governance and this needs to be a joint responsibility adopted by both NHS organisations and individual health professionals. Dependable local delivery is also supported by professional self-regulation and lifelong learning by staff.

The NHS performance assessment framework, the Healthcare Commission and national and patient and user surveys play a major part in the process of monitoring standards.

Increasingly, clinical governance is being seen as indivisible from other governance issues that NHS organisations face. Hence, clinical and non-clinical risks are usually now reported on in one uniform risk management system.

Serious adverse events can result from healthcare. *An organisation with a memory*, a report drawn up by an expert group chaired by the chief medical officer of England, concentrated on learning from adverse events in the NHS. This has led on to the creation on the National Patient Safety Agency which is collating and making more sense of how the service might avoid serious adverse incidents from recurring. Guaranteeing safe care is a core component of good quality care. Good reporting systems and encouraging a culture of openness are crucial for a safer service.

Clinical audit, introduced with

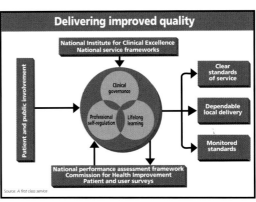

Delivering improved quality

National Institute for Clinical Excellence
National service frameworks

Patient and public involvement

Clinical governance

Professional self-regulation

Lifelong learning

Clear standards of service

Dependable local delivery

Monitored standards

National performance assessment framework
Commission for Health Improvement
Patient and user surveys

Source: A first class service

5 — The advance of clinical governance

funding in 1990 enabled health practitioners to demonstrate locally how patients were not always getting appropriate interventions or were receiving inappropriate care. Through the development of clinical audit it has been possible to identify local problems, to find that most are common and that solutions mostly require a shared approach. Moreover, most people now realise that although professional practice and performance underpin good care, many problems with the quality of care — both the calamitous and the endemic — can be related to organisational failings.

Yet, at the same time, publicised failings of health professionals raise concerns about professional competence and the procedures for accreditation and self regulation.

Getting the right number of appropriately trained healthcare professionals working well together is crucial for significant improvements in the quality of care. Simply working people harder is unlikely to benefit patients. Pay is important but conditions probably more so. Attention needs to be paid to the working conditions of all NHS staff. Staff who are looked after and valued are more likely to deliver good quality care to patients.

While many of the problems of quality of care are linked to organisational problems, the people delivering care must be technically competent. Professionals must also have skills and attitudes to enable them to work and develop in a changing environment.

Further reading

An organisation with a memory. Report of an expert group on learning from adverse events in the NHS. Chaired by the chief medical officer. TSO, 2000.

Department of Health. *A first class service: quality in the new NHS*. 1998.

Continuing professional development (CPD)

Considerable store should be set by clinical staff on maintaining and developing individual healthcare expertise and knowledge as part of the ethos of being a member of a health profession and in the implementation of clinical governance. Clinicians need to keep their skills up-to-date and track developments within their specialty.

Continuing education and lifelong learning link into the NHS human resources agenda (chapter 2). *Working together* states that NHS organisations must provide programmes on education and training; and personal and organisational development, particularly around clinical governance. Locally, NHS employers can use personal development plans (PDPs) for their staff to ensure they renew skills regularly.

Continuing medical education (CME) and continuing professional development (CPD) programmes support doctors and other health professionals. A network of postgraduate medical centres, for instance, which are often based at district hospitals, has done much to keep GPs and related professionals up with the latest developments.

Bodies such as the medical royal colleges, the Royal College of Nursing and a number of other health professional bodies regard encouraging continuing professional development as a key responsibility. CPD is becoming a compulsory element of remaining on health professional registers.

Clinical governance

Clinical governance was created to provide NHS organisations and individual health professionals with a framework within which to build a single, coherent, local programme for quality improvement.

Clinical governance includes work to:
• identify and build on good practice
• assess and minimise the risk of untoward events
• investigate problems as these arise and ensure lessons are learnt
• support health professionals in delivering quality care.

The government wants to see consistently high quality healthcare for all patients, regardless of where they live, and wants to tackle unacceptable variations of service across the country and improve equity of access. Clinical governance is the umbrella concept within which clinical audit, evidence-based healthcare, professional self-regulation and lifelong learning sit. It encompasses both quality improvement and accountability, and depends on effective methods of changing practice.

What all the initiatives embraced by clinical governance have in common is the visible influence of management and organisational culture on service delivery.

What is clinical governance?

The Department of Health defines clinical governance as 'a framework through which NHS organisations are accountable for continuously improving the quality of their services and safeguarding high standards of care by creating an environment in which excellence in clinical care will flourish'.

NHS organisations have a statutory duty of assuring the quality of clinical care. Health authorities, NHS trusts and primary care trusts as well as clinical practitioners such as GPs, dentists, optometrists and community pharmacists have to have in place mechanisms to ensure high quality clinical services.

NHS trust chief executives are accountable for the clinical standards within their organisation. They are required to produce reports on clinical quality in the same way as they do for financial performance. Each trust has to have a designated senior clinician responsible for ensuring clinical governance systems are in place and functioning correctly. The legal duty of clinical governance also requires all doctors to participate in a national audit programme for their specialty.

Non-executive directors are expected to make sure that processes of clinical governance are established, developed and tailored to the needs of their organisation and its service users. They need to ensure that executives deliver the agreed clinical governance objectives and scrutinise how they do this.

Strategic health authorities are responsible for ensuring that there are coherent strategies across local health services and that local clinical governance programmes are linked to the health improvements set out in local delivery plans.

Primary care trusts and individual health professionals within primary care are expected to develop the quality of services and to demonstrate that they are doing so through reporting arrangements. Prescribing and referral patterns are key focuses in clinical governance work.

PCTs have been required to nominate a senior health professional (usually a GP) to take the lead on clinical standards and professional development. Much of the role of improving primary care in each primary care trust has been taken on by this

5 — The advance of clinical governance

clinical governance lead. They are expected to relate to a lead on clinical governance in each practice.

The role of clinical governance is linked to that of using scarce resources cost effectively. Better prescribing, as well as better diagnostic procedures and use of primary and secondary services may generate savings, which can then be used to further develop primary (or secondary) care.

National service frameworks, National Institute for Health and Clinical Excellence's guidelines and National Patient Safety Agency reporting should be implemented as part of clinical governance, and the Healthcare Commission's action at a local level will be triggered by lapses in clinical quality it uncovers.

The Healthcare Commission is seeking to ensure that guidelines and clinical effectiveness information are acted upon to improve performance. Outliers, or persistently poor performers, may be required to defend their position. If necessary, they receive development support or, if all else fails, an entire management team could be removed and replaced at the behest of the Health Secretary.

To turn clinical governance into reality requires the drawing together of a number of strands of professional endeavour and managerial commitment into a cohesive programme of action within each NHS organisation.

www.dh.gov.uk/PolicyAndGuidance/
HealthAndSocialCareTopics/
ClinicalGovernance

Clinical effectiveness

The development of a knowledge-based health service is dependent primarily upon the use of high quality research evidence by those making clinical, managerial and policy decisions. This can only occur if sound information is made easily available to the appropriate audiences. The NHS Centre for Reviews and Dissemination (CRD) is helping to provide the NHS with important information on the effectiveness of treatments and the delivery and organisation of healthcare by offering rigorous and systematic reviews on selected topics, a database of high quality reviews and a dissemination service.

CRD is a facility commissioned by the NHS R&D programme. It is the sibling organisation of the UK Cochrane Centre.

CRD produces systematic reviews both in-house and by commissioning and supervising selected academics and healthcare professionals. Reviews cover the effectiveness of healthcare interventions relevant to the NHS. An expert panel of consultants is recruited for each review to advise and help ensure accuracy and relevance to the NHS.

CRD is one of the agencies which has been commissioned to undertake evidence-based technology appraisals of significant new and existing interventions on behalf of the National Institute for Health and Clinical Excellence (NICE).

Over the past few years, CRD has been involved in a major programme to promote improved quality and coordination of care in those cancers identified as major service priorities (breast, colorectal, lung, gynaecological and upper gastrointestinal). The national cancer guidance group has had the responsibility of developing high quality guidance on these site specific cancers for commissioners of cancer services.

Dissemination

The majority of the CRD's dissemination

The Healthcare Commission

Clinical standards in every part of the NHS in England are monitored by the Healthcare Commission (described as the Commission for Healthcare Audit and Inspection in NHS legislation). It evaluates and refines local systems designed to safeguard clinical quality. The commission is a statutory body set up under the Health and Social Care (Community Health Standards) Act 2003, which succeeded the Commission for Health Improvement (CHI) in April 2004.

It has brought together the work of CHI, the health value for money work of the Audit Commission and the private healthcare role of the National Care Standards Commission. The commission inspects the NHS and private healthcare sector and reviews the quality of patient care and how well the NHS is using its funds. It is also responsible for licensing private healthcare provision.

The Healthcare Commission is independent of the NHS and government and reports annually direct to parliament. It is designed to offer an independent guarantee that systems to monitor, assure and improve clinical quality are in place in hospitals, primary care and community services. Its aims are to reduce variations in clinical quality across the country and rapidly to eliminate malpractice.

The commission's functions involve both the NHS and the independent healthcare sector and include:
• assessing the performance of NHS organisations by reference to standards published by government
• seeking to promote improvements

in the provision of healthcare
• identification of where, and how well, public resources are used to provide healthcare
• publishing annual ratings of all NHS organisations in England, and an annual report to Parliament on the state of healthcare
• working with the Commission for Social Care Inspection to ensure integration of healthcare and social care inspection
• carrying out independent reviews of complaints about NHS services in England
• acting as the leading inspectorate in relation to healthcare — coordinating the activities of other bodies involved in inspection
• investigation of serious failures in health services
• reporting to the Health Secretary any serious concerns about the quality of public services or how they are run.

The commission is chaired by Professor Sir Ian Kennedy and its chief executive is Anna Walker.

Healthcare Commission, Finsbury Tower, 103 Bunhill Row, London EC1Y 8TG . Tel: 020 7448 9200. www.healthcarecommission.org.uk

NHS Quality Improvement Scotland

Scotland has one main body for clinical effectiveness. NHS Quality Improvement Scotland is a special health board and is chaired by Lord Naren Patel.

It has been formed by the merger of three organisations: the Clinical Standards Board for Scotland, the

Health Technology Board for Scotland and the Scottish Health Advisory Service.
The organisation:
• promotes best practice through evidence-based guidelines, clinical audit and support for implementation of changes in the care progress
• sets standards, provides advice and gives national leadership on improving the quality of care

• through a programme of visits to NHS boards and services, reviews and monitors the performance of NHS organisations
• investigates serious failures in clinical service delivery.

NHS Quality Improvement Scotland, Elliott House, 8 Hillside Crescent, Edinburgh EH7 5EA. Tel: 0131 623 4300. www.nhshealthquality.org

activities focus on raising awareness of important messages from research, and providing research intelligence in easily accessible forms.

The core dissemination products which the CRD uses include the *Effective Health Care* series of bulletins. These are distributed as widely as possible to relevant audiences throughout the NHS. The bulletins are available via the internet. In addition to the core dissemination process, summary articles relating to each *Effective Health Care* bulletin are published in healthcare journals.

It is also important for users of NHS services to know about the latest research evidence, and CRD works with voluntary organisations and the lay and professional media to raise awareness of its publications.

Databases

In addition to printed reports three databases have been produced by CRD which are publicly available: the Database of Abstracts of Reviews of Effects (DARE), the NHS Economic Evaluation Database (NHS EED) and the Health Technology Assessment (HTA) Database.

DARE is a collection of records of high quality research reviews of the effectiveness of healthcare interventions, and the management and

organisation of health services. Trained reviewers and information staff within CRD have identified systematic reviews, from reports published throughout the world, and have evaluated them according to a set of quality criteria. Several hundred structured abstracts of systematic reviews are on DARE and cover a wide spectrum of healthcare topics.

The NHS EED is a database of abstracts of published economic evaluations of healthcare interventions. Health economists throughout the UK evaluate published cost-benefit analyses, cost-effectiveness analyses and cost-utility analyses from a variety of sources. Records normally include a structured summary and an assessment of the quality of the studies, together with details of any practical implications for the NHS.

The HTA Database contains information on healthcare technology assessments and is produced in collaboration with the secretariat of International Network of Agencies for Health Technology Assessment (INAHTA). This database contains records of ongoing projects being conducted by members of INAHTA as well as publications reporting completed assessments.

These databases are available free of charge and can be accessed in a variety of ways including the internet

Clinical audit

Clinical audit is the systematic and regular evaluation by health professionals of the care they provide. By pinpointing good and bad aspects of clinical practice it helps quality standards to be maintained. Clinical audit has been in operation for some years, with some success, and is now part of the NHS' overall clinical governance activities. It complements professional self-regulation and should be part of a clinician's continuing professional development. It also links in with the national service frameworks, which contain standards for particular services, thereby providing focus points.

The audit process, known as the audit cycle, involves identifying areas of care to be audited; implementing changes necessary; and periodically reviewing these, taking into account any new evidence. The national confidential enquiries are examples of national clinical audits.

Clinical audit is a clinically-led scheme covering primary and secondary care, supported by the royal colleges, other national organisations and local audit advisory groups. An interface between clinical audit and a trust's management board is important because of the resource implications of poor clinical performance.

From 1999 all clinicians have been required to take part in the national audit programme appropriate to their specialty and this facilitates the comparison of clinicians' individual performance with national averages. This process is linked to clinical governance, with doctors having to share the results of their own individual audits with their hospital's medical director and its lead clinician responsible for clinical governance.

(www.york.ac.uk/inst/crd/crddatabases.htm). Both DARE and NHS EED are also available on disk and CD-ROM as part of he Cochrane Library.

CRD information service

The CRD information service is available to health professionals, researchers, managers and information workers. It answers enquiries about systematic reviews and economic evaluations relating to healthcare, and acts as a help desk for the CRD databases.

NHS Centre for Reviews and Dissemination, University of York YO10 5DD. Tel: 01904 321040. www.york.ac.uk/inst/crd

NHS research and development

The aim of the NHS research and development strategy is to support a knowledge-based health service in which clinical, managerial and policy decisions are based on sound information about research findings and scientific developments. The research programmes under this strategy focus on the needs of the health service.

The Department of Health currently allocates about £650m a year (2005/06) through a portfolio of national research programmes and the NHS R&D programme. Professor Sally Davies is the director of research and development at the Department.

The policy research programme aims to ensure that Department policy is based on reliable evidence of needs and of what works best. The research portfolio covers healthy living and social wellbeing, disease prevention, the role of the environment in health, social care for adults and children, the organisation of the NHS, and strategies for

5 — The advance of clinical governance

treating particular diseases or conditions.

The national NHS R&D programme, which is also managed by the DH, investigates a range of healthcare matters and supports the application of research-based knowledge across all healthcare sectors. The programme was recast from a relatively large number of time-limited programmes into three programmes:
• health technology assessment (HTA)
• service delivery and organisation (SDO) R&D programme

Clinical guidelines

Clinical guidelines provide a checklist for a clinician so that they can be sure they are providing the best and most appropriate treatment for each individual patient. Guidelines or protocols often set out a treatment pathway and suggest the different options which can be taken according to signs, symptoms, tests results and the patient's wishes. An important function of guidelines is to stop the use of established yet unduly hazardous treatments. They also should discourage health professionals from adopting ineffective, yet possibly expensive treatment options.

Guidelines have become a component of the clinical governance scheme. They apply to a specific disease or family of diseases, plus treatments and/or groups of patients.

Guidelines in the past have been drawn up by teams of enthusiastic clinicians or local and national professionals organisations, such as the medical royal colleges. The National Institute for Health and Clinical Excellence has a central role in propagating national guidelines and is developing its own series.

• new and emerging applications of technology (NEAT) programme.

HTA forms the largest single programme of research. Health technologies include all devices, equipment, drugs and procedures across all sectors of healthcare. It aims to answer questions such as: Does this treatment work? At what cost? How does it compare with alternative treatments?

Many existing treatments have yet to be assessed and this is an important area for the NHS. The programme has the capacity to fast-tract topics to meet the need for timely research; for example, to provide evidence for the National Institute for Health and Clinical Excellence.

SDO promotes the use of research evidence to improve the organisation and delivery of healthcare. The programme was launched in 2000 and the first projects addressed research needs in the area of continuity of care.

NEAT promotes the use of new technologies. It aims to fill the funding gap for applied research that exists between generating fundamental knowledge (the remit of the research councils) and using mature technologies for manufacturing products for commercial gain (the remit of industry).

NHS R&D funding

The Department also manages NHS R&D funding. Policy on this funding was set out in the 2000 report *Research and development for a first class service*. It specified two main streams of support: NHS support for science and NHS priorities and needs R&D funding.

NHS priorities and needs R&D funding reflects the full range of NHS responsibilities for public health and healthcare in community, primary, secondary and tertiary settings. NHS support for science has aimed to target funding more closely on formally funded R&D, working to an activity and cost formula for allocations.

NHS research funding has been used to support R&D vital to improvements in medicine and health, which is of relevance to the NHS, and is undertaken in hospitals, general practice and other healthcare settings. The direct costs of this research is often funded by other bodies such as research councils and charities. The Department pays the service support (but not treatment) costs of the research (£400m in 2005/06 allocated directly to NHS providers).

The Department also funds research undertaken by non-departmental public bodies.

Other major government health R&D funders include the Medical Research Council and the Higher Education Funding Council for England, which provide funds to universities for medical and dental research. Medical charities and industry are also major funders of medical research.

Social care research is also sponsored by the Economic and Social Research Council, by local authorities and charities.

The Department has concordats with the Medical Research Council and other research councils and has a statement of partnership governing the NHS, universities and other funders.

A research governance framework sets out the standards, delivery mechanisms and monitoring arrangements for all research funded by the DH.

The 2004 Budget

In March 2004, the Chancellor of the Exchequer announced that the NHS would receive an extra £25m a year for four years to fund research in the treatment and cure of four major diseases — Alzheimer's, stroke, diabetes and mental health as well as developing new medicines for children.

A new NHS strategy: *Best research for best health*

In January 2006, the Department launched a modernised NHS strategy in England. The strategy aims to ensure the NHS supports the government's commitment to positioning the UK as the best place in the world for health research, development and innovation.

The proposed changes include:

- modernising the way research in the NHS is funded — to ensure a transparent system of funding that more accurately reflects the levels of health research conducted by NHS trusts
- establishing a set of academic medical centres — to serve as the nation's premier research hospitals and compete with other top clinical research institutes throughout the world
- creating the National Institute for Health Research — a virtual institute to work with the UK clinical research collaboration to coordinate the research infrastructure of the NHS. This would bring together, for the first time, all elements of NHS and Department of Health research.

The strategy states that the Department will spend over £650m a year on research, development and innovation. There will be a three-year NHS R&D funding transition period.

Consumer involvement

The NHS R&D strategy has always aimed to involve consumers, patients, carers and other members of the public in all stages of the R&D process. The consumers in NHS research group was established in 1996. The group's support unit has published guidelines for researchers on how to involve consumers. The group reports annually, holds national

5 — The advance of clinical governance

conferences and has established the principle that every major committee or advisory body in NHS R&D programmes should normally have two consumer representatives.

NHS intellectual property

In June 2004 the Department of Health appointed Dr Marie Smith as director of intellectual property for the NHS. She oversees nine NHS innovations hubs across the country with the aim of ensuring that the NHS reaps the full financial rewards of research by tapping into the commercial potential of ideas.

The NHS innovations hubs supply intellectual property services to NHS organisations in partnership with universities.

Through co-funding of the Department of Health, Department of Trade and Industry and the regional development agencies, the hubs aim to bring commercial opportunities to healthcare using local business and knowledge networks.

NHS Centre for Reviews and Dissemination

The NHS Centre for Reviews and Dissemination (CRD), based at the University of York, was established in 1993 to commission and support experts to undertake specific systematic reviews into key NHS topics. It works closely with the UK Cochrane Centre and takes account of overseas research and work ` funded in the UK by non-NHS organisations.

Further information

Office of the Director of Research and Development, Room 330, Richmond House, 79 Whitehall, London SW1A 2NS.

Department of Health R&D website: www.dh.gov.uk/PolicyAndGuidance/ ResearchAndDevelopment

Department of Health. *Best research for best health: a new national health research strategy — the NHS contribution to health research in England.* January 2006.

UK clinical research collaboration. www.ukcrc.org

The National Research Register (NRR) holds information on all research funded through the DH and NHS R&D programmes and data on R&D receiving support in trusts. It contains details on several thousand projects. The register is freely available through the internet, www.update-software.com/national.

The DH Research Findings electronic Register (ReFeR) is a freely available database, providing prompt sight of the findings of completed projects from the NHS R&D programme and the DH policy research programme. It can be accessed via the DH R&D website.

Centre for Reviews and Dissemination, University of York, York YO1 5DD. www.york.ac.uk/inst/crd

Effective healthcare bulletins, 71 Clarendon Road, Leeds LS2 9PL.

The UK Cochrane Centre, Summertown Pavilion, Middle Way, Oxford OX2 7LG.

The National Institute for Health and Clinical Excellence

The new National Institute for Health and Clinical Excellence (NICE) was formed on 1 April 2005, when the National Institute for Clinical Excellence took on the functions of the Health Development Agency to create a single excellence-in-practice organisation responsible for providing national guidance on the promotion of good health and the prevention and treatment of illness. The new institute was described in the White Paper *Choosing health: making healthier choices easier.*

NICE originally started work in April 1999 as a special health authority that produced formal advice for NHS clinicians and managers in England and Wales on the clinical and cost effectiveness of new and existing technologies — including medicines, diagnostic tests and surgical procedures. In Scotland, the institute's advice has been given effect and it is also reflected in Wales and Northern Ireland.

NICE produces guidance in three areas:
- public health — guidance on the promotion of good health and the prevention of illness for those working in the NHS, local authorities and the wider public and voluntary sector
- health technologies — guidance on the use of new and existing medicines, treatments and procedures in the NHS
- clinical practice — guidance on the appropriate treatment and care of

people with specific diseases and conditions within the NHS.

The guidance is being produced by three centres within NICE: the centre for public health excellence, the centre for health technology evaluation and the centre for clinical practice.

Public health guidance

The centre for public health excellence at NICE develops guidance on the promotion of good health and the prevention of illness in theme areas, including those identified explicitly in the Department of Health White Paper *Choosing health: making healthier choices easier.* Topics for guidance products in these areas are referred to NICE by the Department of Health.

NICE has been consulting on the process by which the centre for public health excellence will develop public health intervention guidance and public health programme guidance.

Recent guidelines published by NICE

Hypertension	Aug 2004
Dental recall	Oct 2004
Epilepsy	Oct 2004
Falls	Nov 2004
Head and neck cancer service guidance	Nov 2004
Anxiety	Dec 2004
Depression	Dec 2004
Lung cancer	Feb 2005
Violence	Feb 2005
Post-traumatic stress disorder	Mar 2005
Referral for suspected cancer	Jun 2005
Children and young people with cancer	Aug 2005
Depression in children and young people	Sep 2005
Pressure ulcer management	Sep 2005
Long-acting reversible contraception	Oct 2005
Obsessive-compulsive disorder	Nov 2005
Skin tumours including melanoma	Feb 2006
Nutrition support in adults	Feb 2006

Source: www.nice.org.uk

Wellard's NHS Handbook 2006/07

5 — The advance of clinical governance

Appraisal of health technologies

The Department of Health and the National Assembly for Wales fund NICE. Guidance is issued by NICE on about 25 technology appraisals a year. For the present NICE will not be in a position to attempt to appraise all technologies that are, or are about to be, available.

The Department of Health and the National Assembly for Wales announces the work programme for NICE, listing those treatments to be examined. NICE sets a timetable, commissions an evaluation report and asks for evidence to be submitted. Treatments selected tend to be those of major public health importance, those that raise significant management problems concerning their introduction, or those which bear a significant financial burden to the NHS. Also selected are technologies where NICE guidance will add value. The results of appraisals provide health professions and managers with a single, authoritative source of advice.

The clinical and cost effectiveness of a treatment is compared with current best practice. When cost effectiveness of a treatment is being considered, both direct and indirect costs to the NHS are taken into account.

Pharmaceutical manufacturers are invited to submit full data on clinical and cost effectiveness of a product some four to six months before its launch.

Interventional procedures

NICE also undertakes a programme to assess whether interventional procedures used for diagnosis or treatment are safe enough and work well enough for routine use in the NHS.

Doctors planning to undertake new interventional procedures need to seek approval from their NHS trust's clinical governance committee before doing so, and the chair of the committee should notify NICE's interventional procedures programme (IPP).

Interventional procedures involve making a cut or hole in the body, entry into a body cavity or using electromagnetic energy (including X-rays or lasers) or ultrasound.

Clinical guidelines

NICE clinical guidelines are based on the best available evidence and expert professional advice. They take into account both the clinical and cost effectiveness of the measures recommended and they have to be practical and affordable. The NICE national collaborating centres manage the development of clinical guidelines in collaboration with guideline review panels.

There are seven collaborating centres. They develop best practice clinical guidelines and audit advice for the NHS in England and Wales in the following areas:

- acute care
- cancer
- long-term conditions
- nursing and supportive care
- mental health
- primary care
- women and children's health.

The centres, typically based in royal colleges, collaborate with a number of partner organisations representing both healthcare professionals and patients.

Additionally, NICE draws up protocols for the appropriate referral of patients, with conditions ranging from back pain to cancer, by GPs to secondary care.

Implementation of NICE guidance

While the output from NICE in the form of advice to NHS organisations is not mandatory, it is expected that its recommendations will be accepted. Its guidelines cover most clinical circumstances for which they have been developed and health professionals are being advised to record any reasons for non-compliance with the guidelines in patients' clinical records.

The Department of Health's *Standards for better health* sets out how NHS organisations should respond to NICE guidance. The Healthcare Commission incorporates successive NICE appraisals into its clinical governance monitoring of NHS organisations.

NHS organisations in England have three months from the date technology appraisal guidance is published to fund approved technologies considered appropriate by a clinician.

In 2004, NICE launched a programme of work to support the implementation of its guidance. It has appointed an executive director with responsibility for implementation and has added a section to its website to support those responsible for implementing NICE guidance in the NHS.

In December 2005, it published *How to put NICE guidance into practice*, an implementation guide for NHS organisations.

NICE's structure
The chairman of NICE is Professor Sir Michael Rawlins. Joining him on NICE's board are a complement of 10 other non-executive directors and four executives. The board is appointed by the DH and the Welsh Assembly. The executives include a chief executive, a clinical and public health director, an implementation systems director and a planning and resources director.

There is also a NICE partners' council, formed of representatives from patient and carer groups, the health professions, NHS interests and the healthcare industries, and a secretariat. A citizen's council comprises non-NHS people who aim to ensure NICE deci-

sions reflect public values.

Although based in London NICE is operating in many ways as a virtual institute with many electronic links. It is harnessing the expertise of the royal colleges, professional associations, NHS regions, the R&D sections of the NHS and the healthcare industries. It has appointed members of expert committees, covering appraisal, guidelines and audit.

The National Institute for Health and Clinical Excellence, MidCity Place, 71 High Holborn, London WC1V 6NA. Tel: 020 7067 5800. www.nice.org.uk E-mail: nice@nice.nhs.uk

All-Wales medicines strategy roup
The All-Wales medicines strategy group (AWMSG) provides advice to the minister for health and social services in Wales on medicines management and prescribing, across primary and secondary care. Among its functions are to:
• develop timely, independent and authoritative advice on new drugs and on the cost implications of making these drugs routinely available on the NHS
• advise the Welsh Assembly on the development of prescribing strategy for Wales
• advise the Assembly on the implementation of a range of prescribing recommendations.

(www.wales.nhs.uk/awmsg).

The Scottish Medicines Consortium
The remit of the Scottish Medicines Consortium (SMC) is to provide advice to NHS boards and their area drug and therapeutics committees across Scotland about the status of all newly licensed medicines, new formulations of existing medicines and any major new indica-

5 — The advance of clinical governance

tions for established products. This advice is made available as soon as practical after the launch of the product involved.

The consortium's new drugs committee (NDC) makes recommendations on issues surrounding newly licensed products.

The SMC is chaired by David Webb, professor of therapeutics and clinical pharmacology, Edinburgh University, and the new drugs committee is led by Dr Kenneth Paterson, consultant physician, Glasgow Royal Infirmary.

Each NHS board is expected to develop an implementation protocol to ensure that drugs recommended by the SMC are made available to meet clinical need within three months of publication of that advice.

(www.scottishmedicines.org.uk)

Equivalent bodies elsewhere

The entry of new technologies is increasingly being managed by healthcare systems themselves through health technology assessment (HTA) and horizon scanning. A number of countries have set up equivalent bodies to NICE, and health technology assessment agencies around the world are government supported.

Many countries, such as Sweden and the Netherlands, have horizon scanning centres. A European-wide initiative known as EuroScan is in operation. It has in membership HTA organisations in nearly 10 countries from Europe and elsewhere (www.euroscan.bham.ac.uk). In 2000 the EU-sponsored European Collaboration for Assessment of Health Interventions began work. Agencies are liaising through the International Network of Agencies for Health Technology Assessment.

National confidential enquiries

The national confidential enquiries have been set up over a number of years to examine clinical performance and serious avoidable events. Information is furnished on a confidential basis from around the NHS to provide a wide picture.

The first enquiry, established in 1951, was designed to examine the cause of death in women at the time of childbirth and thus minimise untoward deaths. In the late 1980s a major exercise was launched to audit hospital deaths occurring during or soon after surgery.

In 1998 the government announced that participation in the enquiries would be compulsory for all relevant clinicians as part of the new legal duty to achieve clinical quality.

The three current enquiries are:
• *National confidential enquiry into patient outcome and death (NCEPOD)*
Function: to review the management of patients undergoing medical and surgical care
• *Confidential enquiry into maternal and child health (CEMACH)*
Function: to audit deaths of mothers up to one year after delivery, late fetal losses, stillbirths and deaths in infancy up to 12 months
• *National confidential inquiry into suicide and homicide by people with mental illness (NCISH)*
Function: to perform a national audit of suicide and homicide by people with a history of mental illness.

In April 2005 responsibility for the confidential enquiries was transferred from the National Institute for Health and Clinical Excellence to the National Patient Safety Agency.

The National Patient Safety Agency

Within certain healthcare areas it is possible to identify regular patterns of error, which, if selectively targeted, can lead to a reduction in the risk to patients. The National Patient Safety Agency (NPSA) — established in July 2001 — has launched a mandatory reporting and learning system for logging failures, errors and near misses across the NHS, so as to improve patient safety by reducing the risk of harm. The NPSA expects reports to come from staff, patients and patient groups with the aim of making the NHS as error proof as possible.

Chief medical officer Professor Sir Liam Donaldson has said that the agency's system of recording adverse events should be at the heart of a shift to a more blame-free, open NHS, where lessons are shared and learnt.

The NPSA, a special health authority, collects and analyses information on adverse events from NHS organisations, patients and carers. It also specifies national goals and establishes tracking mechanisms where risks are identified.

The organisation's first public safety alert, issued in 2002, concerned the prevention of accidental injection with potassium chloride concentrated solutions. For 2003/04 NPSA identified more than 20 areas of work it would pursue. These include the labelling and packaging of medicines, wrong site surgery and the risks associated with the anaesthetics process.

The agency aims to ensure that where risks are identified, work is undertaken on producing solutions to prevent harm.

In 2003 the NPSA published *Seven steps to patient safety* to provide NHS staff with an overview of patient safety and to update them on the tools that it was developing to support them:

1. *Build a safety culture*
   Create a culture that is open and fair
2. *Lead and support your staff*
   Establish a clear and strong focus on patient safety throughout your organisation
3. *Integrate your risk management activity*
   Develop systems and processes to manage your risks and identify and assess things that could go wrong
4. *Promote reporting*
   Ensure your staff can easily report incidents locally and nationally
5. *Involve and communicate with patients and the public*
   Develop ways to communicate openly with and listen to patients
6. *Learn and share safety lessons*
   Encourage staff to use root cause analysis to learn how and why incidents happen
7. *Implement solutions to prevent harm*
   Embed lessons through changes to practice, processes or systems.

From January 2004, former health minister Lord Philip Hunt of Kings Heath took up the post of chair of the organisation.

Building a safer NHS for patients, published in April 2001, introduced the NPSA and set out the government agenda for promoting patient safety. It followed the recommendations of the report *An organisation with a memory* (June 2000). The report seeks to make adverse event reporting consistent, and to clarify the role of organisations to respond effectively to all service failures. It focuses on local and national action to establish a system which ensures lessons from adverse events are learnt across the NHS and which tackle the estimated 850,000 incidents and

5 — The advance of clinical governance

errors occurring in the NHS each year. It also sets out procedures for handling situations where there are potential risks to patients of poor outcomes of care, or harm, or where such events have already taken place.

The NPSA has developed the following three formats to disseminate its advice and solutions to NHS staff:
- a patient safety alert requires prompt action to address high risk safety problems
- a safer practice notice strongly advises implementing particular recommendations or solutions
- patient safety information suggests issues or effective techniques that healthcare staff might consider to enhance safety.

Patient safety alerts and safer practice notices (box) are distributed via the Safety Alert Broadcast System (SABS) in England, and direct to NHS organisations in Wales. Patient safety information is sent to targeted groups of healthcare staff where it is of direct relevance and interest.

From 1 April 2005, the NPSA's work has also encompassed:
- safety aspects of hospital design, cleanliness and food (transferred from NHS Estates)
- ensuring research is carried out safely, through its responsibility for the Central Office for Research Ethics Committees (COREC).

It is supporting local organisations in addressing their concerns about the performance of individual doctors and dentists, through its responsibility for the national clinical assessment service (NCAS), formerly known as the National Clinical Assessment Authority.

It also manages the contracts with the three confidential enquiries. This responsibility has been transferred from NICE.

Some alerts and advice issued by the NPSA

Safer patient identification — 22 Nov 2005

Being open when patients are harmed — 15 Sept 2005

Reducing the harm caused by misplaced naso and orogastric feeding tubes in babies under the care of neonatal units — 18 Aug 2005

Protecting people with allergy associated with latex — 26 May 2005

Ensuring safer practice with Repevax and Revaxis vaccines — 29 Apr 2005

Improving emergency care for patients who breathe through their neck — 7 Mar 2005

Correct site surgery alert — 2 Mar 2005

Advice to the NHS on reducing harm caused by the misplacement of nasogastric feeding tubes — 22 Feb 2005

Update on producing patient information on methotrexate usage — 30 Nov 2004

Improving the safety of patients with established spinal injuries in hospital — 15 Sept 2004

Clean hands helps to save lives — 2 Sept 2004

Improving infusion device safety — 20 May 2004

Standardise your crash call number to 2222 — 18 Feb 2004

Update on the implementation of recommended safety controls for potassium chloride in the NHS — 6 Nov 2003

Administering vincristine — 1 Apr 2001

Wellard's NHS Handbook 2006/07

Further information

NPSA. *Building a memory: preventing harm, reducing risks and improving patient safety. The first report of the national reporting and learning system and the patient safety observatory.* July 2005.

NPSA, 4 Maple Street, London W1T 5HD. Tel: 020 7927 9500. www.npsa.nhs.uk

The National Clinical Assessment Service. www.ncaa.nhs.uk

The Central Office of Research Ethics Committees. www.corec.org.uk

The Confidential Enquiry into Maternal and Child Health. www.cemach.org.uk

The National Confidential Enquiry into Patient Outcome and Death. www.ncepod.org.uk

The National Confidential Enquiry into Suicide and Homicide by People with Mental Illness. www.national-confidential-inquiry.ac.uk

Health and social care awards

People whose hard work, innovation, commitment, dedication and talent are improving the standard of health and social care in the public and voluntary sectors throughout England are eligible to be considered for a national health and social care award.

The annual awards are supported by the Department of Health and the government.

A selection process involving health and social care professionals, patients, users and carers is applied to each application. Final decisions are made by a national selection panel.

Winners receive £15,000 to help share their best practice with others or develop their service further.

www.healthandsocialcareawards.org

Accreditation and inspection

Hospitals, other health facilities and specialty services may have their organisation, management and clinical practice evaluated by an external body — a process known as accreditation. This leads to recognition that the service concerned has achieved defined standards.

In 2000 the Commission for Health Improvement began the most significant form of inspection of NHS organisations. From April 2004 CHI became the Healthcare Commission and its powers were strengthened.

Important parts of the accreditation process are preparatory work to achieve pre-set standards and initial self assessment, prior to an inspection by outside assessors. Following the inspection, the accrediting body submits a report to the organisation which may indicate areas for improvement. Once the required standard has been met, accreditation is awarded for a fixed term.

Examples of accreditation and inspection programmes include:
• Clinical negligence: Clinical Negligence Scheme for Trusts
• Clinical data: Data Accreditation Programme
• Clinical pathology: Clinical Pathology Accreditation UK
• Health records: Accreditation and Development of Records
• Palliative care: Macmillan Cancer Relief Fund
• The Health Quality Service.

The word accreditation, in the context of healthcare, may also be applied to:
• recognition by an authorised body of a training programme or trainee
• recognition that a licensing body is competent to issue certificates of compliance under ISO or EN standards.

5 — The advance of clinical governance

Risk management in the NHS

Life is inherently risky and in an organisation as large and complex as the NHS, adverse events will occur. With improving patient safety a high priority, there is now a real drive in the NHS to reduce risk.

The Department of Health estimates that 10 per cent of inpatient episodes lead to adverse incidents and about half of these are preventable.

Since 1995, NHS trusts have had a direct financial incentive to invest in risk management in the form of subscription discounts awarded to trusts meeting risk management standards under the Clinical Negligence Scheme for Trusts (CNST). The CNST was set up by the Department of Health as a national risk pooling arrangement for trusts and is operated by the NHS Litigation Authority. The Health Secretary's overall aim for the authority is 'to promote the highest possible standards of patient care and to minimise the suffering resulting from any adverse incident, which do nevertheless occur'.

CNST provides a central fund for trusts to call on in the case of substantial claims. It avoids the situation where a trust could be technically bankrupted and limited in its ability to continue providing healthcare following a very substantial award against it in the courts.

By joining CNST, trusts in England are able to turn an unknown and variable liability into a more predictable overhead. Minimum standards of clinical risk management are set for members. In Wales, the All-Wales Risk Pool provides a more wide-ranging fund for health authorities and trusts.

Increasing use has been made by the courts of structured settlements for plaintiffs. In these, costs are paid over the lifetime of the individual or for an agreed period to help to support them. These have benefits for the NHS and patients alike.

However, it is not sufficient for organisations and individuals involved in NHS care to learn and to improve practice only from things that go wrong. The 1997 publication *The new NHS: modern, dependable* and the 1998 *A first class service* introduced a strategy to improve the quality of clinical care in the NHS based on:

- setting national standards through national service frameworks
- ensuring standards are met through clinical governance, revalidation and appraisals for clinicians
- monitoring implementation using the Commission for Health Improvement (now the Healthcare Commission).

Thus risk management activity must be proactive as well as reactive. In the 2001 *Building a safer NHS for patients* the Department of Health published plans to introduce a mandatory national reporting scheme for adverse incidents and near misses and this was swiftly followed by the establishment of the National Patient Safety Agency (NPSA). In *Doing less harm,* the NPSA sets out key requirements for healthcare providers, the cornerstone of which is the need to establish the underlying causes of serious incidents through root cause analysis. Of the 10 requirements, the key is that of organisational learning and change — 'organisations will need to demonstrate that they learn from individual incidents, from aggregate reviews and from wider experiences, with that learning translating into improvement strategies which are implemented and monitored to ensure a sustained improvement'.

Dimensions of risk

The British Medical Association (*Patient*

safety and clinical risk, December 2002) usefully identifies five categories of levels of risk:
• patient's perception of risk
• the risk of individual clinical incompetence or malpractice
• the risk of systems failure
• risks imposed by costs constraints
• risks inherent in clinical procedures.

Risk can be defined as the product of the likelihood or probability of an adverse event occurring, and the consequences or impact that event would have. The Department of Health quantifies risk by a system that produces a numerical value for the risk itself. However, the key to successful risk management lies in developing a culture in which mistakes are openly reported and potential mistakes actively sought out and addressed. Neither will occur where a response to an adverse event is one of blame and retribution, and trusts are realising that such a negative culture is the greatest barrier to organisational learning.

One of the difficulties in changing culture is the need to balance positive organisational learning with a clear understanding that all individuals in the organisation must acknowledge that they have to bear the risks, which are properly their responsibility. The BMA points out that this process of assigning responsibility ought to be made more explicit. The government has a responsibility for the risk of cost constraints; health service managers must bear the risks of systems failure; doctors must acknowledge that their individual errors will contribute to an adverse outcome. Patients must bear the risks inherent in a particular course of treatment and of their personal characteristics and lifestyle choices. The BMA points out, even if all of the preceding risk could be eliminated, no patient undergoing

treatment could ever do so entirely free from risk of an adverse outcome, and 'the risks associated with a particular course of treatment must be weighed against the risks and benefits of alternative options, and discussed with the patient. It is then the patient's right and responsibility to choose which of these risks he or she prefer to accept'.

Clearly there is much to be done in terms of managing expectations and cultural change. However, much else has been done, the framework is in place and many trusts are achieving substantial advances in their approach to risk management with a consequent reduction in adverse events.

Clinical negligence

In October 2005 the NHS Redress Bill was published. This gives the Health Secretary the power to establish an NHS redress scheme and place a duty on commissioners and providers of hospital services to ensure that patients receive a more consistent, speedy and appropriate response to clinical negligence. Under the scheme, in lower value cases (up to an expected ceiling of £20,000) patients will receive explanations, apologies and financial redress without the need to go to court. Patients will also be able to receive redress in the form of care.

The Bill sets out arrangements for England and framework powers for Wales only. The scheme, which is expected to come into operation in England in 2007/08, is largely based on proposals made in Making amends, a 2003 report by the chief medical officer for England Liam Donaldson.

NHS organisations will be expected to review adverse events and begin

5 — The advance of clinical governance

investigations themselves, and report any incidents which may fall within the scheme to the NHS Litigation Authority. The authority will decide on liability, and compensation where warranted. All members of the scheme will have to appoint a person responsible for learning from mistakes.

Patients will be able to opt out of the scheme at any time before settlement and go down the litigation route. They will also receive independent legal advice before accepting the settlement offered. However, patients accepting a package under the scheme will not subsequently be able to litigate for the same injury through the courts.

The NHS paid out £503m for clinical negligence in 2004/05, of which about £150m went on legal costs. Small claims account for about 10 per cent of all clinical negligence payouts each year. The scheme will obviously reduce expenditure on legal costs. Currently, the legal and administrative costs of settling claims exceed the money actually paid to the victim in the majority of claims under £45,000 and take up an even higher proportion of smaller claims.

The scheme will include care and compensation for severely neurologically impaired babies, including those with severe cerebral palsy if their impairment was birth-related and they fulfil other eligibility criteria.

Under the proposals, the redress scheme will initially be applied to NHS hospitals. If it is successful, the Department of Health will look at how it can be extended to cover primary care.

Documents and information collected for identifying adverse events should be protected from disclosure in court in keeping with moves in other countries to promote openness in reporting errors.

Complaints

The NHS, like all other services, receives many complaints and comments on service delivery. It is expected that any complaint about NHS services is investigated and complainants receive a quick, full, written reply from the relevant chief executive or general manager.

Patients are now more conscious of their rights and therefore more willing to complain, stimulating an increase in the number of complaints that the service receives. Many complaints arise from a breakdown in communication, so it is important that communication channels are reviewed and adapted regularly. Well-handled complaints can make good relations with service users and even enhance them; but key to this is ensuring that complaints are taken seriously and are dealt with promptly. An ideal approach to handling complaints is one which is open, clear and where the complaint is answered from the complainant's point of view.

Responses to complaints should not be defensive and errors should be openly admitted to and, where appropriate, an apology given. Wherever possible, the problem causing the complaint should be rectified and the complainant should be made aware of any action taken to avoid a similar situation arising again. Complaints can also be used as a stimulus for improvements in service delivery and staff development.

Through the NHS Plan the government pledged to reform the complaints procedure so that it was more independent and responsive to the needs of patients. In an evaluation of the former procedure the role of conveners was criticised and the system was not seen to be sufficiently independent or transparent.

Establishing complaints procedures

The boards of NHS trusts and primary care trusts are required to establish and publicise written complaints procedures reflecting directions and regulations. Family health practitioners are required to set up, publicise and operate practice-based complaints procedures for local resolution of complaints, which meet national criteria and to co-operate in any independent review (see below).

Where NHS care is provided by the independent sector the contracts will provide for similar complaints arrangements to be in place.

Complaints manager. Trusts and primary care trusts must have a designated complaints manager, who is readily accessible to the public and who is either directly accountable to the chief executive or, in the case of large trusts, at least has direct access. Family health practitioners must also identify to patients and clients someone who is responsible for handling complaints, possibly a senior partner or practice manager.

Patient advice and liaison services. Every NHS trust and primary care trust in England has established its own patient advice and liaison service (PALS) to provide information and on-the-spot help for patients, their families and carers. PALS staff listen and provide relevant information and support to help resolve users' concerns quickly and efficiently. They liaise with staff and managers, and, where appropriate, with other PALS services, health and related organisations, to help resolve complaints so avoiding the need for patients to make a formal complaint in most cases. They also act as one of the gateways to independent advice and advocacy support for people wanting to pursue formal complaints and act as a force for change and improvement within the organisation as a whole.

Separation of complaints and disciplinary procedures. Complaints and disciplinary procedures are kept separate, although it is recognised that some complaints may throw up information about serious matters which indicate a need for disciplinary investigation. Where a decision is made to embark on such an investigation, the complaints procedure will automatically cease in respect of those issues, but may continue if there are other aspects of the complaint still to be resolved. A similar approach will need to be adopted in a case which has indicated the need for a referral to one of the professional regulatory bodies.

Possible claims for negligence. The complaints procedure should continue as normal until the complainant explicitly indicates an intention to take legal action in respect of the complaint, in which eventuality the matter will necessarily be referred to lawyers.

Time limit of six months for making complaints. Patients, or whoever is complaining on their behalf, should normally make a complaint within six months from the incident that caused the problem, or within six months of the date of discovering the problem (provided that this is within 12 months of the incident). However, there is discretion for the time limit to be extended.

Independent complaints advocacy services

Independent complaints advocacy services (ICASs) across the NHS in England are designed to offer support to individuals who wish to make a complaint about their NHS care or treatment. Responsibility for ICAS is devolved in Northern Ireland, Scotland and Wales.

Patients have a statutory right to this support when they raise concerns. Feedback indicates that the public value access to this free, confidential and independent service. Relationships with local patient advice and liaison services together with common understanding of roles and responsibilities are improving services for patients.

The Commission for Patient and Public Involvement in Health sets standards for and monitoring provision of ICAS.

The NHS complaints procedure

A two-stage procedure for dealing with NHS complaints applies, with minor variations, across the whole UK. Complaints about hospitals and primary care services are dealt with in similar fashion at two clear levels:

• Local resolution — a quick and informal way to complain direct to the provider of the service, under which the NHS trust/PCT or family practitioner — that is GP practice, dentist, pharmacist or optometrist — will respond to the complainant and try to provide a satisfying answer.
• Independent review (see below).

Local resolution

All trusts and PCTs have to put in place a local resolution process, which lays emphasis on complaints being dealt with quickly and, where possible, on the spot. The process should be fair, flexible and conciliatory, with the complainant being given the opportunity to understand all possible options for pursuing the complaint.

Meeting patients' immediate health needs. Staff should deal with complaints rapidly and, if circumstances

permit, in an informal manner. They should also bear in mind that their first responsibility is to ensure that the patient's immediate healthcare needs are being met.

Referrals to the complaints manager. Where the member of staff who receives a complaint is unable to investigate it adequately or feels unable to give assurance, the matter should be referred to the complaints manager. Similarly, complainants who prefer to make their complaint to someone not involved in their care should be referred to the complaints officer or the chief executive.

Full and positive response. All complaints, whether written or oral, should receive a full and positive response and the offer of an apology and/or explanation as appropriate. Responses to complaints involving matters of clinical judgement need to be agreed by the clinician concerned. All written complaints must receive a response in writing from the chief executive.

Obligation on family health practitioners. Family health practitioners are required to have in place a practice-based complaints procedure which complies with national criteria. The practice must nominate one person to oversee the administration of the procedure, ensure the procedure is publicised and that it is clear how and where complaints are lodged.

PCTs assist if a complainant does not wish to complain directly to the practice or is having difficulty in so doing. PCTs use lay conciliators where the complainant agrees to use this process. Alternatively, PCT staff act as intermediaries to secure an investigation by or an explanation from the practice.

Completion of local resolution. NHS bodies and practices are advised to

Wellard's NHS Handbook 2006/07

round off the local resolution stage by giving a written summary of the investigation and its conclusions to the complainant. Any letter concluding the local resolution stage of a complaint should indicate the right of the complainant to seek an independent review.

Performance targets. The guidance lays down a number of performance targets for the speed with which complaints should be resolved:

- on the spot or within two working days for oral complaints
- an initial acknowledgement of formal written complaints within two working days
- full investigation and resolution of all types of complaints within 20 working days (10 working days in the case of a family practitioner).

Where these targets are not met, the complainant needs to be informed of the delay and the reasons for it, as well as the revised timetable for resolving the matter.

Local monitoring and recording of complaints

Trust and health authority boards must receive at least quarterly reports on complaints in order to:

- monitor arrangements for local complaints handling
- consider trends in complaints
- consider any lessons to be learned which could be used to improve services.

This monitoring, and actioning the lessons learned from complaints and related staff developments is a key element of clinical governance.

Reform of the complaints system and independent reviews

The NHS (Complaints) Regulations 2004, which apply in England alone, came in to force on 30 July 2004. These regula-

tions moved responsibility for the review of complaints about the NHS to the Healthcare Commission, to bring independence to the second stage of the procedure. Such a review takes the form of an investigation by commission staff and, where appropriate, by a panel of lay people. The regulations also consolidated the directions governing complaints about NHS bodies, and introduced some minor changes to the existing local resolution procedure in secondary care, such as the requirement to have a senior person in the body responsible for the oversight of complaints.

The separate directions and regulations relating to complaints handling by primary care practitioners continue to apply.

The reforms are in response to an independent evaluation of the existing procedure and recommendations made in *NHS complaints reform: making things right*, published by the DH in March 2003.

NHS foundation trusts

The regulatory requirements on local resolution do not apply to NHS foundation trusts. Such trusts are able to develop their own local systems for handling complaints. However, where a complainant is unhappy with the outcome of any investigation of their complaint by the foundation trust, or the trust has no local complaints procedure in place, the complainant can ask the Healthcare Commission for an independent review of their complaint.

Role of the health service ombudsman

The health service commissioner (ombudsman) has jurisdiction in England, Wales and Scotland over the whole range of NHS complaints, other

5 — The advance of clinical governance

than contractual and personnel matters, and any matter in respect of which the aggrieved person had or has the right of appeal or recourse to a tribunal or the courts. Staff involved in complaints have the right to complain to the ombudsman if they consider they have suffered hardship or injustice through the complaints procedure.

The ombudsman's remit is to investigate cases of maladministration. This covers bias, neglect, inattention, delay, incompetence, ineptitude, perversity, arbitrariness, faulty procedures and rudeness.

The ombudsman's investigations are thorough and lengthy. The ombudsman has the power of the High Court to compel the production of documents - and the attendance and examination of witnesses. The ombudsman has the power to pass information discovered in the course of an investigation to a professional regulatory body and/or to an employing authority if the ombudsman believes that is necessary in order to protect patients or the public.

When the investigation is completed a report is sent to the complainant and to the authority concerned.

The ombudsman reports annually to the Health Secretary, who in turn lays the report before Parliament. In addition, the ombudsman publishes each year, with the authority of parlia-ment, volumes of selected cases, with the aim of the service learning lessons from them.

If a trust, PCT or practitioner fails to grant the remedies which the ombudsman has recommended it is probable that the ombudsman will refer to the matter in the annual report and also bring it to the attention of the parliamentary select committee which reviews the ombudsman's work. That committee has the power to summon members and employees of a trust or PCT and also family practitioners and their staff. (General inquiries: Tel: 0845 015 4033. www.ombudsman.org.uk)

Further information

NHS complaints policy. www.dh.gov.uk/PolicyAndGuidance/OrganisationPolicy/ComplaintsPolicy

NHS Executive. *Complaints. Listening ... acting ... improving. Guidance on implementation of the NHS complaints procedure. DH*, 1996.

Department of Health. *NHS complaints reform. Making things right. March* 2003.

Department of Health. *Guidance to support implementation of the NHS (Complaints) Regulations 2004.* August 2004.

6 — The public health agenda

Public health programmes have achieved some spectacular successes in recent years. Sustained campaigns against smoking have brought huge reductions in coronary heart disease and a steady decline in lung cancer. A vigorous response to the threat of AIDS averted the catastrophe which has devastated Africa. New immunisation programmes have reduced markedly meningitis in children, with every child in Britain now immunised — unless their parents unwisely declined the offer — against *Haemophilus meningitis* and against groups A and C meningococcus.

But it is important not to be complacent. There has been a steady improvement in life expectancy in the UK since 1970. Over the same period in Denmark it remained stagnant. There is nothing inevitable about improvement in public health: it takes persistent effort.

The key priorities for public health work are:
• lifestyle programmes: smoking, teenage pregnancy
• disease programmes: coronary heart disease and the cancers
• preventive programmes: immunisation, particularly influenza.

Smoking rates have declined steadily over the past 40 years due to effective public campaigns and continuous work in school to guard children against the dangers of starting to smoke. More recently attention has been turned to helping those who have difficulty giving up. Basic advice is available from any health professional, but in addition smoking cessation clinics have been set up for smokers who want to quit but cannot without help. The government has helped to create the right climate for tobacco control by banning tobacco advertising.

Teenage pregnancy rates in the UK are among the highest in Europe. Tackling the problem requires full and frank sex education of school children, and ready access to contraception for those who want it. Again the government is playing its part by allowing adults and children over 16 to obtain the 'morning after' pill from pharmacies. This will not solve the problem but it is a useful step.

Much of the face to face work of public health is delivered by health promotion specialists, who have the knowledge and skills needed, for example, to run smoking cessation groups, set up exercise programmes for older people or work with teachers on sex education materials. These hands-on public health workers are often based in primary care trusts and will help these organisations to fulfil their role in health improvement.

Strategies for health

The 1999 government's strategy for health in England (*Saving lives*) set targets for reducing deaths from coronary heart disease and stroke, cancer, suicide and accidents. More recently an updated public health White Paper, *Choosing health*, is being put into action. Implementation of these strategies is being driven through national service frameworks. Although local freedom is important, the scientific basis for preventing death does not vary from one end of the country to the other. Meeting national targets requires the uniform application of best practice, solidly founded on research evidence. National clinical directors (czars) have been appointed (for example, Mike Richards for cancer, Roger Boyle for coronary heart disease) to champion the process.

The service framework for coronary heart disease was released in 2000 and

Tackling obesity

The Health survey for England 2004 reveals that the proportion of adults who were categorised as obese (body mass index [BMI] over 30) increased from 13.2 per cent of men in 1993 to 23.6 per cent in 2004 and from 16.4 per cent of women in 1993 to 23.8 per cent in 2004. While the proportion of adults with a desirable BMI decreased in the same years from 37.8 to 27.2 per cent among men and from 44.3 to 35.8 per cent among women. Between 1995 and 2001, mean BMI increased among boys (from 17.6 to 18.1) and girls (from 18.0 to 18.4) aged 2–15.

The National Audit Office estimated that obesity accounted for 18 million days of sickness absence and 30,000 premature deaths in 1998. On average, each person whose death can be attributed to obesity lost nine years of life. Treating obesity costs the NHS at least £500m a year. The wider costs to the economy could be a further £2bn each year.

The Department of Health says obesity:
• is linked to life-threatening illnesses such as coronary heart disease, type 2 diabetes and some forms of cancer
• is rapidly increasing in children, creating long-term health risks.

The national service framework for coronary heart disease sets standards for the NHS on reducing obesity, promoting healthy eating and increasing physical activity at a local level.

Along with the provision of advice, support and counselling on diet and exercise for people with weight problems, about 55,000 patients each year will be prescribed anti-obesity drugs to help them lose weight.

Healthy living centres are also improving the health of local communities, for example by running diet and nutrition classes.

Preventing a further increase in obesity in future generations obviously means tackling the problem in childhood.

The Department of Health's £42m national school fruit scheme is providing children aged six with a free piece of fruit on each school day. The scheme is part of the government's wider five-a-day programme for England to increase the amount of fruit and vegetables eaten by everyone.

The government is also investing £581m in physical education and sports facilities and has pledged that children will get at least two hours a week of physical activity and sports within and outside school.

The chief medical officer's (CMO) report for 2002 concluded that the growth of overweight and obesity in the population — particularly among children — was a major concern. It had the potential to lead over the next three decades to thousands of extra cases of heart disease, certain cancers, arthritis, diabetes and many other problems. The CMO wrote: 'Unless this time bomb is defused the consequences for the population's health, the costs to the NHS and losses to the economy will be disastrous.' With a coordinated response from health and local authority services and across government and with the co-operation of the food, sports and leisure industries it was still possible

Wellard's NHS Handbook 2006/07

to mitigate its impact on future generations.

Within the overall health improvement debate set by the *Choosing health* White Paper, the public were consulted in 2004 on *Choosing a better diet*, a document which sets out priorities for a food and health action plan.

National Audit Office. *Tackling obesity in England.* February 2001. TSO.

Department of Health. *On the state of the public health. Annual report of the chief medical officer 2002.* July 2003: 37–45.

National diet and nutrition survey, volume 4, adults 19–64. Food Standards Agency and Department of Health. February 2004. www.foodstandards.gov.uk

Storing up problems: the case for a slimmer nation. Royal College of Physicians, Faculty of Public Health, Royal College of Paediatrics and Child Health. February 2004.

House of Commons, Health Committee. *Obesity.* May 2004.

Health survey for England 2004. www.ic.nhs.uk/pubs/hlthsvyeng2004upd

---

a number of detailed targets were set. Meeting some of them is expensive — more money has been needed for more heart surgery and for drugs, particularly clot busting (streptokinase) and cholesterol lowering (statins). But care also needs to be well organised: hospitals need to be able to offer rapid access chest pain clinics to speed diagnosis. GPs have to establish patient registers and practice clinics to make sure patients' needs are not overlooked. The NHS also still needs to do more to put rehabilitation from heart attacks on a better footing. About half of the decline in death from coronary heart disease over the past decade has been due to changes in lifestyle — particularly smoking and diet — while the other half is the benefit of treatment including quite simple treatments such as aspirin.

The theme of the NHS cancer plan is the need for a team approach to treatment. Doctors in different specialties (surgeons, oncologists, radiologists, pathologists) need to work together; and different hospitals have to coordinate their work under the leadership of a cancer centre. Achieving consensus in cancer networks requires considerable patience. The plan has laid great emphasis on reducing the wait for treatment, with the goal of ensuring that no patient waits more than a month for treatment.

The service framework for mental health was issued in 1999. As with the other frameworks there is an emphasis on ensuring uniformly good services throughout the country. Collaboration again emerges as a theme, though in mental health the form this takes is good collaboration between GPs and specialist services.

Reaching the target for accidents depends on action both within and outside the NHS. Road traffic is the main cause of accident deaths in young people, so most of the health gain will come from road engineering and traffic law. NHS efforts will tend to focus on accidental death in old people, particularly death from falls. Recent years have seen the first clear evidence that

6 — The public health agenda

incidents of the latter can be prevented, by programmes which combine home safety checks, medication review and exercise programmes for frail older people. Primary care trusts can use the combined talents of health visitors, GPs and health promotion staff to mount effective programmes.

Tackling inequality in health is also important. Because illness is often rooted in poverty, primary care trusts need to work with local government and other agencies to create healthy communities in disadvantaged areas. This is the concept of the spearhead primary care trusts. But the benefit of eradicating specific causes of illness should not be overlooked. There is a strong social class gradient in childhood accident deaths.

Epidemiology

The success of local efforts to improve health needs to be tracked. A good selection of information on disease, for every district in England, is published as the *Public health common data set* (PHCDS). This includes death rates, statistics on cancer, hospital admission, and teenage pregnancy and population data. NHS public health departments can provide more detailed analyses for their own areas. Information on lifestyle (smoking, eating and exercise) and disability (backache, arthritis, incontinence) comes from national surveys. Accurate estimates can be made of local disease from these national surveys once allowance is made for age

structure and the ethnic make-up of the local populace.

Needs assessment

The original concept of the 1990 reforms of the NHS was that health authorities would assess the health needs of a population and trusts would provide services to meet that need. Under such a system, no trust would lobby to provide a service that was not needed, and each health authority would deploy its resources to meet all needs that arose (since the NHS guarantees that patients will get the treatment they need). This was a laudable idea, but one deeply hostage to what the

Trends in CHD mortality (men and women under 65)

As standardised per 100,000

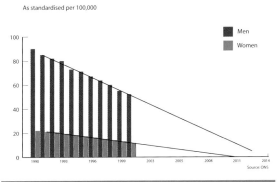

Men
Women

Source: ONS

Death rates from all circulatory disease in England 1993-2003 and target and projection for the year 2010 (persons under 75)

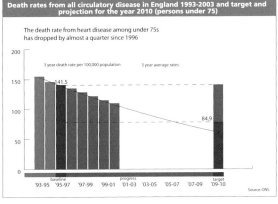

The death rate from heart disease among under 75s has dropped by almost a quarter since 1996

3 year death rate per 100,000 population   3 year average rates

141.5

84.9

baseline   progress   target
'93-95 '95-97 '97-99 '99-01 '01-03 '03-05 '05-07 '07-09 '09-10

Source: ONS

Wellard's NHS Handbook 2006/07

word 'need' means, particularly when coupled to the word 'assessment'. In practice it is, of course, impossible to assess all the needs of all the residents of even the smallest primary care trust.

Often the most effective way of making an assessment is to look at whatever the present service is, and then judge whether it seems hard-pressed (long waits for appointments, numerous complaints), relaxed (trivial conditions offered immediate lengthy treatment) or about right. Such an evaluation may not be scientific but it can be used for almost any service or treatment.

Occasionally specific needs can be estimated, where the treatment is specialised and the research base strong. The numbers of people likely to need a cochlear implant, a bone marrow transplant or treatment for end stage renal failure, for example, are reasonably predictable. Regional specialist commissioning groups commission most of these specialised services. The key task for public health specialists on such groups is to assess claims for the effectiveness of new treatments.

Screening

For most people, the term 'screening' implies some form of test; for example, a smear test or a cholesterol test. Screening programmes often start because a scientist has devised a test that allows early diagnosis of disease. Haphazard screening based on a test, without thought for the whole programme, can be counter-productive.

A screening programme must be well thought out, properly staffed and fault-lessly executed. A lesson learned the hard way is that if screening cannot be done with the utmost efficiency, it may be better not to do it at all. Meticulous attention to detail is absolutely essential. Typically a screening programme tests 1,000 people to discover one with disease.

Screening policy in the NHS is now decided by advice from the UK screening committee (www.nsc.nhs.uk). The library page on this website contains a number of useful information sheets on different screening programmes.

Cancer. The biggest national screening programmes are for breast cancer and cervical cancer. These programmes, together with improvements in treatment and a fortuitous change in the biology of the cancers, have achieved substantial reduction in deaths from these diseases. Considerable effort goes into quality control of these programmes.

The next big cancer screening programme for the NHS is for bowel cancer. The programme is being rolled out across the country from April 2006 over three years. Men and women aged 60–69 years will be screened for colorectal cancer every two years. Faecal occult blood testing involves analysing

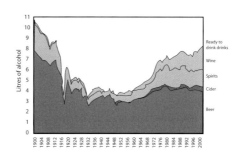

Alcohol consumption in the UK

1900-2000 per capita consumption of 100 per cent alcohol

Litres of alcohol

Ready to drink drinks
Wine
Spirits
Cider
Beer

6 — The public health agenda

stool samples and this method is being introduced in phases among men and women in their sixties. Large scale pilots of a second method of bowel cancer screening, flexible sigmoidoscopy, will be carried out in people in the late fifties.

Meanwhile the Medical Research Council is researching the case for ovarian cancer, but it will be several years before results are known.

Mother and child. A range of tests is done on pregnant women by most maternity units to detect abnormalities in the fetus. Only two are endorsed by national policy, both for communicable

National screening programmes

Breast cancer
Cervical cancer
Chlamydia
Colorectal cancer
Cystic fibrosis
Diabetic retinopathy
Down's syndrome
Fetal anomaly
Newborn bloodspot
Newborn hearing
Sickle cell and thalassaemia

Pilot programme
Diabetes, heart disease and stroke (DHDS) pilot project

Alcohol harm reduction

In March 2004 the government unveiled plans to forge partnerships with the health and police services, the drinks industry, and communities to combat the range of problems caused by alcohol misuse in England.

The *Alcohol harm reduction strategy for England*, which was published by the Prime Minister's strategy unit, sets out measures to:
• tackle alcohol-related disorder in town and city centres
• improve treatment and support for people with alcohol problems
• clamp down on irresponsible promotions by the industry
• provide better information to consumers about the dangers of alcohol misuse.

The document records that alcohol misuse is costing around £20bn a year through crime and disorder, injuries and illness, and lost productivity in the workplace.

Each year there are:
• over 30,000 hospital admissions for

alcohol dependence syndrome
• up to 22,000 premature deaths
• at peak times, up to 70 per cent of all attendances at accident and emergency departments related to alcohol use.

The cross-government approach seeks to create partnerships at local and national levels which can address existing problems but are also flexible enough to adapt to changing needs.

The strategy identifies a need for greater awareness of alcohol misuse issues among health service staff, and an improvement in their ability to deal with them. It calls for improved treatment services and better help for the most vulnerable — such as drug addicts, the mentally ill, homeless and young people. They often have multiple problems and need clear pathways for treatment from a variety of sources.

www.strategy.gov.uk

disease (HIV and hepatitis B virus). The aim of this screening is to prevent infection passing to the baby. Most units also screen for syphilis. In each case, if the mother's infection is detected before birth, the risk to the baby can be reduced by treatment. Maternity units also screen for Down's syndrome. A national programme for screening for chlamydia infection in women is also underway.

Diabetes, heart disease and stroke prevention. A pilot is underway to screen for diabetes and encourage healthy lifestyle changes in people aged 40 and over considered at high risk for diabetes on the basis of a prior diagnosis of cardiovascular disease and/or being overweight. The project has aimed to reach 90 per cent of the eligible population in nine pilot PCTs during 2005, prior to its evaluation.

Conclusion

No two public health departments are quite alike, but the common themes are:
• leadership for public health programmes
• analysing health needs
• helping PCT staff to take knowledge-based decisions
• working with clinical staff on local policies and strategies
• working with health promotion specialists to secure healthy lifestyles.

> ### The 2004 public health White Paper — *Choosing health*

In November 2004 the government published the White Paper *Choosing health. Making healthy choices easier.* It aims to give people the choices to change their lifestyles by tackling the public health issues of smoking, obesity, sexual health, alcohol and mental health. The delivery plan for the initiative was published in March 2005.

New measures in the White Paper, which are backed by £1bn funding, include:
• increasing the number of smoke-free workplaces
• curbing the promotion of unhealthy foods to children
• clearly labelling the nutritional content of food
• introducing personal NHS-accredited health trainers
• providing faster access to sexual health clinics
• tackling social and geographical inequalities in health.

Choosing health details the support that will be available to help people make and carry out the right decisions for their own health. From 2006, NHS-accredited health trainers will give support to people who want it, in the areas with the highest need. From 2007 they will be operating progressively across the country.

Health trainers will often come from local communities and will offer practical advice and connect with locally available services and support. Individuals will be able to contact their trainer through their health centre, walk-in centre or via NHS Direct. Health trainers will help develop personal health guides and offer a stock take so that

6 — The public health agenda

people can see how their way of life might be affecting their health.

The White Paper identifies a range of activity, including the following:

- the national clinical directors will work with communities to identify where there may be scope to extend prevention in their clinical areas.
- primary care trusts will receive funding to give greater priority to areas of high health need. Eighty eight PCTs have been chosen to spearhead this work
- from 2006, NHS stop smoking services will be offered on the choose and book system
- some 3,000 community matrons will take the lead in providing personalised care and health advice. They will also provide a greater focus on patients with complex health problems
- new approaches will be developed to help people with mental illness manage their own care and aspects of their health
- capital and revenue funding will help to modernise the range of sexual health services.

Delivering choosing health: making healthier choices easy sets out how the commitments should translate into practical benefits for local communities. The plans include a range of actions to help children make healthier choices.

The document outlines the priorities for action at national and local levels and what should be done by whom and when. It lists 45 big wins that are expected to make the greatest impact on health in the shortest period of time. It describes new partnerships between industry, the voluntary sector and professional groups, and new services delivered by local authorities and the NHS.

Choosing a better diet includes action on:

- advertising and promotion of foods to children
- simplified food labelling
- obesity education and prevention
- nutritional standards in schools, hospitals and the workplace.

Choosing activity brings together the commitments relating to physical activity in *Choosing health* as well as other actions across government, which should contribute to increasing levels of physical activity.

Department of Health. *Choosing health. Making healthy choices easier.* November 2004.

Department of Health. *Delivering choosing health: making healthier choices easy.* March 2005.

Department of Health. *Choosing a better diet: a food and health action plan.* March 2005.

Department of Health. *Choosing activity: a physical activity action plan.* March 2005.

The public health observatories

In 2000 eight public health observatories were established across England. Wales, Scotland and Northern Ireland have equivalent bodies or are developing them. Their role is to monitor disease patterns at local level, drawing together information to facilitate local public health priority-setting and planning.

The observatories identify gaps in health information and evaluate progress by local agencies in improving health and cutting inequality. They also look ahead to give early warning of future public health problems.

www.pho.org.uk

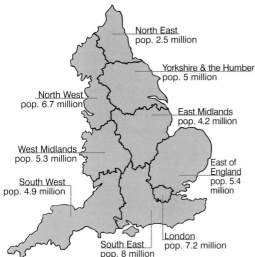

North East
pop. 2.5 million

Yorkshire & the Humber
pop. 5 million

North West
pop. 6.7 million

East Midlands
pop. 4.2 million

West Midlands
pop. 5.3 million

East of England
pop. 5.4 million

South West
pop. 4.9 million

London
pop. 7.2 million

South East
pop. 8 million

Spearhead primary care trusts

Primary care trusts manage funding to deliver health equality targets. In November 2004, former Health Secretary John Reid named the 88 most deprived PCTs that would be the first to pilot initiatives such as health trainers, enhanced stop smoking services and more school nurses, as set out in the 2004 White Paper *Choosing health*.

This spearhead group of PCTs is receiving extra funding. The PCTs covering 70 local authority areas, were identified using information on deprivation, mortality from cancer and heart disease as well as life expectancy to determine the areas which face the greatest health challenges. Over a

quarter of the population in England is covered by the areas, including large urban areas such as Liverpool, Manchester, Birmingham and parts of London.

Health action zones

The health action zone (HAZ) initiative was launched in 1998 to encourage new approaches to improving health, and modernising service systems, through multiagency partnerships. The initiative was concerned with new ways of tackling health inequalities in some of the most deprived areas in England.

Twenty six local health action zones were set up. A sum of £290m was made available for the three years from 1999/2000, with some further funding from 2002/03.

Primary care trusts within the HAZ areas were responsible for deciding how HAZ resources would be used and for ensuring that HAZ activities helped PCTs deliver on health equality targets. HAZs were performance managed by the strategic health authorities.

Each HAZ developed its own priorities and targets, reflecting local needs of the population. Some selected a number of focus areas such as improving health and opportunities for children and young people, improving elderly services or integrating mental health provision.

All HAZs established governing partnership boards involving health and local authorities, primary care trusts, NHS trusts and a range of other partners such as community groups, business and higher education. Where they developed new service models, different and more fluid partnership approaches were needed.

Wellard's NHS Handbook 2006/07

6 — The public health agenda

Reducing health inequalities

Health inequalities targets in the areas of life expectancy and infant mortality were announced by the Health Secretary in February 2001. These were aimed at narrowing the health gap in childhood and throughout life between socioeconomic groups and between the most deprived areas and the rest of the country.

For the first time, health inequalities were made a priority for the NHS in the priorities and planning framework for 2003–06 *Improvement, expansion and reform: the next three years.* The framework set out the need to identify a single set of local priorities with partners, supported by tools such as equity audits, and an approach that is responsive to community needs.

In July 2003, the Department of Health issued a further plan for tackling health inequalities over three years. The document provides a detailed toolkit for local organisations to change the way they deliver services to improve the health of disadvantaged groups. It establishes the foundations needed to achieve the national target for 2010 of reducing inequalities in health outcomes by 10 per cent as measured by infant mortality and life expectancy at birth. It calls for this to be done in the most disadvantaged areas faster than elsewhere.

Primary care trusts are taking the lead locally in driving forward health inequalities work in the NHS, and are expected to work closely with NHS trusts, local authorities and other partners to take concerted action on public health and prevention, health services and the wider determinants of health such as housing, transport, education.

Other NHS interventions to support narrowing of health inequalities more broadly than the target areas include:

- identification of local health inequalities, including improving data quality and collection to identify groups or areas with high health need/poor health outcomes
- providing local leadership by developing and sustaining close partnership working, identifying a single set of local priorities and taking concerted action with partners to tackle health inequalities, including influencing community strategies. Contributing to the development of the local strategic partnership to realise its potential for health improvement and tackling inequalities
- supporting Sure Start, contributing to regeneration and leading the development and delivery of the health domain of local neighbourhood renewal strategies in the most deprived areas
- making the NHS a power for regeneration to stimulate local economies and enhance the employability of disadvantaged groups, through its local employment and purchasing procedures and capital programmes.

Progress towards implementation of these interventions forms part of the assessment framework for NHS organisations.

In October 2004, NHS chief executive Sir Nigel Crisp appointed Surinder Sharma as equality and human rights director for the NHS. His role is to help to tackle inequalities in all aspects of health and social care delivery.

In February 2004, Sir Nigel launched his 10-point leadership and race equality action plan. It challenges NHS leaders to demonstrate personal leadership particularly in two areas: making race equality a core part of improving health services for all, and ensuring a workforce and leadership that is diverse and inclusive.

In the context of the Race Relations (Amendment) Act 2000, NHS organisations have a statutory duty to promote race equality. They were asked to review and consult on their race equality schemes and publish a new three-year scheme by may 2005.

HM Treasury/Department of Health. *Tackling health inequalities. Summary of the 2002 cross-cutting review.* November 2002.

Department of Health. *Tackling health inequalities. A programme for action.* July 2003.

Department of Health. *Department of Health race equality scheme: 2005–2008.* May 2005.

Department of Health. *Promoting equality and human rights in the NHS — a guide for non-executive directors of NHS boards.* July 2005.

Department of Health. *Tackling health inequalities: status report on the programme for action.* August 2005.

Commission for Racial Equality
www.cre.gov.uk

'Saving lives: our healthier nation'

The work surrounding the *Choosing health* initiative is based on previous national strategy development and action. The 1999 White Paper *Saving lives: our healthier nation* set out the government's proposals for specific improvements in healthcare and disease management in England. Targeting cancer, coronary heart disease and

stroke, accidents, and mental illness the key objectives were 'to save lives by preventing up to 300,000 untimely and unnecessary deaths' and 'to achieve better health for everyone and especially for the worst off'. The target areas accounted for three quarters of all deaths under the age of 75. The deadline for achieving objectives was the year 2010, by which time:

- **Cancer** death rates in people under the age of 75 would be reduced by at least a fifth (from 69,000 to 55,000)
- **Coronary heart disease and stroke** death rates would be reduced in people under the age of 75 by two fifths (from 69,000 to 41,000)
- **Death by accident** would be reduced by a fifth (from 10,000 to 8,000) and serious injury by at least a tenth
- **Suicide and undetermined injury through mental illness** would be reduced by at least a fifth (from 4,500 to 3,600).

To achieve the four *Saving lives* targets it was proposed to:

- secure more funding for the health service
- begin an offensive against smoking, as the biggest preventable cause of illness and premature death
- integrate national and local government work
- stress health improvements as key to the work of the NHS (that is, prevention rather than treatment)
- press for high health standards for all, and especially those on lower incomes.

Proposals for increasing the length and quality of life were eclectic. A government-wide agenda would seek to address underlying social causes of inequality, for example, combating poverty, improving education and work opportunities, and improving housing stock.

6 — The public health agenda

Health organisations and local authorities would build into their health improvement programmes for 2000/03 plans to implement action on the four national targets, as well as local targets specific to the health needs of local populations, and proposals to tackle local health inequalities.

Partnership was a key element in the achievement of the *Saving lives* objectives. A new three-way partnership was proposed, between individuals, communities and government.

Individuals and health
The onus was being placed upon individuals to be responsible for their own health by increasing physical activity, improving diet and quitting smoking.

To encourage physical activity and participation in sport, a sports strategy was published in 1999. Its aim was to provide affordable, local sports and leisure opportunities, to encourage exercise on prescription (exercise as a cost effective alternative to long-term medication), and to promote specific sports programmes which encourage activity among people with certain medical conditions, for example, obesity.

The particular health needs of mothers and young children were addressed in Sure Start, a cross-government programme to provide support to parents and local communities. It would be targeted on specific areas of need.

The healthy citizens programme had three principle strands:

NHS Direct — A 24-hour nurse-led telephone helpline.

Health skills — The expansion of training for first aid skills.

The expert patient programme to help people with long-term illnesses. Department of Health. *Saving lives: our healthier nation.* Cm 4386. TSO, 1999.

Department of Health. *Reducing health inequalities: an action report.* TSO, 1999.

Acheson D. *Independent inquiry into inequalities in health report.* TSO, 1998.

The clean hospitals programme

As part of a nationwide clean-up campaign, the Department of Health has made funds available to NHS trusts to improve the cleanliness and patients' environment within NHS hospitals.

The purpose of the money has been to achieve cleaner and better conditions for patients, visitors and staff. The expectation has been that improvements are immediate, tangible and sustainable.

Trusts were asked to appoint an environmental champion for their board, and self and external assessments have been used to monitor progress. The Department of Health's patient environment action teams (PEATs) have been conducting annual inspections to make sure that standards are being maintained and improved upon.

The PEAT teams are volunteer NHS managers, patients and patient representatives who provide an independent and unannounced review of standards at hospitals and report on their findings.

PEAT assessments look at 24 cleanliness and other patient environment issues relating to wards, reception and waiting areas, A&E and outpatients, corridors, furnishings, linen, the external appearance of hospitals and the amenities provided to patients and visitors.

Based on the assessments hospitals are rated either excellent, good, acceptable, poor or unacceptable.

In 2004 the environmental results of the PEAT for England were: (see below)

The national standards of cleanliness have been revised and renamed the national specifications for cleanliness to avoid confusion with the Healthcare Commission's *Standards for better health*. They are incorporated into guidance on contracting for cleaning, which also includes guidance on minimum cleaning frequencies.

The NHS *Healthcare facilities cleaning manual* provides guidance and best practice on the effective cleaning of healthcare premises.

In another initiative, the NHS Plan contained a target to have housekeepers working with nurses. In 2004 the target was achieved with 70 per cent of larger hospitals employing such staff.

The housekeepers aim to support the delivery of clinical care by:
• ensuring that wards are clean
• ensuring that food is enjoyable and enjoyed
• providing a warm and welcoming environment
• ensuring that there are suitable measures on the ward to protect patients' privacy and dignity
• applying a range of skills that complement the clinical work and allow nurses to nurse.

www.cleanhospitals.com

Better hospital food

The better hospital food programme aims to improve food services for

Patient environment					
2005	Excellent	Good	Acceptable	Poor	Unacceptable
Percentage of hospitals	10.3	44.8	40.1	4.6	0.2

6 — The public health agenda

ients. In almost 90 per cent of acute hospitals, patients can access drinks and light refreshments around the clock.

In 2003 PEAT inspectors found that 71 per cent of hospitals provide snack boxes for patients who miss main mealtimes, or feel like eating something lighter. Two thirds of hospitals offer patients additional snacks on at least two occasions each day. And at least three new dishes, designed by leading chefs, are available at 60 per cent of hospitals. For food, 56 per cent of sites inspected received an amber rating and 44 per cent achieved a green rating. No sites received a red rating.

In 2004 the results for England were: (see below)

www.betterhospitalfood.com

Campaign to tackle smoking

Smoking is the UK's leading cause of preventable death, resulting in around 120,000 deaths a year from cancer, heart disease and other causes. The government has run a sustained programme to tackle smoking, including help for smokers to quit through the NHS. Around seven in ten smokers say they want to quit.

The government's White Paper on tobacco, *Smoking kills,* was published in 1998. The aim was to cut the number of people smoking by 1.5 million by 2010. About 13 million adults in the UK smoked and, according to the Department of Health, more than 120,000 people a year died from smoking.

The programme was designed to protect children from the effects of tobacco and to help seven out of ten adult smokers who said they wanted to give up.

Measures included:
- an NHS smoking cessation programme, with advice clinics and support for adults wanting to quit
- counsellors offering a week's supply of nicotine replacement therapy — free of charge to those smokers least able to afford it
- a mass media publicity campaign
- further curbs of tobacco advertising and promotion
- choice for non-smokers in public houses and restaurants
- code of practice for smoking at work
- tobacco tax increases
- a drive against smuggling.

More recent anti-tobacco initiatives include:
- new targets to reduce smoking rates among manual groups from 32 per cent in 1998 to 26 per cent in 2010 (in the *NHS cancer plan,* September 2000)
- the launch of a tobacco education campaign to support the NHS Smoking Helpline (0800 169 0169)
- the launch, in 1999/2000, of the NHS stop smoking service
- an enforcement protocol on underage sales
- specialist smoking cessation services for pregnant women (0800 169 9169)
- support to a European draft directive to strengthen the law on tar, nicotine and carbon monoxide yields, health

Hospital food					
2005	Excellent	Good	Acceptable	Poor	Unacceptable
Percentage of hospitals	32.4	51.5	14.8	1.3	0

warnings and tobacco additives
- the availability on NHS prescription, from June 2000, of bupropion (Zyban), a non-nicotine smoking cessation treatment
- the availability on NHS prescription, from April 2001, of nicotine replacement therapy, in addition to its availability over the counter in pharmacies
- the investment of £209m in a three-year campaign to deter smuggling.

From February 2003, tobacco advertising on billboards and in the press and magazines was banned across the UK under the Tobacco Advertising and Promotions Act 2002. A ban on in-pack promotion schemes and remaining direct marketing became effective in May 2003. The Act also restricts internet advertising, is bringing to an end sponsorship of tobacco products through sporting events and limits the promotion of tobacco products in places where they are sold.

The chief medical officer's report for 2002 devoted a section to the health risks of second-hand smoke (passive smoking). Professor Sir Liam Donaldson argued that 'major action to clear the air of cigarette smoke in workplaces and public places would be the final brick in the wall'. Inhaled second-hand smoke can cause lung cancer (increasing the risk by 20–30 per cent in people who live with smokers) and heart disease (increasing the risk by 25 per cent in people who live with smokers), and is causally linked to other conditions such as lower respiratory illness and asthma. Second hand smoke contains 50 known or suspected cancer causing agents and 100 chemical poisons. The report called for smoke-free work areas and campaigns for smoke-free public places.

In December 2004, the General Household Survey showed that there were around 1.2m fewer smokers in England since the 1998 Smoking kills White Paper and 400,000 had quit during 2004. The proportion of the population who smoke had declined from 28 per cent in 1998 to 25 per cent in 2003. Some £138m has been made available to stop smoking services over the three years 2003/04 to 2005/06.

To back the chief medical officer's call for a complete, rigorously enforced smoking ban in all NHS healthcare facilities, the Health Development Agency (HDA) and Pharmacy Health Link published a paper which recorded that while 99 per cent of NHS hospitals in England had a no-smoking policy, only 10 per cent were completely smokefree. It urged NHS organisations to take action to eliminate tobacco use from all premises. They should, argued the document, also provide comprehensive support for smokers and help those wishing to give up. At the same time the HDA issued Guidance for smokefree hospitals trusts.

2005 saw controversy in England about proposals to ban smoking in all enclosed public spaces and workplaces. While countries such as Ireland and Australia had successfully implemented such bans, the government in London appeared to be in two minds about the issue. However, the Health Bill due to go through Parliament in 2006 will contain such a ban after all.

Smoking kills. TSO, December 1998.

Department of Health. On the state of the public health. Annual report of the chief medical officer 2002. July 2003: 15-25.

Pharmacy Health Link, Health Development Agency. The case for a completely smokefree NHS in England. January 2005.

Health Development Agency. Guidance for smokefree hospitals trusts. January 2005.

6 — The public health agenda

www.ash.org.uk

www.givingupsmoking.co.uk

Healthy living centres

A network of some 350 healthy living centres (HLCs) has been developed across the UK. The aim has been for them to promote health, helping people of all ages to maximise their health and wellbeing, whatever their capacity for fitness in the traditional sense. Their focus is on health as a positive attribute which helps people get the most out of life, embracing both physical and mental wellbeing.

HLCs may involve a range of part-nerships at local level, for example the voluntary, public and private sectors working with each other, local GPs and local people. There is no central blue-print for the centres — the scheme is designed to be flexible so that projects can be specifically tailored to meet the differing needs of different communi-ties. The range of services on offer can include, for example, exercise classes to help tackle coronary heart disease, nutrition advice and health information which enables adults to make informed choices about their diet and lifestyle.

The healthy living centres initiative is UK-wide and is partly funded by £300m the Big Lottery Fund. The first grants were approved early in 1999.

Priority has been given to projects in areas where general health was below average or where groups who would particularly benefit from them find existing faculties off-putting or difficult to get to.

The health education bodies

Wales Centre for Health

The Wales Centre for Health is an independent body working to improve public health and reduce health inequalities in Wales. It was fully established as an Assembly sponsored public body on 1 April 2005.

The centre acts as a focal point for multidisciplinary advice, debate and professional development. The broad functions of the centre, as defined in the Health (Wales) Act 2003, are to:

- develop and maintain arrangements for making information about matters related to the protection and improvement of health in Wales available to the public
- undertake and commission research into such matters
- contribute to the provision and development of training in such matters.

The centre is playing an important part in establishing networks and liaising and engaging with relevant professions and organisations to improve health and wellbeing.

In August 2005 the centre published the *Health in Wales* report. It maps health issues according to geographical area, and highlights the health and social problems which exist in the south Wales valleys, particularly Merthyr Tydfil.

Wales Centre for Health (Canolfan Iechyd Cymru), 14 Cathedral Road, Cardiff CF11 9LJ. Tel: 029 2022 7744. www.wales.nhs.uk/sites/home.cfm?orgID=369

Wellard's NHS Handbook 2006/07

NHS Health Scotland

Health Scotland is a special health board created in April 2003 by bringing together the Public Health Institute of Scotland (PHIS) and the Health Education Board for Scotland (HEBS).

Health Scotland provides a national focus for improving health, and works with the Scottish Executive and other partners to take action to improve health and reduce inequalities in Scotland.

NHS Health Scotland. Edinburgh office: Woodburn House, Canaan Lane, Edinburgh EH10 4SG. Tel: 0131 536 5500. Glasgow office: Clifton House, Clifton Place, Glasgow G3 7LS. Tel: 0141 300 1010. www.healthscotland.com

Northern Ireland Health Promotion Agency

The Health Promotion Agency for Northern Ireland, established in 1990, develops and implements programmes to promote good health and prevent disease. It provides policy advice to the Department of Health, Social Services and Public Safety, coordinates regional health promotion activities, undertakes public information campaigns, provides training, carries out research and works with the wider health and personal social services and other sectors in helping to implement the health promotion elements of the regional strategy.

Health promotion is an important part of the work of many disciplines in the health and personal social services. However, dedicated health promotion staff are employed in the agency and in the health promotion departments of health and social services trusts.

The Health Promotion Agency for Northern Ireland, 18 Ormeau Avenue, Belfast BT2 8HS. Tel: 028 9031 1611. www.healthpromotionagency.org.uk

Control of infectious diseases and health protection

For most of the past century improv- proved social conditions and sanita- tion, followed by medical interventions such as immunisation and antibiotics, led to a steady decrease in the burden of infection. However, in recent years infectious agents have tightened their grip on the developing world and re- emerged as an important public health problem in the UK. Infectious diseases such as tuberculosis, HIV/AIDS, menin- gitis, E coli O157 food poisoning and new variant CJD regularly capture media attention, but the continuing role of the NHS and partner organisations in controll- ing such diseases is less well known.

The arrangements for the control of infectious disease were revised after the 1988 report of a committee of inquiry chaired by the then chief medical officer (the Acheson report).[1] This inquiry had been undertaken in response to the deficiencies found by public inquiries into the management of two major outbreaks of communi- cable disease which caused 19 deaths from Salmonella infection and 28 from legionnaires' disease. The key responsibilities of health authorities/ boards and NHS trusts have subse- quently been set out in health service guidelines issued in 1993[2] and their importance have been emphasised in priorities and planning guidance from the Department of Health. Following *Shifting the balance of power* and *Getting ahead of the curve*[3] the health protection responsibilities (including communicable disease control) of health authorities in England have transferred to primary care trusts, which are now supported in delivering these responsibilities by the Health Protection Agency.

6 — The public health agenda

Responsibilities of primary care trusts (health authorities and boards)

Every PCT/HA/HB should assign executive responsibility for surveillance, prevention and control of communicable disease and infection to a named medical consultant (box 1), known in England, Wales and Northern Ireland as the consultant in communicable disease control (CCDC). In Scotland the generic term consultant in public health medicine is used. In England, the CCDC is part of the local team of the Health Protection Agency; in Wales, they are part of the National Public Health Service for Wales; in Scotland part of Health Protection Scotland, and in Northern Ireland, the CCDC/CPHM is part of the Health Board Department of Public Health. The CCDC has usually also been appointed by the matching local authorities as proper officer to discharge certain of their legal powers and responsibilities; for example, the receipt of notifications of infectious diseases and the power to exclude potentially infectious people from work or school. The work of the CCDC covers both these legally notifiable infections (meningitis, food poisoning, tuberculosis, hepatitis, etc) (box 2) and any other infections of public health importance such as legionnaires' disease, HIV and influenza.

The work of the CCDC and their support staff include surveillance (identifying cases of infection requiring public health action and monitoring of trends), outbreak investigation and proactive work to reduce the burden of infection in the community. This involves close liaison with local authorities (especially environmental health and education departments), microbiologists, hospital doctors, general practitioners, community health staff, and agencies such as the Health and Safety Executive. Such liaison must include the preparation and updating of joint plans for managing both individual cases of infectious disease and outbreaks. In addition, many CsCDC also assist in discharging the PCT/HA/HB's responsibilities in other related areas such as immunisation (to meet government targets for immunisation uptake), the AIDS Control Act, chemical incidents, environmental hazards, emergency planning, port health, control of infection in nursing and residential homes and certain areas of advice to local authorities.

It is important that PCTs understand that the creation of the HPA does not relieve them of their responsibilities in relation to health protection and communicable disease control. Strategic health authorities have an increasing role in ensuring that local health protection arrangements are adequate.

Support to local teams

The Acheson report recommended the provision of specialist support at a regional and national level. In England and Wales this was provided by the regional (regional epidemiologist) and national centres of the Public Health Laboratory Service Communicable Disease Surveillance Centre (CDSC) and regional and national specialist PHLS laboratories: all of these have been absorbed into the HPA. Northern Ireland and Wales also have national communicable disease surveillance centres. Support to HBs in Scotland is available from Health Protection Scotland. Both the HPA and Health Protection Scotland are also responsible for national surveillance of infectious disease and advice to government.

Many NHS trust and PCT staff also play an important role in control of

Box 1. Responsibilities of consultants in communicable disease control (CsCDC) and their staff

Core activities:

- setting up and maintaining surveillance systems
- analysing trends in infectious disease incidence
- investigation and control of outbreaks
- proper officer for Public Health Act and regulations
- liaison with others involved in control of infectious disease
- advice to local authorities, primary care staff and public
- infection control advice and support to nursing and residential homes and to schools
- advice to PCTs on commissioning services to prevent, control and treat infection
- prevention and health promotion programmes
- teaching and training of others
- continuing education, audit and research.

Variable activities:

- district immunisation coordination
- district HIV prevention coordination
- tuberculosis contact tracing
- port health
- chemical incident planning and management
- investigation of environmental hazards
- decontamination lead under HSC 2000/032
- emergency planning.

communicable disease in the community including microbiologists, clinical medical staff, health visitors, tuberculosis nurses, sexual health contact tracing staff, school nurses and health promotion officers. It is important to bear in mind the public health role of such staff when commissioning services and when organisational changes are underway.

Control of hospital infection

Modern hospitals collect together as patients a group of people who are particularly vulnerable to infection due to age, disease and treatments which affect the immune system. These patients inevitably risk coming into contact with others admitted with infectious diseases, or patients and staff carrying potentially harmful organisms. Practices such as the increase in invasive medical procedures and mass catering are further potential sources of infection. In addition, the frequent need for antibiotics favours the emergence in hospitals of resistant bacteria such as methicillin-resistant *Staphylococcus aureus* (MRSA).

Nearly one in ten patients in acute hospital at any one time has an infection acquired after admission to hospital. Such infections increase the risk of patients dying in hospital (perhaps contributing to 20,000 deaths annually in the UK) and prolong their length of stay, causing substantial increased costs to the hospital. The cost to the NHS of hospital acquired infection is estimated at £1bn a year. There is evidence that a good hospital infection control service can reduce hospital acquired infection by about one third and that this is an extremely cost-effective use of NHS resources.[4] Hospital infection control is therefore an important area in the drive to improve quality through the clinical governance

6 — The public health agenda

Box 2. Notifiable diseases

Doctors in England and Wales have a statutory duty to notify the proper officer (the local consultant in communicable disease control) of suspected cases of certain infectious diseases under the Public Health (Control of Diseases) Act 1984 and the Public Health (Infectious Diseases) Regulations 1988. The proper officers are required every week to inform the Centre for Infections (CfI) of each case of each disease that has been notified. CfI has responsibility for collating these weekly returns and publishing analyses of local and national trends.

The diseases are:
- Acute encephalitis
- Acute poliomyelitis
- Anthrax
- Cholera
- Diphtheria
- Dysentery
- Food poisoning
- Leprosy
- Leptospirosis
- Malaria
- Measles
- Meningitis
- Meningococcal septicaemia (without meningitis)
- Mumps
- Ophthalmia neonatorum
- Paratyphoid fever
- Plague
- Rabies
- Relapsing fever
- Rubella
- Scarlet fever
- Smallpox
- Tetanus
- Tuberculosis
- Typhoid fever
- Typhus fever
- Viral haemorrhagic fever
- Viral hepatitis
- Whooping cough
- Yellow fever

framework for the NHS.

Health service guidelines on hospital infection control were issued in 1995.[5] The chief executive of every hospital trust is responsible for ensuring that there are effective arrangements for infection control. Every hospital should have a specialist infection control team (ICT) which usually consists of an infection control doctor supported by one or more infection control nurses. The ICT organises all aspects of surveillance, prevention and control of infection in the hospital including staff education, preparation of policies and audit of practices. Every hospital should also have an infection control committee which represents the main forum for regular routine consultation between the ICT and the rest of the hospital, including discussion and endorsement of a regularly updated hospital outbreak plan and an annual prevention and control programme. In order to be effective ICTs need to be integrated into the management structure of the trust and to be adequately resourced, including arrangements for cover of leave and out-of-hours advice. Community and psychiatric hospitals and other community care units should contract for appropriate infection control support to managers and staff with a local acute unit.

The National Audit Office undertook a study into the management and control of hospital acquired infection in acute trusts in 2000.[6] The main problems identified were:
- many service agreements between HAs (now PCTs) and trusts did not cover provision of infection control services
- lack of detailed specification in service agreement
- in the majority of trusts, direct chief executive involvement in hospital-

Wellard's NHS Handbook 2006/07

acquired infection was low and infection control was insufficiently incorporated into routine management activities

- a significant number of trusts did not have:
  - an infection control programme
  - a separate budget for infection control
  - adequate surveillance systems for hospital-acquired infection
  - infection control training for staff
  - necessary policies and procedures
  - audit of practice
  - adequate isolation facilities
- most trusts had an inadequate number of infection control nurses and inadequate clerical support for the infection control team.

Action for NHS trusts to rectify these

Box 3. Antibiotic resistance

There is growing concern about the increasing resistance of micro-organisms to the antibiotics used to treat infection. In the UK the need for more concerted action to prevent, control and delay antibiotic resistance has been identified by the House of Lords Select Committee on Science and Technology. The chief medical officer asked the standing medical advisory committee (SMAC) to examine and make recommendations on this issue. This committee reported in 1998.

Main recommendations of the report:

- patient education not to expect antibiotics
- four areas for reducing prescribing by GPs:
  - no antibiotics for simple coughs and colds
  - no antibiotics for viral sore throats
  - short course only for cystitis
  - limit telephone prescribing
- decision support systems to be developed for prescribing in hospital
- monitoring of antibiotic resistance by hospitals for local use and to feed into national surveillance
- national prescribing guidelines needed

- local guidelines based on national version and local data
- national strategy for surveillance of resistance
- international co-operation
- high priority for research
- improved infection control in hospital and community
- reduction of antibiotic use in agriculture
- co-operation with pharmaceutical industry to develop new antibiotics.

The government has issued a health service circular (below) which sets out action for the NHS in response to these reports.

Further reading

House of Lords Science and Technology Committee. *Resistance to antibiotics and other antimicrobial agents: seventh report from the Science and Technology Committee: session 1997-98.* TSO, 1998 (HI 81; Vol 1).

Standing Medical Advisory Committee sub-group on antimicrobial resistance. *The path of least resistance.* London: Department of Health, 1998.

HSC 1999/049. *Resistance to antibiotics and other antimicrobial agents.*

6 — The public health agenda

deficiencies are identified in HSC 2000/002.[7] A study undertaken in the West Midlands region would suggest that potentially serious deficiencies can also be identified in a number of community and mental health trusts in terms of level of staffing, contractual arrangements, cover for leave, integration into management and updating of outbreak plans.[8]

Recently, attention has been refocused on the failure to ensure basic precautions such as hand washing, hospital cleaning and decontamination of surgical instruments. HSC 2000/032 required trusts urgently to undertake a thorough review of their decontamination arrangements in the light of problems identified in a snapshot survey of current practice, and the possibility of transmission of vCJD due to inadequate disinfection.[9]

The Department of Health has sponsored national surveillance of healthcare associated infections, starting with a scheme to monitor MRSA bacteraemia rates in all hospital trusts: these trust-specific data are available to the public. Cleanliness and infection control are also included in the healthcare standards being monitored by the Healthcare Commission. All this makes hospital infection control a legitimate area for performance improvement for strategic health authorities.

In November 2004, former Health Secretary John Reid announced the ambition target of reducing bloodstream MRSA infections in NHS hospitals by half by 2008. He asked all NHS trusts to identify high sources of infection and draw up comprehensive action plans to prevent or isolate MRSA in order to achieve this reduction

In June 2005, a delivery programme to reduce healthcare-associated infections was published by the Department of Health.[10] Five high impact interventions (box 4) are at the centre of the programme.

The future
The work of the NHS in controlling communicable disease is likely to

---

Box 4. Delivering the best clinical practice for infection control

Five high impact interventions have been developed for the clinical practice related to infection control, each with distinct evidence-based elements of the clinical process.
  They are:
• preventing the risk of microbial contamination
• central venous catheter care
• preventing surgical site infection
• care of ventilated patients (or tracheostomy where appropriate)
• urinary catheter care.

Clean your hands campaign
A national campaign to encourage healthcare staff to wash their hands was launched in September 2004. Alcohol-based disinfectant hand rubs have been placed next to all beds in acute hospitals. A pilot study by the National Patient Safety Agency indicated that this would save 450 lives a year nationally and dramatically reduce extended hospital stays. The campaign also aims to raise awareness generally about the importance of hand washing and encourages patients to ask staff if they have cleaned their hands.

www.npsa.nhs.uk/cleanyourhands

change substantially over the next few years. Organisational changes, such as those at the HPA, are affecting the way that public health interventions are organised. Further changes are likely as the chief medical officer's strategy, *Getting ahead of the curve*, continues to be implemented in England and the other countries review their services (box). Other factors creating new demands on public health services, resulting from new infectious disease challenges are:
• the awaited review of the law relating to communicable infectious disease control
• the threat of a deliberate release

of a biological, chemical or radiation hazard
• technological advances (for example, the introduction of a vaccine against some forms of meningitis)
• quality initiatives (for example, screening patients in general practice for Chlamydia infection)
• the identification of new infectious agents, for example SARS
• the identification of infectious causes for many chronic diseases (for example, stomach ulcers)
• continuing global changes (for example, increased international travel and environmental changes)
• the overuse of antibiotics (box 3).

The matron's charter

When Chris Beasley was appointed as chief nursing officer in 2004 she stated that her top priority was tackling hospital infections.

'All staff covered by *Agenda for change* (the new NHS pay system), whether nurses, healthcare assistants, porters or cleaners must show that they can develop and apply the appropriate knowledge and skills to reduce the risk of healthcare associated infections. Personal development plans will give staff and managers an opportunity to identify how to raise standards of cleanliness,' she said.

In October 2004, *A matron's charter: an action plan for cleaner hospitals* was published. This reinforces the role of hospital matrons in relation to cleanliness but also points out that it is something that is the responsibility of all staff.

The charter sets out ten broad commitments that are expected to be adopted everywhere in the NHS:

• keeping the NHS clean is everybody's responsibility
• the patient environment will be well maintained, clean and safe
• matrons will establish a cleanliness culture across their units
• cleaning staff will be recognised for the important work they do — matrons will make sure they feel part of the ward team
• specific roles and responsibilities for cleaning will be clear
• cleaning routines will be clear, agreed and well publicised
• patients will have a part to play in monitoring and reporting on standards of cleanliness
• all staff working in healthcare will receive education in infection control
• nurses and infection control teams will be involved in drawing up cleaning contracts, and matrons have authority and power to withhold payment
• sufficient resources will be dedicated to keeping hospitals clean.

6 — The public health agenda

Continuing control of infectious disease relies upon maintaining services able to respond adequately to such changes.

This section is based on a contribution by Dr Jeremy Hawker, Regional Epidemiologist for the West Midlands region with the Health Protection Agency

References
1. Committee of inquiry into the future development of the public health function. *Public health in England*. HMSO, 1988.
2. HSG[93]56. *Public health: responsibilities of the NHS and the roles of others.*

Winning ways

In December 2003, the chief medical officer Professor Sir Liam Donaldson set out proposals which seek to revolutionise the way potential infections are handled in hospitals and other healthcare settings. In *Winning ways. Working together to reduce healthcare associated infection in England*, he announced a drive against healthcare acquired infections including antibiotic resistant organisms.

The report set out a number of actions:
• every NHS trust would identify a director of infection control — a senior figure with the power to impose tough new rules on each hospital in order to cut infection levels
• he or she would lead dedicated infection control teams, charged with ensuring every possible step is taken to minimise the risk of infection
• a system which had proved its worth in cutting food poisoning in the catering trade would be introduced to the NHS
• a drive would be launched to ensure staff follow tried and trusted techniques for cutting infection rates through frequent hand washing and disinfection
• minimum necessary use of procedures most likely to produce

infection, such as catheters and intravenous drips
• the Healthcare Commission would be asked to make infection control a priority when assessing hospital performance
• £3m would be spent on research and development into hospital acquired infections.

It is estimated that 100,000 people a year pick up some form of infection while in hospital. The cost of hospital acquired infection is high — estimated at around £1bn a year.

A new working group bringing together NHS frontline staff such as modern matrons, ward housekeepers and allied health professionals, would work out ways to improve the prevention and control of healthcare associated infection in their everyday work.

Towards cleaner hospitals and lower rates of infection: a summary of action, published in July 2004, sets out an action plan based on work already underway.

Department of Health. *Winning ways. Working together to reduce healthcare associated infection in England*. Report from the chief medical officer. December 2003.

Department of Health. *Towards cleaner hospitals and lower rates of infection: a summary of action*. July 2004.

3. Chief medical officer. *Getting ahead of the curve: a strategy for combating infectious diseases (including other aspects of health protection).* January 2002.
4. Office of Health Economics. *Hospital acquired infection.* London: OHE, 1997.
5. HSG[95]10. *Hospital infection working group of the Department of Health and Public Health Laboratory Service. Hospital infection control: guidance on the control of infection in hospitals.*
6. National Audit Office. *The management and control of hospital acquired infection in acute trusts in England.* TSO, February 2000.
7. HSC 2000/002. *The management and control of hospital infection.*
8. Hawker JI. Arrangements for the control of infection in hospitals. *Communicable Disease and Public Health* 1999;2:54-8.
9. HSC 2000/032. *Decontamination of medical devices.*
10. Department of Health. *Saving lives: a delivery programme to reduce healthcare associated infection including MRSA.* June 2005.

The Health Protection Agency

One of the main recommendations of the national strategy for control of infectious disease, *Getting ahead of the curve*, was the creation of the Health Protection Agency (HPA) to integrate the specialist services at local, regional and national levels that are dedicated to protection of the population against biological, chemical and radiological threats to health.

Changes are also occurring in the rest of the UK. Wales has absorbed its local and regional communicable disease control staff into the National Health Protection Service for Wales and some other health protection functions will become part of the HPA.

Health Protection Scotland was established in November 2004 to strengthen and coordinate health protection work in the country. The organisation took over the functions of the Scottish Centre for Infection and Environmental Health.

A review of public health functions and health protection arrangements has also been conducted in Northern Ireland.

Getting ahead of the curve also recommended that intensified action was required to control:
• healthcare associated infection
• tuberculosis
• antimicrobial resistance
• blood-borne and sexually transmitted viruses.

National action plans cover each of these areas.

Other proposals included a programme of new vaccine development, strengthened and integrated surveillance, a strengthened approach to infection in childhood, action on chronic disease caused by infections, enhanced programmes of professional development and a review of public health law.

The strategy placed clear public health duties on all NHS laboratories, including a duty to report infections of public health importance and the use of standard operating procedures. Although most of the functions of the Public Health Laboratory Service, including specialist national and regional laboratories, transferred to the HPA, local public health laboratories,

6 — The public health agenda

which mainly provided clinical diagnostic microbiology services, have come under the management of local NHS trusts. As NHS pathology managed clinical networks become established in strategic health authority areas, the laboratories become a part of them.

In April 2003 the Health Protection Agency started work as a special health authority for England and Wales, chaired by Sir William Stewart, former chief scientific advisor to the government. The chief executive is Dr Pat Troop, former deputy chief medical officer. The HPA has taken over many of the functions of:

- the Public Health Laboratory Service (PHLS)
- the Centre for Applied Microbiology and Research
- the National Focus for Chemical Incidents
- the National Poisons Information Service
- local PCT consultants in communicable disease control (CsCDC) and their support staff
- certain Department of Health staff, including health emergency planning advisors.

On 1 April 2005, the agency was established as a non-departmental public body, replacing the HPA special health authority and the National Radiological Protection Board and with radiation protection as part of health protection incorporated in its remit.

The responsibilities of the HPA are to:
- identify and respond to health hazards caused by infectious diseases, chemicals, poisons or radiation
- anticipate and prepare for emerging and future threats
- provide specialist support to the NHS, local authorities and other agencies
- provide specialist health protection services, including a rapid response to emergencies
- advise the public, professionals and government on the best ways to protect health.

Primary care trusts remain responsible for health protection for their local populations, although much of the necessary activity is carried out on their behalf by the local teams of the HPA (CsCDC, public health nurses and support staff). In addition, PCTs are providing support services and sometimes accommodation to these local teams. These arrangements are covered by memoranda of understanding and service level agreements between PCTs and the HPA, which are overseen by the regional director of public health.

The HPA has a large network of staff based regionally and locally throughout England (and working with locally based colleagues employed within the devolved administrations), a central office based in London and three major centres, at Colindale, Porton and Chilton.

The Centre for Infections at Colindale is the base for communicable disease surveillance and specialist microbiology. The Centre for Radiation, Chemical and Environmental Hazards is based at Chilton, and the Centre for Emergency Preparedness and Response, focusing on applied microbiological research and emergency response, is based at Porton.

Health Protection Agency, 7th Floor, Holborn Gate, 330 High Holborn, London WC1V 7PP. Tel: 020 7759 2700. www.hpa.org.uk

Chief Medical Officer. *Getting ahead of the curve: a strategy for combating infectious diseases (including other aspects of health protection).* January 2002.

Wellard's NHS Handbook 2006/07

142

Acute services

In the UK, acute services are traditionally viewed as being secondary care or hospital-based healthcare services, to which patients are referred by their general practitioners, or to which people refer themselves by attending an accident and emergency department. Acute services are typically considered to be of a more specialist nature than primary care services, having more sophisticated technology, more specialised staff, and serving a larger catchment population. Tertiary care refers to those highly specialised services for rare and complex conditions, where a patient has been referred by a secondary care (hospital) consultant.

NHS acute care services are currently provided in the following settings:
• district general hospitals (DGHs)
• treatment centres
• specialist tertiary centres
• community hospitals.

The apparently simple distinction between primary and acute care services is increasingly being challenged. For example, minor surgery, a wide range of diagnostic services, and some consultant outpatient clinics now frequently take place in general practice. Likewise, some of the work carried out in accident and emergency departments and in other hospital clinics can in many cases be undertaken by primary care professionals.

Challenges facing hospital services
Hospital services face a number of challenges which arise from the wider health policy environment:
• political pressure to reduce waiting times
• continuing development of new technologies
• pressure caused by high bed occupancy rates

• the detrimental effect of delayed discharges on efficiency
• the call for more sub-specialisation and centralisation of services
• a central drive to improve the quality of services
• the financial uncertainties associated with the system of payment by results.

Increasing demand
In recent years demand for hospital services, in particular emergency care, has steadily increased. The government has made the provision of adequate arrangements for coping with emergency pressures an important NHS priority and has targeted resources towards the provision of health and social care initiatives to counter these pressures.

Reforming emergency care
In October 2001, in *Reforming emergency care* the Department of Health's winter and emergency services team (WEST) reported that people were having to wait too long for care and treatment at each stage in the emergency care system.

Earlier work in upgrading A&E departments, improving ambulance response times and integrating GP out-of-hours cover has been supplemented by measures set out in *Reforming emergency care,* namely:
• recruiting more A&E consultants
• investing in additional nursing staff
• buying additional planned operations for NHS patients to free up emergency capacity
• investment in social care to reduce delayed discharges
• increasingly separating the elective and emergency workload
• provision of 24-hour diagnostic services
• separation of patients with minor

New approaches to care — 7

injuries/illnesses from those with serious conditions, and treating both groups in a timely fashion (the see and treat approach)
• adopting new ways of working and skill mixes of staff
• improvements in information technology
• appointment of emergency care leads in each organisation.

The implementation of many of these measures is having a dramatic effect on the productivity of NHS emergency care teams.

From January 2005, the NHS has been working to the target of 98 per cent of patients waiting no longer than four hours in A&E from arrival to admission, transfer or discharge.

Waiting lists and times and booking

Exacting targets have been set for NHS trusts, with the focus being primarily on reducing maximum waiting times. Booking elective admission or appointment dates with patients is intended to make accessing the NHS more convenient, by introducing patient choice and reducing the uncertainty associated with traditional waiting lists for elective treatment. As part of the government's strategy for modernising the NHS, booking is also intended to reduce patients failing to attend and cancellations.

The impetus for booking was increased through the national booked admissions programme and the NHS Plan target of having all NHS services booked by the end of 2005.

New technologies

Technological advances are constantly enabling changes in clinical practice. The rapid growth in the use of minimally invasive surgery demonstrates the potential of new technology to impact on the demand for acute hospital facilities, although much day case activity may not reflect substitution for inpatient activity. IT-enabled initiatives such as telemedicine or extensions to NHS Direct offer the potential to shift care increasingly to non-hospital settings.

Bed use and availability

In 1998, the government instigated the national beds inquiry, with a brief to assess the appropriate number of beds for the NHS and to advise on future bed requirements in the light of different policy options.

The NHS Plan announced a commitment to increase the number of intermediate care beds by 5,000 by 2004, in addition to 1,700 extra non-residential intermediate care places. The Plan emphasises the focus for acute services on rapid assessment, stabilisation and treatment. The extra 2,100 general and acute beds by 2004 announced in the Plan represented an increase of about 2 per cent.

Average daily available acute and general hospital beds, England	
1992/93	153,208
1996/97	140,515
1997/98	138,046
1998/99	136,427
1999/00	135,079
2000/01	135,794
2001/02	136,584
2002/03	136,678
2003/04	137,278

Referral to outpatients, England

Year	GP written referral requests for outpatient appointments ('000)
1998/99	8,917
1999/00	9,061
2000/01	9,271
2001/02	9,369
2002/03	9,444
2003/04	9,523
2004/05	9,600

Day surgery

Day surgery is the admission of selected patients to hospital for a planned surgical procedure with them returning home on the same day. It provides benefits to all involved:

- Patients receive treatment that is suited to their needs and which allows them to recover in their own homes. The risk of hospital-acquired infection is reduced.
- Clinicians can provide high quality care for appropriate patients, and release inpatient beds for more major cases.
- Trusts improve their throughput of patients, facilitate booking, and reduce waiting lists.
- Primary care trusts can commission cost-effective care.

During the early 1990s there was considerable growth in the use of day surgery and the NHS Plan predicts that 75 per cent of all elective operations will be carried out in this way.

In August 2002 the Department of Health published a guide to assist trusts in improving their performance in day surgery and to unlock the potential for further improvement.

Treatment centres

A series of treatment centres is being created rapidly to increase the number of planned surgical operations. By separating elective tests and surgery from emergency work productivity can be improved. The centres also provide scheduled diagnostic and treatment services.

Treatment centres can be run by NHS trusts, primary care trusts or by an independent provider. They may be stand alone new builds, refurbished sites or virtual treatment centres — defined services within an existing hospital building, using care pathways to ensure process efficiency and improve the patient's overall experience of care.

There are 44 NHS-run treatment centres fully open across England, and two are in development. Over 240,000 patients have been treated in NHS centres since the start of the programme in April 2003. There are also 14 independent sector sites delivering a full service and three sites delivering an interim service.

Centralisation or a local service?

There are a number of factors which are leading to a trend towards the concentration of certain services into a smaller number of hospital centres. The changes taking place in the medical workforce are important. Following the implementation of the *New deal* for junior doctors, and the *Modernising medical careers* initiative, junior doctors spend less time delivering patient care and more time studying or practising medicine under direct consultant supervision. To provide adequate and legal shift patterns for junior doctors (under the European working time directive), with appropriate consultant supervision, hospitals are linking up with clinical teams in other hospitals, hence providing care in a network model, with the service covering a larger population base.

A joint report by the BMA, the Royal College of Physicians and the Royal College of Surgeons on the provision of acute services in 1998 concluded that the average sized district general hospital, serving a population of 250,000 to 350,000, would remain the backbone for some time to come. However, the report recommended that the ideal size of a unit to provide fully comprehensive medical and surgical care was a hospital or integrated group of hospitals covering a population of 450,000 to 500,000.

Similarly, where hospitals served smaller rural populations, closer clinical and managerial links with adjacent acute service providers was essential.

The medical organisations called for a major expansion in the number of consultants to provide up-to-date high quality medical and surgical services. The NHS Plan responded with a commitment to increase the number of consultants by 7,500 by 2004.

A consultation document published by the DH in February 2003 has had a counter-balancing influence on the big is best movement. *Keeping the NHS local* records that smaller hospitals will be supported to develop new roles at the heart of local communities. It argues that new resources and models of care show that 'small can work', with the potential for a wider range of safe, effective, high quality care to be offered in smaller hospitals than previously thought possible.

The document includes guidance for the NHS on service change and proposes some service models.

Possibilities include:
• increasingly sophisticated day surgery

• networking between small and large hospitals, including telemedicine
• new ways of providing hospital services at night.

Configuring hospitals

To enhance the range of secondary care services available near to patients' homes, many acute hospitals have to be reconfigured. The Department of Health's configuring hospitals project was designed to guide and support this change. A section of the Department's website (www.dh.gov.uk/ PolicyAndGuidance/OrganisationPolicy/ SecondaryCare/ConfiguringHospitals) explains the background to the project and reports progress.

The hospital at night

The hospital at night project, launched in 2003, has redefined how medical cover can be provided in hospitals during the out-of-hours period. The project has required a move from cover requirements defined by professional demarcation and grade, to cover defined by competency.

The Department of Health worked with professional bodies and the NHS to identify the core competencies required to staff a hospital at night and develop working time directive compliant staffing models to provide these, which are both clinically sound and acceptable to both patients and public.

One team of appropriately skilled, alert and motivated staff covers most of the hospital at night. It works to agreed protocols and has the competencies to cover a wide range of interventions but has the capacity to call in specialist expertise when necessary.

The project aims to:
• mitigate the effects of full shift working by junior medical staff
• reduce duplication

- take away inappropriate tasks
- have more effective bleep and call policies
- have better use of technologies.

An evaluation report, published in August 2005, found hospital at night helped improve patient care. It had no negative impact on doctors' training and it had not affected the achievement of NHS performance targets.

The national orthopaedic project

The demand for orthopaedic treatment has grown steadily for the past 20 years. The growth has occurred in the numbers of patients seen per year and the numbers of interventions per person. At the same treatments have become more complex and more conditions can now be treated.

The national orthopaedic project was set up in January 2004 to help speed up access to surgery. An April 2005 report on the project showed that:

- the number of patients waiting longer than six months for orthopaedic surgery had fallen by 55 per cent from 57,000 in January 2004 to 25,700 in February 2005
- average waiting time for orthopaedic patients had also fallen — from over 19 weeks in 1998 to an average of just over 12 weeks
- a troubleshooting team working with the 40 most challenged health economies helped to implement fast processes — the improvement rate of these sites was 15 per cent quicker than in all other sites.

Towards integrated care

Changes to acute services are part of a wider trend towards integration of care provision in the NHS, which have been given new emphasis by the government. Clinical teams are working in increasingly integrated networks of care, within and across hospitals.

Acute services continue to face pressures to use their resources in the most efficient manner. More services are being delivered by PCTs in the community, taking advantage of continuing advances in medical and information technology. At the same time, some services will be concentrated in larger specialist centres. As the alternatives to care in a traditional DGH acute setting increase, so will the challenge to ensure that the patient's journey is optimal.

Further reading

Reforming emergency care. DH, October 2001.

Day surgery: operational guide. Waiting, booking and choice. DH, August 2002.

Keeping the NHS local — a new direction of travel. DH, February 2003.

The implementation and impact of hospital at night projects: an evaluation report. DH, August 2005.

Ham, C. Does the district general hospital have a future? *BMJ* 2005;331:13331-3.

Hospital at night project. www.modern.nhs.uk/hospitalatnight

Intermediate care

Services promoting rehabilitation have continued to be squeezed by pressures related to acute and long-term care, leaving relatively few alternatives to more frequent or longer stays in hospital, entry into residential care and nursing homes, or complex packages of support at home. Increasing throughput in the acute hospital sector has reduced the time available for inpatient rehabilitation, and a lack of services for rehabilitation practice in the community can mean that many older people do not achieve their full potential for rehabilitation.

The result has been a distorted system of care, spiralling expenditure and inefficient use of scarce resources. However, the government has been committed to policies designed to promote independence through the modernisation of health and social care services, and intermediate care has emerged as a key part of the agenda for change.

An evolving concept

The pressures on the NHS, particularly those on acute hospitals, and on local authority social services began to focus the debate. Pressures on acute beds led to reductions in lengths of stay and calls to ensure that acute beds should only used by people who needed acute care. It was recognised that many people who were placed in long-term institutional care, often fully funded by the local authority, might instead have been able to go home from hospital if they had been given the time and therapeutic support to recover. At the same time, many community health and social care services lacked funding, staff and other resources to deliver the necessary post-discharge care. These were powerful drivers for the development of care and support for people, (especially but not exclusively older people) who no longer needed the level of care that acute hospitals provided, but who nevertheless needed significant support if they were to regain their maximum level of independence. A number of other drivers have been identified.

The following working definition was arrived at by the King's Fund: intermediate care is a *function* of

services, the function being to facilitate transitions from medical dependence (experiencing oneself as a patient) and social dependence to day-to-day independence (experiencing oneself as a person). A range of services had the potential to fulfil this function as people moved from hospital to home, where the objectives of care were not primarily medical, the patient's discharge destination was anticipated, and a clinical outcome of recovery (or restoration of health) was desired. Over time the definition has broadened to take in services designed to prevent hospital admission. Specifically excluded are services like convalescence or hotel beds that do not have therapeutic input.

The concepts of transition and restoration are also central to the function of services that are called, or offer, rehabilitation.

A number of different services were originally described as having the potential to provide intermediate care in different settings. These included: community hospitals, community care centres, inpatient nursing beds, supported discharge schemes, and hospital at home schemes. However, there can be a lack of consensus on the aims, the intensity of care and the target group for intermediate care. Commissioners and service providers need to agree explicit criteria for success in order to be able to plan and deliver effective care to meet defined needs, as well as to enable evaluation.

A common vision?

In February 2000, former Health Secretary Alan Milburn raised the profile of intermediate care. In the context of the national beds inquiry he put the case for a programme to 'build a bridge between home and hospital' for older people. He envisaged a set of intermediate care services in a variety of forms, specifically designed around the needs of older patients for a period of rehabilitation and recovery. Some would be in specially designated hospital wards run by nurses, some in step-down facilities in the community and some would be improved care services in the home. He identified the scope for NHS collaboration with the independent sector and other providers, and for the breaking down of traditional demarcations between staff groups, giving way to more flexible and fluid team working.

This vision set the tone for the government's change agenda, through modernising health and social services, to promote independence, facilitate earlier hospital discharge, prevent unnecessary hospital admissions and prevent premature and unnecessary admissions to long-term care. Subsequent Department of Health publications, notably the response to the national beds inquiry and the NHS Plan, have outlined changes which are aimed to increase the availability of rehabilitation and intermediate care.

The NHS Plan

The NHS Plan states that intermediate care and related services for older people should:
- promote independence
- improve quality of care
- deliver the right care, in the right place, at the right time.

It outlines increased resources for developing intermediate care and related services for older people in the form of £900m cash investments, specific commitments to the provision of more beds, increased levels of services and new types of services in line with the above service models.

Other changes, though not directly linked to the development of intermediate care, are nonetheless important to service improvements generally and thus impact on rehabilitation and intermediate care, for example:
- increased staff numbers
- service integration
- a commitment to changing ways of working (including the introduction of a single assessment process, which must take account of a person's potential for rehabilitation)
- changes in organisational arrangements (including the use of Health Act flexibilities)
- incentives for joint working.

The NHS Plan contained a commitment by the Department of Health to issue clear guidelines on likely future requirements for beds and types of services which should be available in all areas. Meanwhile, it called on PCTs, NHS trusts and local authorities, building on services already in place, to start the planning and development of new intermediate care services.

Implementing change

Challenging timetables were laid out in the NHS plan implementation programme. It identified priorities for expansion and reform, but recognised that change on the proposed scale would take a long time. Providers are expected to deliver high quality pre-admission and rehabilitation care to older people to help them live as independently as possible by:
- reducing preventable hospitalisation
- ensuring year-on-year reductions in delays in moving people aged 75 and over on from hospital.

Intermediate care change teams began the process of supporting this development work locally. But there were tensions between managing winter pressures by short-term/quick fix

New approaches to care — 7

expedients and longer term planning for sustainable change to whole health and social care systems. It remains easier to commission a new stand-alone project using short-term funds, than to re-engineer a whole service system to deliver a more rehabilitative approach to care, by changing working practices and integrating services across the care continuum.

The national service framework (NSF) for older people also contains information crucial to the development of intermediate care (box 1).

Guidance to support developments

In January 2001 intermediate care guidance was issued (HSC 2001/01: LAC (2001)1. *Intermediate care*). It goes some way to clarifying the important issues for service commissioners and providers. Perhaps most importantly, it provides a standard definition on intermediate care to be used in planning and monitoring service development (box 2). There are now five clear criteria, *all of which must be met.* Particularly welcome is the emphasis on cross-professional working, assessment, individual care-planning involving service users and carers,

and active rehabilitation.

Many services might claim to have been offering intermediate care, but would not meet this tighter definition. Further development work is needed within existing teams and across agencies to achieve the required single assessment framework, single professional records and shared protocols.

The guidance suggests a range of service models for intermediate care:
• rapid response

> ## Box 2: Standard definition of intermediate care
>
> Intermediate care includes services that meet *all* the criteria below. Services that:
> • are targeted at people who would otherwise face unnecessarily prolonged hospital stays, or inappropriate admission to acute inpatient care, long-term residential care, or continuing NHS inpatient care
> • are provided on the basis of a comprehensive assessment, resulting in a structured individual care plan that involves active therapy, treatment or opportunity for recovery
> • have a planned outcome of maximising independence and typically enabling patients/users to remain living at home
> • are time-limited, normally no longer than six weeks and frequently as little as one to two weeks or less
> • involve cross-professional working, with a single assessment framework, single professional records and shared protocol.
>
> HSC 2001/01: LAC (2001)1. *Intermediate care.*

> ## Box 1: Intermediate care: the national service framework for older people
>
> The NSF sets out in more detail:
> • the key interventions
> • the evidence base
> • service models
> • performance indicators
> • milestones.
> Department of Health. *National service framework for older people.* March 2001.

- hospital at home
- residential rehabilitation
- supported discharge
- day rehabilitation.

There is an expectation that new services will be developed in settings such as patients' homes, community hospitals, rehabilitation centres, nursing or residential care homes and possibly in step-down facilities within acute hospitals. To simplify arrangements and encourage the take-up of services, the guidance suggests that intermediate care should be free at the point of use.

Improving outcomes for older people

There is a real opportunity to make major improvements to the care and support of older people giving them a better chance to regain control over their lives and live independently at home after a period of illness or injury. This is what older people themselves say they want. Their views have been taken account of in government policy, backed by substantial increases in funding to develop new types of support and care.

Intermediate care certainly has the potential for improving the quality of life of many thousands of older people by helping them to live as independently as possible. It will be some time before it will be possible to be able to judge if the policy directives and the investment of significant amounts of money in service developments achieve the anticipated outcomes.

Clinical care networks

Because the patient's pathway through the healthcare system is all important and the interfaces between NHS organisations tend to be where there

are difficulties, the emergence of clinical care networks has assumed considerable significance. They are designed to be able to deliver seamless services for the patient.

Formal NHS networks involve groups of health professionals and organisations working in a coordinated manner, ideally unconstrained by boundaries to ensure equitable provision of high quality services. Networks coordinate, deliver and resource services, and have links to other parts of the health and social care system.

They are becoming particularly important as a way of coordinating services for patients who require care across a range of institutions. Cancer networks have often been the first to be established but the idea is being used in a range of other areas such as coronary heart disease, vascular surgery and critical care. Cancer networks have the main responsibility for delivering the cancer plan.

Networks can play an important part in helping to break down traditional barriers in the NHS between units and organisations and can play a part in empowering patients and staff in influencing the way that staff work together.

NHS networks may be used to sustain services which would otherwise be vulnerable due perhaps to the small numbers of patients involved locally. They are a good way of making the best use of scarce specialist resources, improving access to care and standardising care.

Networks can also stimulate innovation and facilitate learning and research.

Clinical care networks however require different managerial and performance management skills and run counter to traditional lines of

Wellard's NHS Handbook 2006/07

New approaches to care — 7

accountability. It is important to decide whether lines of accountability rest within the network or devolve back to the participating organisations. New commissioning skills are needed and networks need direct funding. Rather than being direct commissioners of care, it may be appropriate for networks to be facilitators of effective commissioning by primary care trusts. They can be costly and difficult to set up and sustain.

Networks need to establish management boards that enable them to a work as genuine joint enterprises of partner organisations. They typically have a network manager and lead clinician and they should involve the public in their decision-making. There should be a clinical governance framework for the network.

Further reading

NHS networks. www.networks.nhs.uk

NHS Confederation. *Clinical networks. A discussion paper.* 2001.

NHS service delivery and organisation programme. *Networks Briefing. Key lessons for network management in health care.* 2005. www.sdo.lshtm.ac.uk

Maternity services

Just over 600,000 babies are born in the UK each year and the NHS spends around £1bn a year on maternity services. Over recent years, the maternity service has been the site of rapid reform, characterised by a high degree of user involvement in intense professional and political debate. Much of this has focused on the special character of maternity care — providing a service for users who are in the main healthy and well, but who can develop acute care needs.

In the second half of the last century, maternity care became almost completely medicalised, with nearly all births occurring in hospital settings, and heavy use of medical interventions in even the most straightforward of births. While the UK's maternity services are among the best in the world, with low rates of infant and perinatal mortality, this medicalisation continues to cause concern for the following reasons:

- In its rush to ensure that childbirth be a safe experience for women and their infants, the NHS may forget that the transition to motherhood is primarily a social and emotional experience for most women. In neglecting this truth, women and their families have been alienated from the processes of childbirth.
- This medical focus may undermine the public health role of maternity care. For example, the emphasis on childbirth has resulted in a neglect of women's needs in the postnatal period, leading to significant rates of undetected morbidities, postnatal depression, and failure to sustain breast feeding. The long-term consequences of these are significant for the nation's health.
- Routine interventions carry significant costs and lead to higher costs. For example, use of induction, augmentation, electronic monitoring and epidural — while all of clinical value in certain situations — seem to lead to higher rates of caesarean section. The rate of caesarean section in England in 2003/04 was 22.7 per cent, and in some areas up to 30 per cent. This is far in excess of the WHO recommended rate of 10–15 per cent, and it carries significant costs to both the woman herself and to the NHS. In May 2004, the National Institute for Health and Clinical Excellence issued guid-

ance on how caesarean section rates might be reduced.

With obstetrics accounting for over half of the NHS litigation bill, and national modernisation strategies emphasising the importance of integrating health and social care needs, the maternity service has some serious choices to make in its future development.

Women-centred care

The last significant policy shift in maternity care followed the publication of the 1992 House of Commons Health Committee (Winterton) Report. This emphasised the right of women to be full partners in their care, exercising informed choice and being offered a range of real options. It was the catalyst for change in all four UK countries. In England, it led to the Department of Health setting up an expert maternity group, chaired by former health minister Baroness Julia Cumberlege, which in 1994 published its report *Changing childbirth*. This established that:

- women should be able to choose their care giver during pregnancy and childbirth: this could be a midwife, GP, obstetrician or a combination of these
- women should be able to choose the type of care they want, including whether to give birth in hospital or at home
- as far as possible women should be cared for by the same person, or by the same small group of people, throughout pregnancy, birth and the postnatal period
- women should be fully informed about the options open to them, so that they can decide what best suits them.

The implications of this for the organisation of NHS care have included:

- enabling the woman to book with a midwife direct, if that is her prefer-

ence, and giving midwives direct access to maternity unit beds
- basing antenatal care as near to the woman's home as possible, preferably in community settings
- reorganising midwives' working patterns to better meet women's needs, most notably though the introduction of caseload schemes to improve continuity of carer
- developing different settings for care, such as midwife-led birth centres
- involving women in the planning of maternity care (at both individual and service levels)
- ensuring that services reflect the needs of all women, including those who are disadvantaged or experiencing complex problems
- ensuring that all women have a named midwife who is known to them and to whom they can turn for advice
- identifying for each woman (after discussion with her) a lead professional who will have a key role in the planning and provision of care.

Changing childbirth was widely welcomed by both the users and providers of maternity care. It has significantly changed attitudes and expectations and has resulted in a number of improvements in care, including:

- increasing awareness of user involvement and empowerment
- the development of innovative models of care, such as caseload midwifery and midwife-led birth centres
- initiatives to facilitate informed choice, such as the Department of Health-funded *Informed choice* leaflets, developed by the Midwives' Information and Resource Service (MIDIRS) and the NHS Centre for Reviews and Dissemination
- an increasing emphasis on evidence-

based care, and the development of midwifery research.

However, its impact on practice has been less sustained, for a range of reasons including resources, professional territorialism, cultural tradition, and managerial reluctance to empower midwives. In its large-scale study of 1997, the Audit Commission found that services were still unduly shaped by tradition and service convenience, rather than user preference or effectiveness, and that women still had concerns about a number of aspects of care. Nevertheless, *Changing childbirth* is still sanctioned government policy, and fits

The Human Fertilisation and Embryology Authority

The development of methods of assisted conception affects family life and it is important that the legal, social and ethical implications are considered in order to protect the public. The Human and Fertilisation and Embryology Act 1990 arose largely from the 1984 Warnock committee report, following the birth of the first test-tube (in vitro fertilisation, IVF) baby in 1978. The Act makes provisions to regulate and monitor treatment centres and to ensure that research is carried out in a responsible way. This is done by means of a licensing system.

Three areas of activity are covered by the Act:
• any fertilisation treatment which involves the use of donated eggs or sperm (for example, donor insemination, DI), or embryos created outside the body (IVF). These are referred to as licensed treatments
• storage of eggs, sperm and embryos
• research on human embryos.

During 2005 a consultation exercise was run by the Department of Health to see how the Act might be amended to take account of technologies and techniques that have emerged in recent years.

The Human Fertilisation and Embryology Authority (HFEA) inspects and licenses centres on behalf of the government. It also:
• publishes a code of practice giving guidance to centres on how they should carry out their licensed activities
• keeps a confidential register of information about donors, patients and treatments
• publicises its role and the services which licensed centres provide
• gives advice and information
• keeps the whole field of fertility treatment and research under review.

The HFEA has 21 members, who have broad experience and are appointed by UK health ministers.

The authority produces an annual patients' guide to DI and IVF clinics, which lists all licensed centres and gives their success rates for DI and IVF. The guide is available free by telephone or from the HFEA website.

It is proposed the HFEA will merge with the Human Tissue Authority in 2008 to form the Regulatory Authority for Fertility and Tissue which will be responsible for regulation and inspection relating to the whole range of human tissue, including blood, organs, tissue, cells, gametes and embryos.

The Human Fertilisation and Embryology Authority, 21 Bloomsbury Street, London WC1B 3HF. Tel: 020 7291 8200. www.hfea.gov.uk

Wellard's NHS Handbook 2006/07

neatly with current policy priorities such as user involvement, public health and the move to a primary care-led NHS.

The government says that its highest priority must be to tackle inequalities in access to services and health outcomes for women and their babies.

In 2001, it provided £100m to improve 200 maternity units around the country. This funding was used to provide women with en suite bath-rooms, single rooms for mothers in early labour, new home from home area and birthing pools.

In 2003, the Department of Health announced a link with the organisation Dr Foster to produce local maternity guides for prospective mothers. The guides are designed to allow women to compare local services and encourage them to think about the sorts of services they and their families would like to use.

Current challenges

The work of *Changing childbirth* has been taken forward by the *National service framework for children, young people and maternity services*. The maternity services standard in the framework, which was issued in Sep-tember 2004, addresses the require-ments of women and their babies during pregnancy, birth and after birth. It includes women's partners and their families; and it addresses and links to pre- and post-conception health promotion and the child health promo-tion programme.

The standard calls for:
- flexible individualised services de-signed to fit around the woman and her baby's journey through pregnancy and motherhood, with emphasis on the needs of vulnerable and disadvantaged women
- women being supported and encour-aged to have as normal a pregnancy

and birth as possible, with medical interventions recommended to them only if they are of benefit to the woman or her baby
- midwifery and obstetric care being based on providing good clinical and psychological outcomes for the woman and baby, while putting equal emphasis on helping new parents

Folic acid campaign

For some years the health education bodies on behalf of the Department of Health have been working to raise awareness of the benefits of folic acid. The main aims of the ongoing campaign are to inform all women planning a pregnancy and other women of child-bearing age about how folic acid can help improve the chances of having a healthy baby.

Folic acid is a B vitamin which is found naturally in many foods. By increasing their intake of this vitamin when planning a pregnancy, women can significantly reduce the risk of having a baby with a neural tube defect (NTD) such as spina bifida.

Women have been advised to increase their intake of folic acid as soon as they stop using contracep-tion up until the twelfth week of pregnancy. To achieve this, women need to do three things:
- take a daily 400 microgram folic acid supplement
- choose foods fortified with folic acid such as some breads and breakfast cereals
- eat foods naturally rich in folic acid such as leafy green vegetables.

Department of Health. *Thinking of having a baby: folic acid — an essential ingredient in making babies.* May 2004.

New approaches to care — 7

prepare for parenthood.

The national service framework calls for integrated services delivered through managed maternity and neonatal care networks. These are linked groups of health professionals and organisations from primary, secondary and tertiary care, and social services, working together in a coordinated manner, to ensure an equitable provision of high quality, clinically effective care. Pregnant women may require care from a variety of sources or professionals, provided through such managed care or social services networks, as well as support from peers and local support groups. Knowing which path to follow, and who is responsible for providing what, will help to reduce clinical variation, eliminate duplication of services, maintain quality of care and adherence to clinical or other guidelines and give professionals agreed control over the care of the delivery process.

The Healthcare Commission and maternity services

The risks associated with obstetric care have recently prompted the Healthcare Commission to turn its attention to maternity services. It commented in its 2005 report on the state of healthcare that investigations had uncovered significant problems in some maternity services such as poor standards of cleanliness, overcrowding and inadequate support for women whose first language was not English. To date, the commission and its predecessor, the Commission for Health Improvement, have carried out three investigations of serious failings in maternity services. As part of these investigations, they interviewed and surveyed a wide range of women using services. While many rated the quality of their care highly,

they did highlight some areas of concern including:

• not enough time for doctors and midwives to properly explain what was happening
• inadequate information and support for women and their families, whose first language was not English, as well as a lack of cultural understanding among staff
• overcrowding and poor standards of cleanliness, particularly in toilets and bathroom areas, in some wards (more than a quarter of women in one trust said the ward was not clean enough)
• the quality of food (in one trust, only 40 per cent rated the food as good or very good)
• lack of advice and support on issues such as feeding and bathing, handling, settling and looking after the health and recovery of the baby as well as that of the mother (at one trust, 15 per cent of women received no such information while in hospital)
• delays caused by faulty equipment
• lack of information and insufficient support for bereaved families.

The commission is likely to be persistent about the need to tackle such issues, and can be expected to take very seriously the performance of NHS trusts where there is an unexpected high rate of maternal and infant mortality.

Maternity services survey

On a brighter note, the Department of Health announced the results of a survey in December 2005 which revealed that some 80 per cent of women were pleased with the care they got when they had a baby. Women rated highly the professionalism of staff and widely accessed and appreciated postnatal services.

At the same time it was announced that Gwyneth Lewis would be clinical lead for maternity services in England. She is a consultant in public health medicine with 20 years experience of working at the DH.

The public health agenda

The new public health agenda is making peculiar demands of maternity care. The *Independent inquiry into inequalities in health* (Acheson report) recommended that high priority be given to policies aimed at improving health and reducing health inequalities in women of childbearing age, expectant mothers and young children. Recent government policies have made clear the expectation that maternity services — and midwives in particular — develop their contribution to public health and family wellbeing, for example through closer participation with Sure Start, increased support for parenting and family life, extended care in the postnatal period, and participation in initiatives to address smoking cessation, teenage pregnancy and domestic violence.

While the maternity services are willing, by and large, to meet these challenges, they are struggling with some constraints on their capacity to do so. One has been the crisis in midwifery staffing, endemic in London but present in all parts of England and across the UK, which means that even basic standards (for example, of one-to-one midwifery care in labour) may be difficult to meet. In addition, reconfiguration is taking place across the UK, with smaller maternity units being closed — sometimes for good reason, but occasionally down to short-term expediency steps which do not meet the government's long-term policy agenda and are not likely to improve long-term health outcomes.

Nevertheless, there is plenty of reason to feel positive about the future contribution of maternity care to the public's health. It is a service which is well valued by its users, and which has a long and positive record of partnership between users and providers. It has much to teach other areas of the NHS about integration across sectoral and professional boundaries, and about the marrying of health and social care needs. Above all, it is uniquely placed to contribute to the long-term achievement of national targets for public health — since women's wellbeing during pregnancy, childbirth and the early days of parenthood are crucial to the long-term health of the entire family. In short, maternity care is much more than just a delivery service; it justifies commitment and investment from all in the NHS.

Further information

House of Committee Health Committee. *Maternity Services.* (Winterton report). The second report of the Health Committee. HMSO, 1992.

Department of Health. *Changing childbirth.* HMSO, 1993.

Audit Commission. *First class delivery. Improving maternity services in England and Wales.* Abingdon: Audit Commission Publications, 1997.

Department of Health. *Making a difference: a strategy for nursing, midwifery and health visiting.* 1997.

Acheson D, chair. *Independent inquiry into inequalities in health.* TSO, 1998.

Standing Nursing and Midwifery Advisory Committee. *Midwifery: delivering our future.* Department of Health, 1998.

New approaches to care — 7

Royal College of Obstetricians & Gynaecologists, Royal College of Midwives. *Towards safer childbirth.* RCOG: London, 1999.

Department of Health/Department for Education and Skills. *National service framework for children, young people and maternity services. Maternity services.* September 2004.

Child health services

Child health services need to meet the health requirements of infants, children and adolescents (defined as those under school-leaving age) by provision of healthcare and integration with other agencies. The services are the subject of a national service framework (chapter 8). Child health services are provided by a wide range of health professionals both in the community and hospitals. It is important for each primary care trust to know about its local child population and health status characteristics before it plans to purchase a clinical service. The health requirements of children cannot be divorced from the wider needs of the family, which can be influenced by such factors as poverty, homelessness and social class.

Children in the United Kingdom

According to the 2001 Census, the total UK population of children and young people less than 19 years was 14.77m. During that year in England and Wales there were 594,634 live births and 40.1 per cent were outside marriage.

One in every 10 babies born in England is to a teenage mother. These children are at high risk of growing up in poverty and experiencing poor health and social outcomes. Infant mortality rates for babies born to mothers under the age of 18 are twice the average.

Teenage pregnancy rates for women in England in 2002 between 13 and 15 years were 7.9 per 1,000. This figure is one of the highest pregnancy rates in this age group in Europe. About half of these pregnancies terminated; the other half led to a confinement. While the overall trend in teenage pregnancy is downward, in some areas of the country rates are level or increasing.

In 2003 there were an estimated 423 infants born to HIV infected mothers in England, Wales and Northern Ireland and there is clear evidence that transmission of infection can be prevented by giving appropriate drugs during pregnancy and avoidance of breast feeding.

Death rates at all ages during childhood are consistently higher in boys than in girls. Newborn deaths are most commonly due to prematurity, death in infancy to congenital abnormalities and in teenagers deaths are most commonly due to injury or poisoning (59 per cent of deaths in boys and 43 per cent of deaths in girls).

Managing the services

For a number of years governments have supported the concept of a comprehensive integrated health service for children, in which parents have an important role to play. There is a need for continuity of care with primary, secondary and community services each working to agreed common objectives.

Despite examples of close collaborative working in some parts of the country, NHS trusts and primary care trusts have had difficulty in creating a truly integrated provision.

Several kinds of doctors, with their associated multidisciplinary teams, based in traditionally separate organisations, look after the health of children.

Wellard's NHS Handbook 2006/07

General practitioners undertake the primary healthcare of all the children in their practice. Preventive services are provided with the primary care team such as giving routine immunisations, carrying out child health development surveillance and providing medical services at normal schools.

Community paediatricians are concerned with the health of the entire child population of their locality, through health promotion and prevention, surveillance and assessment. They supervise the immunisation programme for a district and provide assessment and treatment of children with suspected learning disabilities. Community paediatricians provide specialist services for children with learning disabilities and physical handicaps. They work both in child development centres as well as special schools, liaising closely with teachers. They have a pivotal role in the assessment and follow-up of child abuse and also act as a bridge between health, education and social services.

Hospital paediatricians provide emergency inpatient services for children and outpatient services for children referred by GPs. There is an increasing tendency for paediatricians to develop special interests. The majority of paediatric units have well developed neonatal services to provide intensive care of premature and sick newborn infants. Survival rates of extremely low birth weight babies under 1,000 grams are improving, as is their long-term outlook for normal developmental progress. In district hospitals there should be a paediatrician playing a lead role for services such as diabetes and cystic fibrosis. It is beneficial for overall services for children if community and hospital paediatricians work in the same trust, as prevention and treatment services can

be better coordinated.

Tertiary centre teaching hospitals frequently provide more specialist services such as paediatric endocrinology, cardiology, neurosurgery, surgery, plastic surgery and children's cancer services. They will also be providing more general local paediatric services.

Specialists from teaching hospitals will frequently provide outreach clinics at district hospitals so that the care of children with complex medical disorders can be closely integrated between district and teaching hospitals.

About half of the children attending hospital are seen for trauma or surgical conditions. These children are treated by orthopaedic surgeons, general surgeons, ear, nose and throat, A&E and ophthalmic surgeons.

Child and adolescent psychiatry services need to be well developed to provide complex largely outpatient services for children with emotional and psychosomatic disorders. They need to work closely with paediatric colleagues. All children admitted to hospital should be based on a paediatric ward where there will be children's trained nurses and play therapists and should not be admitted to specialist adult wards which have inappropriate facilities.

Ambulatory paediatrics. Paediatric assessment units have been developed in most acute paediatric units. Thus acutely ill children referred by GPs can be assessed urgently in a hospital setting (sometimes within an A&E department) to decide on whether they need to be admitted or discharged. In the case of the former appropriate emergency medical treatment can be instigated rapidly.

The development of specialist community paediatric nursing teams has encouraged the provision of complex

New approaches to care — 7

treatments in a home setting. For example, a child having active treatment for a tumour can have intravenous antibiotics or nasogastric tube feeding at home if there is sufficient paediatric community nursing back up. Similarly, high quality palliative terminal care can be provided at home or in a children's hospice depending on the needs of the child.

Screening and surveillance

The basis for future health is laid down in childhood, and one of the functions of an integrated service is to arrange a programme of surveillance so that progress in all areas of child health can be observed.

Ten days after birth a health visitor will take over from the midwife the responsibility for the young baby and mother. Subsequently the mother is encouraged to attend child health clinics, where health visitors check the development of the baby and a doctor trained in developmental paediatrics will see the baby.

The aim of the surveillance programme is to screen all children at predetermined intervals. There is a newborn examination, a six week check, a six to nine month check, an 18–24 month check and a pre-school examination at three to four years. The majority of GPs are accredited to undertake child health surveillance.

The programme specifically encompasses health promotion; emphasising the prevention of childhood morbidity by providing support to young mothers, dealing promptly with postnatal depression, providing nutritional advice and helping parents avoid accidents in their homes. Growth screening for short stature is essential, to ensure early treatment of growth hormone and thyroid deficiencies.

Immunisation

Immunisations are crucial in child health for prevention of infectious disease. In the current immunisation programme doses of diphtheria/tetanus/pertussis vaccine combined with Haemophilus influenzae B (Hib vaccine) and inactivated polio vaccine are given at two, three and four months of age, and again as a pre-school booster. A booster dose of Hib has been added at 12 months. The Hib vaccination programme commenced 12 years ago and has resulted in eradication of Hib meningitis and epiglottitis in children. Two doses of mumps/measles/rubella (MMR vaccine) should be given at 12–15 months of age and as a pre-school booster. Because of concerns about complications from this vaccine the immunisation rates have dropped below 75 per cent in some places and this greatly increases the risk of measles outbreaks in these areas. Uptake of the vaccine across the UK between July and September 2003 was 79.8 per cent. The World Health Organisation recommends immunity levels of around 95 per cent totally to prevent outbreaks of the disease. A suggestion was made that the MMR vaccine is linked to autism or Crohn's disease but this has not been substantiated. Furthermore no scientific evidence has been produced to support giving the individual components of the vaccine separately.

From November 1999 the meningococcal C vaccine was introduced and this is added in to the routine immunisations at three and four months, with a booster at 12 months. Additionally the vaccine has been made available to all under 25 year olds and there has subsequently been a dramatic fall in the rate of meningitis and septicaemia due to the meningococcal type C infection. Unfortunately the majority of cases of

Wellard's NHS Handbook 2006/07

meningococcal disease are due to Type B infection and as yet there is no suitable vaccine for this.

BCG immunisation is given to protect against tuberculosis. It is given to high-risk individuals including babies at birth. These are recognised to be Asian babies and other members of the family where an index case of tuberculosis is identified. Most primary care trusts have a teenage school immunisation programme.

Finally, children 13 to 18 years old are given an injection of diphtheria/tetanus and inactivated polio.

Child accidents

In the UK, about one child in four in the population attends an accident and emergency unit in any one year. On average, about 1,000 children die annually as a result of accidents, half in road accidents. It is estimated that about two million children seek professional treatment for accidental injuries; an unknown number, probably of the order of 10,000, suffer some degree of permanent disability or handicap as a result of such injuries.

It is possible to isolate some of the factors involved and in doing so help to plan strategies for cutting the child accident rate. Many methods of reducing injuries such as car seat belts, speed restrictions/road planning for inner cities and cycle helmets have been shown to be beneficial — the latter reduce the risk of serious head injury by 85 per cent.

Black and ethnic minorities

In planning and purchasing services for children, the ethnicity of the population is crucial. Children in minority ethnic groups may have special health problems. For example, one in every 400 babies born into the West Indian community has sickle-cell anaemia.

Rates of tuberculosis among immigrant groups are higher than those for the indigenous population. Nutritional disorders such as iron deficiency anaemia and rickets, which manifest themselves in childhood, are also more common among people of Asian origin. Rare serious metabolic disorders are more common in Asian than in Caucasian children.

Beside the different diseases requiring specialist services, it is important that equal access to services is also provided, as well as translators when needed.

The NHS Plan

Aspects of the 2000 NHS Plan affect the care of children. In particular:

- The plan records that infants born to fathers in unskilled or semi-skilled occupations have a mortality rate 1.6 times higher than those in professional or managerial occupations. Children of women born in Pakistan are twice as likely to die in their first year compared with children born to women in the UK.
- Sure Start projects aim to cover a third of children less than four years of age living in poverty.
- A national antenatal and neonatal screening programme is to be implemented for haemoglobinopathies and sickle cell disease.
- Improving diet and nutrition. There is a realisation that poor diet and nutrition leads to low birth weight, poor weight gain in the first year of life as well as leading to later adult diseases. Initiatives were announced to improve the overall balance of children's diet and in particular to increase their fruit intake.

The Climbie inquiry

In January 2003 the report on the Climbie inquiry was published. Victoria

New approaches to care — 7

Climbie arrived in England from the Ivory Coast and was subsequently killed at the age of eight by the people who had taken responsibility for caring for her. The inquiry team led by Lord Laming made 108 recommendations, 26 of which relate specifically to healthcare services, in response to the failures at every level of the agencies involved.

The report is one of a long line of such inquiries into cases of child abuse and neglect. In response the Health Secretary wrote to all chief executives of local health services and local authorities emphasising their duties towards vulnerable children and the need to reflect them in their budget decisions. The government asked NHS organisations to implement some recommendations within three months and act on others within six months or two years.

Every child matters

Failures to protect the most vulnerable children prompted the publication in September 2003 of the Green Paper *Every child matters*. The aim is to ensure that every child has the chance to fulfil their potential by reducing levels of educational failure, illness, substance misuse, teenage pregnancy, abuse and neglect, crime and antisocial behaviour among children and young people.

The subsequent cross-government programme *Every child matters: change for children* is about radical change in the whole system of children's services to improve outcomes for all children and young people. The five outcomes which children and young people have said are key to wellbeing in childhood and later life are:
• be healthy
• stay safe
• enjoy and achieve
• make a positive contribution

• achieve economic wellbeing.
Every child matters: change for children in health services, published in December 2004, details the support that the government will provide for implementation of the national service framework for children, young people and maternity services (chapter 8).

Much of the scope of the national service framework overlaps with the *Every child matters* programme, and they are in turn linked to:
• the *Choosing health* public health White Paper
• the chief nursing officer's review of the nursing midwifery and health visiting contribution to vulnerable children and young people
• the *NHS improvement plan*
• *National standards, local action*.

The above initiatives provide a context for local action to enable the vision set out in the *Every child matters* programme to be realised. The programme is underpinned by the Children Act 2004.

The chief nursing officer's review, published in August 2004, recommended a number of areas for action, including:
• increasing the number of school nurses
• strengthening the public health role of midwives and nurses
• greater integration and co-location of practitioners within children's centres
• strengthening the children's role of nurses in general practice
• improved leadership on child protection.

Choosing health identifies the health of children and young people as a key priority so that people start on the right path to health and parents are provided with the support they asked for in giving their children a healthy start in life.

This means action in a number of areas:

- more children's centres to enhance the health and wellbeing of children
- an increased number of extended schools, to help make the school a force for health in every community
- encouraging healthy eating and restricting the promotion and marketing of food high in fat, sugar and salt to children
- providing more opportunities for sport and physical activity
- new support and information to young people on sexual health
- preventing the sale of alcohol to children
- preventing the sale of cigarettes to children
- the development of personal health plans for all children.

National standards, local action sets out the health and social care standards for local organisations. It emphasises the importance of addressing the needs of children as well as the adult population, and of working in partnership locally.

National clinical director and children's commissioner

In September 2005 a new national director for children was appointed to spearhead the government's drive to modernise children's health services. The director also plays a major part in encouraging the implementation of the children, young people and maternity services national service framework (chapter 8). The director is Dr Sheila Shribman, who was medical director at Northampton General NHS Trust and registrar for the Royal College of Paediatrics and Child Health.

Dr Shribman has succeeded Professor Al Aynsley-Green, who in March 2005 was appointed as the first chil-

dren's commissioner for England. Professor Aynsley-Green is also Nuffield professor of child health at Great Ormond Street for Children and the

Children Act 2004 — the main provisions

- A children's commissioner to champion the views and interests of children and young people
- A duty on local authorities to make arrangements to promote co-operation between agencies and other appropriate bodies in order to improve children's wellbeing and a duty on partner organisations, including PCTs and NHS trusts, to take part in the co-operation arrangements
- A duty on agencies, including PCTs, to safeguard and promote the welfare of children
- A duty on local authorities to set up local safeguarding children boards and on partners, including PCTs, to take part
- Provision for indexes or databases containing basic information about children and young people to enable better sharing of information
- A requirement for a single children and young people's plan to be drawn up by each local authority
- A requirement on local authorities to appoint a director of children's services and designate a lead member
- The creation of an integrated inspection framework and the conduct of joint area reviews to assess local areas' progress in improving outcomes
- Provisions relating to foster care, private fostering and the education of children in care.

Institute of Child Health, University College London. His remit as commissioner is set out in the Children Act 2004 and he is acting as an independent voice for children and young people, to champion their interests and bring their concerns and views to the national arena. He is working closely with children's commissioners from Scotland, Wales and Northern Ireland.

Children's trusts

A central element of the *Every child matters* programme is the creation of children's trusts. The government is recommending that all areas should have a children's trust by 2008.

The trusts bring together all services for children and young people in an area — planning, commissioning and delivery of children's health services alongside education, social care and other partners.

Other important elements of the integration agenda are:
• a common assessment framework
• information sharing
• a lead professional
• common core competencies for those working with children.

Children in hospital

The best place to treat sick children, whenever possible, is at home. But with many children needing to use hospital services, it is essential that the quality of care provided is targeted to their needs.

The configuration of hospital services for children is a major element of the work of the Royal College of Paediatrics and Child Health. Children are spending less time in hospital, day-care wards and ambulatory services are being promoted, tertiary care needs emphasised and smaller hospitals face difficulties in the wake of the junior doctors' hours initiative and accelerated

specialist training.

Action for Sick Children supports and represents all sick children and their families. It has drawn up a document of rights for children, which has been adopted as the *European charter for children in hospital*. It sets out a number of good practices including:
• children in hospital shall have the right to have their parents or parents' substitute with them at all times
• accommodation should be offered to all parents, and they should be helped and encouraged to stay
• children and parents shall have the right to be informed in a manner appropriate to age and understanding. Steps should be taken to mitigate physical or emotional distress
• children and parents shall have the right to informed participation in all decisions involving their healthcare. Every child shall be protected from unnecessary medical treatment and investigation
• children should be cared for together with children who have the same developmental needs and shall not be admitted to adult wards
• children shall have full opportunity for play, recreation and education suited to their age and condition and shall be in an environment designed, furnished, staffed and equipped to meet their needs
• children shall be treated with tact and understanding and their privacy shall be protected at all times.

In 1997 Action for Sick Children offered practical advice to those involved in commissioning and providing emergency services. Its report *Emergency health services for children and young people* encourages accident and emergency units to provide staff qualified in the care of children and a child-friendly environment.

Health services for adolescents and young people

In recent years there have been increasing concerns that adolescents are not looked after well in the health service and that their needs may fall between paediatric and adult medicine departments with similar problems in psychiatric services.

There are guidelines suggesting that adolescents in hospital are best catered for within a specific adolescent unit. It is recommended that there are 12–15 beds/250,000 of the total population. If possible the unit should be a freestanding ward adjacent to paediatric services. It should be multispecialty and enable children with complex medical and surgical disorders to be looked after. It is also strongly recommended that there are transitional care arrangements for bridging the gap between paediatric and adult services coordinated by a clinical nurse specialist — this is especially important if the two services are in different trusts.

Paediatric intensive care

Concerns about the quality and quantity of paediatric intensive care in the UK resulted in the commissioning of *Paediatric Intensive care: a framework for the future*. The 1997 report outlined the steps to move from the ad hoc provision of services to a more sophisticated service with adequate specialist staff and equipment. The emphasis is on the tertiary paediatric intensive care service providing a lead role in the development and coordination of services in district hospitals. A few larger general hospitals are able to provide back up with the ability to provide children's intensive care for children with single organ failure such as respiratory failure.

The Department of Health endorsed the report which included:
• a nationwide mobile service, which ensures that critically ill children are transferred by doctors and nurses trained in paediatric intensive care, funded and staffed on a 24-hour basis in each geographical area
• travel arrangements made for parents
• the service organised and managed across the whole area
• a lead centre designated in each area
• provision of extra single, isolated beds should cease
• children should only be cared for in centres meeting the standards set out in the report.

A second report *A bridge to the future — nursing standards, education and workforce planning in paediatric care* addresses the nursing issues.

A further review of neonatal intensive care by the Department of Health in 2003 recommended a more structured, collaborative approach to caring for newborn babies by hospitals working closely together in managed networks. It also suggested definitions of categories of care and the designation of units that would provide the various levels of care.

National coordinating group on paediatric intensive care. *Paediatric intensive care: a framework for the future*. NHS Executive, 1997.

Department of Health. *Report of the neonatal intensive care services review group*. April 2003.

Further reading

The Victoria Climbie inquiry. Report of an inquiry by Lord Laming. January 2003. www.victoria-climbie-inquiry.org.uk

Department for Education and Skills. Every child matters. Green Paper. September 2003. www.everychildmatters.gov.uk

Department of Health. Choosing health. Making healthy choices easier. November 2004.

Department of Health/Department for Education and Skills. Every child matters: change for children in health services. December 2004.

Mental health services

Considerable government attention has focused on mental health services over the few years but unsuccessful attempts to reform UK mental health legislation have had an inhibiting effect. The documents which have the most impact in England are: Modernising mental health services, the National service framework for mental health and the NHS Plan.

Mental illness is one of the major problems facing society and one of the most important challenges facing our health and social care agencies. At any one time, around one in six of the working age population in the UK has a mental health problem — about six million people. According to the Department of Health, total investment in adult mental health services in England in 2004/05 was £4.52bn. Yet critics point out that the money has not always been spent in the right way. Mental health services consume around 20 per cent of NHS resources.

Capital investment of £130m is being allocated to strategic health authorities in 2006.

Overall, mental illness in England is estimated to cost over £77bn a year, including the cost of care from the NHS and local authorities, days lost to the economy and costs to individuals and families. People with long-term mental health problems have the lowest employment rate of any group with a long-term illness or disability, with only around 10 per cent in paid work. Around 13 people commit suicide each day, roughly the same number that die on the roads.

The common forms of mental health problems

Diagnosis in psychiatry is complex. Many symptoms occur in more than one diagnostic category and service users often move between diagnoses over time. The most common forms of mental illness are depression and anxiety (often called the neuroses) which affect around one in seven adults of working age at any time. Most treatment of these common forms of mental illness takes place in primary care by GPs, primary care nurses and, increasingly, counsellors. Up to one in three GP consultations involve a mental health problem.

There are many forms of anxiety, including agoraphobia, panic disorder, obsessive-compulsive disorder and post-traumatic stress disorder. It is an unpleasant emotional state characterised by fearfulness and distressing physical symptoms, and can often occur simultaneously with depression. Depression has a range of meaning from a description of normal unhappiness, through persistent and pervasive ways of feeling and thinking, to psychosis.

Wellard's NHS Handbook 2006/07

The so-called major mental illnesses — the psychoses — are much less common and affect around one in 250 members of the 16–65 age group. The major psychotic disorders are schizophrenia, persistent delusional disorders, acute and transient psychotic disorders, manic episodes and bipolar affective disorder. The symptoms of schizophrenia involve variations of the normal brain functions of thinking, perceiving, formation of ideas, and sense of self; typically users suffer from hallucinations (especially auditory hallucinations — voices) and delusions (especially paranoid delusions). People with schizophrenia or other psychotic illnesses are often referred to in policy documents as service users with acute or long-term severe mental illness.

In the case of both the neuroses and the psychoses, the mental health problem is exacerbated — and in some cases prompted — by alcohol or substance misuse. Up to half of users admitted to psychiatric inpatient care are abusing legal or illegal drugs simultaneously with their mental illness, and this proportion has been increasing over recent years.

Another group which present an increasing challenge to mental health services are people with 'personality disorder'. These individuals show consistent, unusual, and often very unpleasant responses to typical personal and social situations which result in them coming to the attention of the criminal justice system. There is some debate about whether many of the people labelled as having a personality disorder are treatable by psychiatrists — are they mad or bad? — and therefore whether they are the responsibility of psychiatric services. Users with psychosis and/or personality disorder can fall foul of the law. When this occurs, users can

find themselves in the category of mentally disordered offender (MDO). There are specialist services for MDOs that are called forensic psychiatric services. It is these services that provide inpatient services with low and medium levels of security, and may also provide community support including arrangements to intercept users entering the criminal justice system (so called court diversion schemes).

The legal framework for mental health treatment

One of the distinguishing features of psychiatry as a branch of healthcare is the power of psychiatrists (in partnership with GPs and social workers) to admit users to hospital without their consent. The Mental Health Act 1983 provides specific statutory authority for compulsory treatment without consent of service users detained in hospital, albeit with explicit safeguards: access to mental health review tribunals; restricting the detention of people deemed to be psychopathically (or personality) disordered to those who are considered to be treatable.

There is currently no power to compulsorily treat (that is, medicate) people in the community. This has led the government to review the 1983 Act, and to issue a White Paper and two draft Mental Health Bills which state the government's intention to introduce provisions in a new Act so that care and treatment orders may be applied to users outside hospital. This power would be part of a staged framework of compulsory powers.

The creation of a new power of preventive detention for people perceived to be dangerous, but who have not committed an offence (or who have served their sentence for a previous offence) is controversial for two reasons. Firstly, the diagnosis personality disorder is unreliable as an indicator of potential dangerousness. Secondly, the current conception of treatment will have to be widened to make all those diagnosed treatable, and detention in a treatment facility which may prevent an offence taking place may come to be defined as treatment (without therapeutic benefit the detention would breach the Human Rights Act 1998).

In January 2005 the Department of Health appointed an advisory group to suggest how the Bill might be implemented. In July 2005 it outlined the next steps for reform and described recommendations it had accepted that had arisen from pre-legislative scrutiny.

Mental health policy

The retraction of the asylums. The policy for mental health services during the 1980s and early 1990s was set out in the 1975 White Paper *Better services for the mentally ill*. A combination of professional resistance and financial constraints impeded progress. Moving beds for long-stay users out of the asylums into community settings proved more difficult to achieve than the transfer of inpatient beds (often accompanied by low secure services) for acutely mentally ill users to district general hospital sites.

Nonetheless, the number of beds for people with long-term mental illness in psychiatric hospitals continued to fall. The biggest remaining asylums are the special hospitals. There are still around 2,000 beds on three sites providing care for a broad spectrum of users, many of whom have been sent there by the courts following conviction for serious offences.

The development of community multidisciplinary teams. Providing

mental health services is a multidisciplinary and multiagency undertaking. Community mental health teams (CMHTs) have become the most common form of multidisciplinary and multiagency team; in 1995, the Department of Health decreed CMHTs to be one of the foundations of local, comprehensive mental health services.

The development of assertive outreach teams can reduce the number of admissions and give rise to shorter lengths of stay for users with psychosis. Specialist 24-hour, 365-day crisis services are designed to deal with users in a psychiatric crisis in the community.

The care programme approach. In July 1984, a former client killed a social worker. This local tragedy was the first of a series of well publicised homicides over the next 15 years by people with mental illness. The recommendations of the inquiry into the care of her assailant exposed the apparent limitations of mental healthcare in the community. In short, there was a failure to provide an effective and coherent mental health system based on coordinated community care. In response the Department of Health framed the care programme approach (CPA) based on the principles of assessment of health and social care needs, the formulation of a care plan to address those needs, the appointment of a keyworker and review of the user's progress.

The growth of the user movement. It was in 1985 that users' councils in psychiatric services and mental health advocacy projects began to develop in Britain. By 1997, most national policy-making, as well as local service planning, involved service user representatives. Access to independent advocacy is to become a right within the new mental health legislation.

Broad policy initiatives which

Box. The standards in the national service framework

Standard one

Health and social services should:
- promote mental health for all, working with individuals and communities
- combat discrimination against individuals and groups with mental health problems, and promote their social inclusion.

Standard two

Any service user who contacts their primary healthcare team with a common mental health problem should:
- have their mental health needs identified and assessed
- be offered effective treatments, including referral to specialist services for further assessment, treatment and care if they require it.

Standard three

Any individual with a common mental health problem should:
- be able to make contact round the clock with the local services necessary to meet their needs and receive adequate care
- be able to use NHS Direct for first-level advice and referral on to specialist helplines or to local services.

Standard four

All mental health service users in the care programme approach (CPA) should:
- receive care which optimises engagement, anticipates or prevents a crisis, and reduces risk
- have a copy of a written care plan which:
— includes the action to be taken in a crisis by the service user, their

carer, and their care coordinator
— advises their GP how they should respond if the service user needs additional help
— is regularly reviewed by their care coordinator
- be able to access services 24 hours a day, 365 days a year.

Standard five

Each service user who is assessed as requiring a period of care away from their home should have:
- timely access to an appropriate hospital bed or alternative bed or place, which is:
— in the least restrictive environment consistent with the need to protect them and the public
— as close to home as possible
- a copy of a written after care plan agreed on discharge which sets out the care and rehabilitation to be provided, identifies the care coordinator, and specifies the action to be taken in a crisis.

Standard six

All individuals who provide regular and substantial care for a person on CPA should:
- have an assessment of their caring, physical and mental health needs, repeated on at least an annual basis
- have their own written care plan which is given to them and implemented in discussion with them.

Standard seven

Local health and social care communities should prevent suicides by:
- promoting mental health for all, working with individuals and communities (standard one)
- delivering high quality primary

mental healthcare (standard two)
- ensuring that anyone with a mental health problem can contact local services via the primary care team, a helpline or an A&E department (standard three)
- ensuring that individuals with severe and enduring mental illness have a care plan which meets their specific needs, including access to services round the clock (standard four)
- providing safe hospital accommodation for individuals who need it (standard five)
- enabling individuals caring for someone with severe mental illness to receive the support which they need to continue to care (standard six).

may influence mental health. Major influences on the lives of people with mental health problems, or at risk of developing mental health problems, may lie beyond mental health services and be affected by wider policy initiatives. The important initiatives which may impact upon mental health are:

• **A public health approach.** The White Paper *Saving lives* set mental health services within a wider, more inclusive approach to mental health. The potential benefits of incorporating mental health strands of work into urban regeneration programmes, for example, have become apparent especially where spearhead primary care trusts have a focus on mental health. The subsequent 2004 *Choosing health* White Paper stresses the importance of everyone in the NHS promoting mental wellbeing and sets out measures for achieving that.

• **The social exclusion agenda and the New Deal.** These initiatives attempt to deal with issues of poverty and marginalisation in society, problems faced in particular by mental health service users. The disability strand of Welfare to Work, along with the creation of a commission to oversee the Disability Discrimination Act, for instance, may offer the prospect of people with mental health problems gaining and/or retaining employment.

• **Partnership.** Changes in the governance of services are also the central themes of the 1999 Health Act. It offers options around pooling of budgets at both commissioning and providing levels, and potential for the extending of powers of NHS trusts to provide social care and of social services departments to provide secondary healthcare. The NHS Plan suggested that health and social care mental health services should be integrated within care trusts.

Modernising services. The 1998 mental health strategy, *Modernising mental health services*, marked a turning point. It was based on the government's perception that care in the community had failed through:
- a group of users who were socially isolated, difficult to engage and in need of long-term care
- overburdened families
- inadequate systems, poor management of resources, and underfunding
- problems of recruitment, retention, and poor staff morale.

To address these failures, the strategy adopted the framework of 'safe, sound and supportive'. As part of the programme to support *Modernising mental health services,* the government committed itself to investing £700m over the following three years. In addition to money for community services, resources would also be found to create up to 500 medium secure places in the NHS by April 2002 and to develop child and adolescent mental health services.

Subsequently, the first national service framework (NSF) for the NHS covered mental health. It has a focus on adults of working age but also covers the complex needs of those graduating from adolescence and those moving into old age. The national service framework sets national standards and defines service models, underpinned by a clear evidence base, and includes performance indicators against which progress can be measured. The standards from the NSF are reproduced in the box. Furthermore, the NSF contained a section on implementation, specifying that each locality had to create a local implementation team (LIT).

In July 2000, the government returned to mental health in the NHS Plan. An additional £300m was promised to provide a number of specific services (table). Professor Louis Appleby presides as national director for mental health — the mental health czar — over a mental health taskforce. In addition to work on the NSF standards, the taskforce is also coordinating work on a series of underpinning strategies: research and development; information; support to clinical decision-making; and workforce planning.

In December 2004, Professor Appleby published an update on the national service framework. It looked at progress five years after its publication. Professor Appleby noted that suicide rates were at their lowest recorded level and staff numbers had increased substantially. Specialist mental health teams had been set up across the country, offering home treatment, early intervention or intensive support for people with complex needs.

Mental health foundation trusts.

In 2006 a number of mental health trusts are likely to be given foundation trust status.

The Mental Capacity Act

The Mental Capacity Act 2005, covering England and Wales, provides a statutory framework to protect vulnerable people, carers and professionals. It makes it clear who can take decisions in which situations and how they should go about this. The Act starts from the fundamental point that a person has capacity and that all practical steps must be taken to help the person make a decision.

It creates a statutory framework for decision-making covering decisions about financial and welfare matters (including healthcare).

The Act creates two new public bodies:

• Court of Protection — the new court will have jurisdiction in relation to the Mental Capacity Act. It will have special procedures and judges.
• Public guardian — this public official will take over from the current public guardianship office. The public guardian will be the registering authority for lasting powers of attorney and deputies.

Under the Act from April 2007, appointing a lasting power of attorney will permit a trusted person to protect another person's interests in decisions about their personal care.

Black and ethnic minority mental health programme

Research shows that people from black and ethnic minority communities can suffer from inequalities in access to mental health services, in their experience of those services, and in the outcome of those services. For example, black and ethnic minority patients

Wellard's NHS Handbook 2006/07

are significantly more likely to be detained compulsorily or diagnosed with schizophrenia.

The Department of Health, in conjunction with other stakeholders, is developing a comprehensive pro-gramme of work to tackle those inequalities. An important part of the programme is implementation of *Delivering race equality in mental healthcare*. This action plan was published in January 2005, along with the government's response to the independent inquiry into the death of David Bennett.

The black and ethnic minority mental health programme is an integral part of the Department's wider pro-gramme for race equality in the NHS. It is led by Professor Kamlesh Patel, head of the centre for ethnicity and health at the University of Central Lancashire and chair of the Mental Health Act Commis-sion. Professor Patel leads a programme board that brings together many of the individuals and organisations responsi-ble for making change happen for black and ethnic minority users of mental healthcare.

The policy for child and adolescent mental health services

A number of reports in the early 1990s identified serious deficits in service provision for child and adolescent mental health services (CAMHS). These proposed ways of making significant service changes and laid the foundation for the development of effective services. Of particular note was the *Health of the nation handbook on child and adolescent mental health* which set out a four-tiered service model that has been widely accepted.

Unfortunately, agencies find it difficult to reach agreement about priorities in the face of workload pressures. Typically, NHS trusts prioritise the small number of children with severe problems who require high-cost services. On the other hand, social services, education departments and primary care health teams are con-cerned about the greater numbers of children with mild to moderate mental health problems who receive little support. Due to this problem, financial constraints, and the continuing priority being given to adult mental health services, implementation of the model has been slow.

The DH's *1996/97 Priorities and planning guidance* for the first time made mental health services for children one of six areas for special monitoring. They were given further prominence in the 1998/99 national priorities guidance for 1999/2000–2001/

Table. Action to be taken as a result of the NHS Plan

- 1,000 new primary care mental health workers
- 500 more community mental health staff to work with GPs, A&E departments and NHS Direct
- 50 early intervention teams for young people with psychosis
- more crisis intervention teams to give coverage in every locality

- a further 50 assertive outreach teams
- women-only day centres in each health authority patch
- more workers to support carers
- additional secure beds and dis-charge support for people leaving secure care
- 300 additional staff to provide prison 'inreach'.

02 and attracted £84m via the NHS modernisation fund and the new mental health grant (administered through social services).

Despite these initiatives, reports on the inadequacies of current services continue to appear.

Older people with a mental health problem

It was an Audit Commission report — *Forget me not* published in early 2000 — which highlighted some major concerns about mental health services for older adults. Among the recommendations the document made were for:

- greater support to GPs to identify problems at an early stage
- improved information and help for carers
- improved specialist care.

Older people — including those with either functional mental illnesses (for example, depression which is very common in later life) or organic illnesses (for example, dementia which afflicts one in 20 people over 65 and becomes increasingly common with advancing years) — are at the heart of the NHS Plan. Specific developments are identified as:

- national standards for residential and nursing homes (where rates of dementia have been estimated to be as high as 80 per cent)
- personal care plans for elderly people and their carers
- £900m investment in intermediate care.

The emphasis on intermediate care in the NHS Plan as an alternative to hospital or long-term care has a number of components:

- rapid response teams
- intensive bed based rehabilitation
- recuperation facilities
- integrated home care teams.

Effective implementation of these components within a locality should make a significant contribution to the quality of life for older people and their mental health, and feature strongly in the mental health component of the NSF for older people.

In November 2005, *Everybody's business. Integrated mental health services for older adults* was published as a service guide. It sets out the necessary components of a modern service for this age group.

Further information

Mental health website: www.dh.gov.uk/ PolicyAndGuidance/ HealthAndSocialCareTopics/ MentalHealth

Department of Health. *Mental health of children and young people in Great Britain, 2004.* August 2005.

Services for people with learning disabilities

People with learning disability have incomplete intellectual development, sometimes accompanied by social or emotional problems. There are around 160,000 adults and 30,000 children with severe or profound learning disabilities in England. Each year, some £3bn is spent on health and social service provision for adults with learning disabilities.

The 2001 White Paper *Valuing people: a new strategy for learning disability for the 21st century* aims to help people with learning disabilities live as independently as possible. It recognises they have greater health needs than the majority of the population, being more prone to mental illness and chronic health problems such as epilepsy. The strategy takes a cradle to grave and cross-government approach

New approaches to care — 7

to improving life chances for people with learning disabilities and their families. Proposals are based on the principles of legal and civil rights, independence, choice and inclusion.

For a number of years there has been a drive to shift care for this client group from hospitals to the community. Smaller scale, dispersed services based in local communities have been developed. At the same time the issues of choice, empowerment and rights that support improvements in the quality of life have been addressed.

These changes were identified as being important as long ago as 1971 in the White Paper *Better services for the mentally handicapped.* An influential report published by the King's Fund in 1980 *An ordinary life* showed that people with a learning disability could and should live in the community in ordinary housing with the same rights and responsibilities as everybody else. With appropriate support to meet the identified needs of individuals, people with a learning disability could benefit immensely and enjoy a quality of life that would be impossible in an institutional setting.

A 1999 report commissioned by the Department of Health described extensive variations in services across the country. In 2001 Rob Greig was appointed to the new position of learning disability director of implementation as part of the government's commitment to improve the life chances of people with learning disabilities. In December 2001 the learning disability helpline in England (freephone 0808 808 1111) was launched, and to help deliver the objectives of *Valuing people* the learning disability taskforce and implementation support team were set up.

In bringing about reforms, the focus of management effort has in many

cases facilitated the organisation in a move towards becoming a provider of social care as well as healthcare services. As the needs of individuals with learning disabilities often do not fall neatly into one category or the other, this makes the provision of a seamless service a reality. The development of care trusts that specialise in caring for this group of people is a logical extension of this trend.

Learning disability partnership boards in each local authority area build on previous inter-agency planning structures and a responsible for services for adults with learning disabilities. They oversee the inter-agency planning and commissioning of comprehensive, integrated and inclusive services.

For supported living programmes to work effectively it is essential for good systems of advocacy to be encouraged. The aim must be to ensure that services are designed to meet the unique combination of needs and wants that individuals have and that those services can be adjusted as needs and wants change over time.

The introduction of health action plans is an important element in the work supporting this client group. A health action plan details the actions needed to maintain and improve the health of an individual and any help needed to accomplish these. It is a mechanism to link the individual and the range of services and supports they need, if they are to have better health. The plan is primarily for the person with learning disabilities and is usually co-produced with them.

In November 2004 the Department of Health found it necessary to issue a note of clarification. The Department and Healthcare Commission had noted a growing number and size of, often remote, independent sector hospitals for people with learning disabilities. While acknowledging that there might be a need for some specialist regional provision, the Department emphasised the principle that local needs should be addressed by local expertise and resources.

Services for people with learning disabilities received over £41m in 2005/06. This funding was allocated to primary care trusts to provide services through the learning disabilities development fund. Priority areas earmarked for funding were:
• day services modernisation
• NHS campuses reprovision — redevelopment of residential services developed by the NHS as a result of the contraction or closure of NHS hospitals
• support for people with learning disabilities from black and minority ethnic communities.

Government plans for the closure of the remaining 20 long-stay hospitals in England by 2006 were announced in December 2003. At the time of the 1971 White Paper *Better services for the mentally handicapped* there were 59,000 adults and children living in long-stay hospitals. In October 2003 the figure was 721 people.

Further information
Learning disabilities website. www.dh.gov.uk/PolicyAndGuidance/ HealthAndSocialCareTopics/ LearningDisabilities

Valuing people website:. www.valuingpeople.gov.uuk

Valuing people. A new strategy for learning disability for the 21st century. Cm 5086. TSO, March 2001.

Department of Health. *The government's annual report on learning disability 2005.* November 2005.

Services for black and minority ethnic people

Britain's black and minority ethnic population has changed significantly since the creation of the health service in 1948. Returns from the 2001 Census reported that the size of the UK minority ethnic population was 4.6m, equivalent to 8 per cent of the total population and an increase of 53 per cent on 1991 figures.

The challenge is to ensure that healthcare is appropriate to the needs of the whole population and this should include access to health services according to identified needs. Significant inequalities have existed in the health and health experience of black and minority ethnic communities. NHS organisations need to ensure that users receive quality healthcare with ease and that they can have the confidence that they will be treated with respect and dignity.

Policy framework
The law. The health service, in the same way as other providers, has an obligation under the Race Relations Act 1976, Section 20. This makes it unlawful for anyone concerned with the provision of goods, facilities or services to the public or a section of the public to discriminate on racial grounds by refusing and/or deliberately omitting to provide them with goods, facilities or services of like quality.

The Race Relations (Amendment) Act 2000 imposes a duty on public bodies to remove discrimination in practice and to deliver equality of opportunity to both staff and service users. NHS organisations were asked to review and consult on their race equality schemes and produce a revised three-year scheme by May 2005.

New approaches to care — 7

The statutory code of practice on racial equality in employment, which comes into force in April 2006 and replaces the Commission for Racial Equality code of practice, outlines employers' obligations.

Concept of equality. Equality in the NHS is understood to mean that all people irrespective of their religion, culture or ethnic background should:

- have equal access to the NHS via appropriate information
- have services which are both relevant and sensitive to their health needs
- be able to use the NHS with ease and have the confidence that they will be treated with respect
- have equal rights of representation on health bodies.

Equality does not mean treating everyone in the same manner, irrespective of different cultural, religious and ethnic backgrounds.

Ministerial and central initiatives. Black and minority ethnic health has been a ministerial theme in the policy developments of the NHS with successive Secretaries of State for Health committing the government to this issue. The Department of Health has taken a number of initiatives in this area.

The new NHS White Papers reaffirmed the government's commitment to tackling inequalities in health and measuring progress through a performance framework, which included 'ensuring that black and minority ethnic groups are not disadvantaged in terms of access to services'.

Health action zones were established in 1998 with one of their key objectives being to reduce health inequalities and this work is being taken over by spearhead primary care trusts.

The NHS Equal Opportunities Unit was behind two significant initiatives aimed at changing practice in the NHS:

- the 'positively diverse' programme, launched in 1998, whose focus is workforce development
- *Tackling racial harassment in the NHS: a plan for action.*

The government's public health policy recognises that health authorities have been identifying priorities, in addition to the four key target areas set out in *Saving lives,* in locally drawn up local delivery plans. Vulnerable people, such as minority ethnic groups, are a possible local priority area.

Tacking health inequalities: a programme for action was launched in 2003 by former Health Secretary John Reid as part of a wider national drive for improving social justice. Backed by 12 government departments, the programme lays the foundation for meeting the government's targets to reduce the health gap on infant mortality and life expectancy by 2010. Reversing this widening gap between social groups is a major challenge and the programme emphasises the need to improve health and the factors that contribute to health faster in disadvantaged areas than elsewhere.

The programme strategy is evidence-based in targeting resources and efforts in the following four delivery themes:

- supporting families, mothers and children
- engaging communities and individuals
- preventing illness and providing effective treatment and care
- addressing the underlying determinants of health.

Equality champion for the NHS

NHS chief executive Sir Nigel Crisp appointed Surinder Sharma as equality and human rights director for the NHS in October 2004. He has been asked to tackle inequalities in all aspects of health and social care delivery, and also to promote the chief executive's action plan on leadership and health equality.

Health issues of specific concern to ethnic groups

The different mortality and morbidity patterns in various minority ethnic populations have been well documented. A number of reports, such as the Department of Health's *Ethnicity and health — a guide for the NHS,* form a good basis for a response from the NHS.

Some genetically determined conditions affect people whose origins are African, African-Caribbean, middle Eastern-Mediterranean and those from the Indian subcontinent. They include blood disorders such as sickle-cell anaemia, thalassaemia major and 6-GPD deficiencies. Tay-Sachs affects Jewish people and systemic lupus erythematosus (SLE) is relatively common in Africans and South East Asians.

In 2000 the results of a national survey of the health of minority ethnic groups in England were published. It included children as well as adults. Among the key findings are:

- higher rates of heart disease among south Asian men and higher rates of stroke in black Caribbean and Indian men
- higher rates of diabetes among the majority of minority ethnic groups
- Bangladeshi men are 60 per cent more likely to smoke than men in the general population
- Pakistani, Bangladeshi and Chinese men and south Asian and Chinese women are less likely to participate in physical activity than the general population.

The survey findings allow healthcare providers to target services better towards minority groups and assist the achievement of the duties imposed upon public bodies by the Race Relations (Amendment) Act 2000.

A number of diseases given priority in *Saving lives* are of specific concern to black and minority ethnic people:

- **coronary heart disease** is a major cause of premature death among people from the Indian subcontinent. Death rates in this group among those aged under 65 are more than 50 per cent higher than the average for England and Wales
- **stroke and hypertension** is common among people from the Caribbean and African Commonwealth. Death rates from stroke among those aged under 65 are nearly twice as great among those born in the Caribbean as the England and Wales average
- mortality from **breast cancers** is low in Caribbeans, Africans and people from the Indian subcontinent, although there is evidence that such cancers could be increasing
- mortality from **cervical cancer** is increased in Caribbean women
- the use of **cancer screening services** is low in black and minority ethnic people
- **mental health.** Diagnostic rates for schizophrenia are high for African-Caribbeans, and are also raised for Asians. British-born African-Caribbeans are diagnosed three to six times more often than the white population
- African-Caribbeans have high **admission rates to psychiatric hospitals** and are disproportionately over represented among compulsory admissions and in specialist facilities for secure detention. These could be a reflection of rigid and culturally-biased diagnostic assessment and treatment

New approaches to care — 7

- **suicide rates** are high in young Asian women
- **HIV and AIDS.** Heterosexual intercourse has been the predominant method of transmission of HIV infection in some black populations. Advice on **contraception** is often provided in a manner inappropriate to the needs of minority ethnic populations
- poor socioeconomic conditions place some black and minority ethnic groups, particularly children, at higher risk of **accidents** in the home.

Other key areas include:

- the incidence of **diabetes** is four to five times greater in Asians than in non-Asians. The associated mortality is three times the national level. Diabetes is also common in African-Caribbeans
- minority ethnic populations are at greater risk of **diabetic renal disease**
- **congenital malformations** are increased in Pakistani babies
- **perinatal mortality** is higher than the British norm in African-Caribbean and Asian babies, in particular Pakistani babies.

Local purchasers in their work on achieving public health targets and health gain should take cognisance of these specific ethnic health conditions which disproportionately affect black and minority ethnic people.

Black and minority ethnic people use services in an atypical manner:

Low utilisation. Services such as antenatal care, early intervention in mental health, chiropody, occupational therapy and physiotherapy, certain sexual health services, screening for cervical and breast cancer are proportionately under-used by black and minority ethnic people.

High utilisation. Studies have shown that black and minority ethnic people are disproportionately over represented among compulsory psychiatric admissions. They are more likely to receive different forms of treatment in hospital and be treated with drugs or electroconvulsive therapy (ECT), and less likely to receive psychotherapy and other early intervention services.

Local purchasers and providers may therefore specify specific service agreements to address this imbalance.

Some minority ethnic groups are reported to have high utilisation of primary care services in inner cities.

Action framework

Many excellent initiatives have been taken by a number of health bodies to improve service provision for black and minority ethnic people. A wealth of knowledge and expertise in black and minority ethnic health has been accumulated by UK organisations. They can be categorised under the following themes:

- **inequality and access:** includes studies done on inequality in access to, and barriers in, utilising services due to organisational and/or individual discriminative practice, or lack of recognition of religious, cultural and linguistic needs of patients
- **organisational commitment:** includes studies which have emphasised the organisational structure; its development of equal opportunities policies in employment and service provision, assessing how ethnic work is being financed, whether a senior manager has been delegated with the responsibility of taking this work forward and whether an effective dialogue exists with the local communities
- **epidemiological trends:** includes studies which are short and long-term clinical studies of given ethnic populations and samples to assess patterns of health, including diabetes,

coronary heart disease and sickle cell anaemia.

Commissioning health for black and minority ethnic people. In 1996 the Department of Health and King's Fund published *Facing up to the difference,* which is a toolkit for creating culturally competent services. This gives practical advice on commissioning healthcare for black and minority ethnic communities and aims to move commissioners beyond an ad hoc approach towards integrating ethnicity within the main work of the organisation. The document proposed a framework for quality standards, as well as a set of standards covering ethnic monitoring, communication and information, religious and spiritual needs, bereavement, gender, diet, personal care, employment, training and handling complaints.

Ethnic minority staff in the NHS
The aim of the programme of action for minority ethnic staff has been to achieve equitable representation of minority ethnic groups at all levels in the NHS, including professional staff groups, reflecting the ethnic composition of local populations.

To achieve progress in service provision to reflect and meet the needs of local populations, parallel measures in employment practices makes good management sense and helps to alleviate discriminative practices.

In order to play a role in NHS strategy setting, it is also crucial that black and minority ethnic people have a presence at board level in proportion to their prevalence in the local population.

Ethnic monitoring — collection of ethnic data
From 1 April 1995, the collection of ethnic group data, for admitted patient care, contract minimum data set and hospitals episode statistics (HES) returns, has been mandatory.

Heart disease
In December 2004 the Department of Health issued *Heart disease and south Asians: delivering the national service framework for coronary heart disease.* This best practice guide aims to support service providers working with south Asian communities to deliver heart disease services. It contains background information on heart disease and south Asians, a selection of best practice cases and details of useful resources.

Culturally appropriate mental health services
Concerns have been expressed over a number of years that mental health services are not being delivered to people from black and minority ethnic communities experiencing mental illness and distress in a way that is appropriate to their needs. In response the Department of Health published in 2004 *Delivering race equality: a framework for action* for consultation.

Other initiatives
Early programmes focused on maternity care and facilitating communication between non-English speaking minority ethnic people and NHS staff. In 1983 the Department took a lead role in inaugurating the Asian Mother and Baby Campaign, which resulted in several health authorities training and employing link workers. Subsequently the National Extension College published guidance and a checklist, which are still useful for local NHS managers and health professionals.

A number of voluntary organisations have joined forces with individual black and minority ethnic people to

New approaches to care — 7

work to improve ethnic healthcare. They include the Sickle Cell Information Centre and the Sickle Cell Society which has produced *A handbook on sickle cell disease: a guide for families.*

The Department of Health-funded NAHAT publication *Action not words* in 1988 was perhaps the first national report in this field that argued for a coordinated strategy to be adopted as a priority across the NHS and linked agencies. The objectives and principles set out are still valid and provide useful targets for healthcare purchasers.

The way forward

Numerous efforts over the years have led many national organisations and individuals to acknowledge the importance of promoting equality of healthcare for black and minority ethnic people. To make further progress on these achievements the NHS needs the continuing commitment of NHS managers to act upon existing information, knowledge and resources. Public health strategy documents make clear the importance the government places on this issue and that it will be monitoring performance.

There are three major challenges for the NHS:
• tackling racism in institutions
• incorporating race equality throughout the policy and practice of the organisation and infusing cultural sensitivity into the culture of service delivery at all levels
• developing collaborative partnerships with local minority communities, that is, moving away from the consultation model and involving communities in the design of services.

The need to provide appropriate services for black and ethnic minorities must continue to be identified and followed through.

Further information

NAHAT. *Action not words.* Birmingham: NAHAT, 1988.

Calman K. *On the state of the public health for 1991.* HMSO, 1992.

Department of Health. *Ethnicity and health — a guide for the NHS.* London: DoH, 1993.

King's Fund Centre. *Checklist on health and race.* London: KFC, 1993.

Social Services Inspectorate. *They look after their own, don't they.* DH, February 1998.

HSC 1999/060. *Tackling racial harassment in the NHS — a plan for action.*

The 1999 health survey for England. Department, June 2000.

Department of Health. *Tackling racial harassment in the NHS — good practice guide.* 2001.

Department of Health. *Tackling health inequalities: a programme for action.* July 2003.

Department of Health. *Heart disease and south Asians: delivering the national service framework for coronary heart disease.* December 2004.

National Institute for Mental Health in England. *Celebrating our cultures: guidelines for mental health promotion for black and minority communities.* December 2004.

Department of Health. *Promoting equality and human rights in the NHS — a guide for non-executive directors of NHS boards.* July 2005.

Department of Health. *Tackling health inequalities: status report on the programme for action.* August 2005.

Commission for Racial Equality. www.cre.gov.uk

Health for asylum seekers and refugees portal. www.harpweb.org.uk

Services for older people

There has been a long standing policy by government to promote the independence of older people. As people age they continue to want the things that make life enjoyable and fulfilling. Like people of any age, they want:

• a reasonable income
• a comfortable home, which is easy to keep warm in winter
• convenient ways to get around their community and travel further afield
• interesting things to do
• choice and control about how they live
• contact with friends and acquaintances
• good health
• effective, good quality services, which meet their needs.

Older people are not a homogeneous group: the accumulation of experience over years makes older people in many ways more diverse than younger people. However, there are clearly factors that make it harder for people to maintain an enjoyable and fulfilling life as they age. Inadequate pensions means that many older people, especially women, do not have a reasonable income. Low income makes it harder to do many things including maintaining and heating your home, travelling, engaging in social activities and eating well. A combination of factors such as bereavement and loss of mobility can also reduce opportunities for social contact as people age. In addition, they are more likely to experience an increase in physical and mental health problems.

This challenges the NHS and other organisations that commission and deliver services for older people to address a range of issues (box 1).

What services do older people use?

Most older people are in good health, for example, 72 per cent of older people living in the community have no dependency. Of those who need support, many receive this from friends and family carers who are often themselves over 65. Four million carers provide some kind of support to older people. However, older people do constitute a significant proportion of users of health, social care, housing and community services. Some two thirds of acute hospital beds are occupied by people over 65. Most domiciliary and residential services are used by older

Box 1. Important issues for NHS and other organisations

• people of all ages should be helped to improve their own health and reduce risk factors
• most older people want to continue living in their own homes — institutional care rarely offers the same level of autonomy and individual choice
• risks to health may be ameliorated through action in services outside the NHS, for example, housing, benefits advice
• loss of mobility and other daily living skills are as detrimental to the quality of life of older people as for any age group
• NHS and other services should be organised around the needs of users, easy to access, well coordinated and provide maximum possible choice and information
• policies for commissioning and provision should assume that people will aspire to a good quality of life irrespective of their age.

New approaches to care — 7

people, especially the over-75s, women and, in the case of day care services, people living alone.

Shortcomings in the current system

The 1999 Royal Commission on Long Term Care identified services that were complicated and confusing to users and carers; a variable quality of and access to services; piecemeal and haphazard developments; perverse incentives, such as divided budgets and ageism.

The NHS Plan

The NHS Plan has aimed to address many of these shortcomings and promote the independence of older people and provision of high quality support at home, rather than institutional care. All the proposals for increasing capacity of the NHS, improving performance, strengthening partnership and service integration, and for delivering on target and on time offer potential improvements for older people who are the largest single group of patients using the NHS.

The NHS Plan highlights four objectives to put older people at the centre of service delivery: to assure standards of care, extend access to services, promote independence in old age and ensure fairness in funding.

Assuring standards:
- the Commission for Social Care Inspection is responsible for ensuring all regulated care services are provided to national minimum standards
- the national service framework (NSF) for older people sets out standards for services used by older people, including those for stroke, falls and mental health problems
- the NSF also explicitly addresses ageism. All NHS organisations are

required to implement local resuscitation policies
- there is a renewed emphasis on recognising the specific needs of older people and respecting their autonomy, dignity and privacy.

Extending access to services:
- an NHS retirement health check has been piloted and breast screening extended to cover all women aged 65 to 70
- a single assessment process for health and social care has been introduced
- a personal care plan is agreed with older people and their carers, identifying their current package of health and social care, care coordinator, monitoring arrangements and key contacts for emergencies
- an information and advice service, Care Direct, provides for older people through telephone, drop-in centres, online and outreach services.

Promoting independence:
- an extra £900m by 2003/04 was announced for investment into intermediate care and related services. Primary care trusts and local authorities have to demonstrate the following services are in place: rapid response teams to provide emergency care at home and help prevent unnecessary hospital admissions, intensive rehabilitation services, recuperation facilities, arrangements at GP practice or social work level to ensure older people receive a one-stop service, and integrated home care teams
- carers are being supported through additional funding to extend services offering a break from caring responsibilities.

Fairness of funding:
- nursing care provided by registered

nurses in nursing homes is no longer charged for

- two initiatives assist people who do not wish to sell their property at the time of entering a care home, to meet charges for care. For the first three months after admission to a residential or nursing home the value of a person's home is disregarded for means testing purposes. For longer - term stays local authorities receive grants to enable loans to be made to individuals as an alternative to selling property
- increasing the value of assets that someone can hold before charges are levied. This aims to counterbalance the effects of increasing property values.

Three other policy issues for services to older people are addressed within the NHS Plan, namely providing better integrated support, reducing health inequalities and strengthening the voice and choice of patients.

The Plan indicated that NHS bodies and local authorities would be required to use powers in the Health Act 1999 relating to pooled budgets, lead commissioning and integrated provision. The development of intermediate care services could enhance health and social care partnerships where health organisations work closely with social care partners to develop comprehensive assessments, appropriate skills and facilities and cost-effective service models.

The Plan signalled the development of care trusts, which commission and deliver local health services as well as social care for older people. The Health and Social Care Act 2001 created powers to establish such trusts.

New arrangements so patients can tell trusts and PCTs about their experience of using health services and can complain when things go wrong, such as patient advice and liaison services

(PALS) and local patients' forums have been put in place.

Measures to ensure people are better informed through, for example, NHS Direct and Care Direct, digital television and smart cards allowing improved access to health records, potentially strengthen older people's exercise of choice. Likewise, other policy initiatives such as direct payments offer opportunities for older people to have greater control and choice over the services they use.

The national director of older people's services Professor Ian Philp has a clear remit to tackle ageism in health and social care and to chair the older people's taskforce which is driving forward the implementation of the NHS Plan and the NSF

Delayed discharges

From January 2004 a system of reimbursement to NHS acute trusts was introduced to help reduce the delayed discharge of older people from hospital. Once a hospital inpatient is medically fit and ready for discharge, social services is responsible for their care. NHS trusts notify local authorities about patients whose discharge is being delayed and they are entitled to charge £100 per day as reimbursement. Introduction of the system has had a markedly positive effect on reducing the number of NHS hospital beds blocked in this way.

Partnership projects

In March 2005, £60m funding was announced by the Department of Health for councils to develop innovative ways to help older people avoid emergency hospital visits and to live independently longer. The partnerships for older people projects (POPP) grant aims to encourage councils in England, together with the NHS and other

New approaches to care — 7

partner organisations, to devise new approaches to establishing sustainable arrangements for supporting older people. In the first phase, more than 150,000 people will receive care designed to keep them healthy and active in 19 projects from May 2006.

Mental health services

Everybody's business was launched in November 2005 with the message that older people's mental health, including delirium, dementia and depression, cuts across health and social care, and mainstream and specialist services. The service development guide is committed to:
• improving people's quality of life
• meeting complex needs in a coordinated way
• providing a person-centred approach
• promoting age equality.

Half of older people in hospital experience mental health problems, and the aim of the guide is to ensure that older people have their needs met wherever they are in the system, without encountering discrimination or barriers to access.

Further information

Older people's website. www.dh.gov.uk/ PolicyAndGuidance/ HealthAndSocialCareTopics/ OlderPeoplesServices

Royal Commission on Long Term Care. *With respect to old age: a report by the Royal Commission on Long Term Care. Research volume 1*. TSO, 1999.

Department of Health. *The national service framework for older people*. 2001.

Care Services Improvement Partnership. *Everybody's business. Integrated mental health services for older adults.* November 2005.

Supportive and palliative care services

In March 2004 the National Institute for Health and Clinical Excellence (NICE) published evidence-based guidance on supportive and palliative care for people with cancer. The guidance also informs the development of effective service models for other disease and patient groups with similar needs.[1] It advises those who develop and deliver cancer services on how to make sure that patients, families and carers are well informed, cared for and supported. The guidance recommends that medical and nursing services are available for patients with advanced cancer on a 24-hour, seven days a week basis, and that equipment can be provided without undue delay. Those providing generalist medical and nursing services should have access to specialist advice at all times.

All people with life-threatening illness will have needs in relation to supportive and palliative care at all stages of the illness, from pre-diagnosis onwards. Most of the care they receive will be delivered by their usual health and social care providers in primary or secondary settings. Some people will require access to specialist services (for example, specialist palliative care services).

Defining supportive care

NICE has decided to adopt the following working definition for supportive care as suggested by the National Council for Palliative Care (NCPC):

Care that helps the patient and their family to cope with cancer and treatment of it — from pre-diagnosis, through the process of diagnosis and treatment, to cure, continuing illness or death and into bereavement. It helps

Wellard's NHS Handbook 2006/07

the patient to maximise the benefits of treatment and to live as well as possible with the effects of the disease. It is given equal priority alongside diagnosis and treatment.[2]

Supportive care is an umbrella term for all the services, generalist and specialist, that may be required to support people with cancer and their carers. It encompasses:
• self help and support
• user involvement
• information giving
• palliative care — including symptom control, psychological, social and spiritual support, end-of-life care and bereavement support
• rehabilitation
• complementary therapies.
It is not a distinct specialty but is the responsibility of all health and social care professionals, who deliver care, that is informed and driven by theories, models and frameworks drawn from diverse sources. It is underpinned by open and sensitive communication and by organisations and teams who work in a coordinated way to ensure the smooth progression of patients from one service to another.

Defining palliative care

NICE has also adopted the NCPC definition for palliative care. Palliative care is:

The active holistic care of patients with advanced, progressive illness. Management of pain and other symptoms and provision of psychological, social and spiritual support is paramount. The goal of palliative care is achievement of the best quality of life for patients and their families. Many aspects of palliative care are also applicable earlier in the course of the illness in conjunction with other treatments.[2]

Palliative care aims to:
• affirm life and regard dying as a natural process
• provide relief from pain and other symptoms
• integrate psychological and spiritual aspects of care
• offer a support system to help patients live as actively as possible until death
• offer a support system to help the family cope during the patient's illness and in their own bereavement.[3]
Palliative care like supportive care is everybody's business. It is delivered by two distinct categories of staff:
• the patient and carers' usual professional carers
• professionals who specialise in palliative care (for example, consultants in palliative medicine, clinical nurse specialists in palliative care).

What patients and carers want from services

As part of the process of developing a supportive and palliative care strategy for cancer patients in England, Cancerlink undertook a questionnaire survey and held a meeting of expert patients and carers.[4] Results from these exercises highlighted the following domains as the key components of good supportive and palliative care:
• **Being treated as a human being.** People want to be treated as individuals, with dignity and with respect for culture, lifestyles and beliefs.
• **Empowerment.** The ability to have their voice heard, to be valued for their knowledge and skills, and to exercise real choice about treatments and services are central to patients' and carers' wishes.
• **Information.** Patients and carers should receive all the information they want about their condition and

possible treatment. It should be given in an honest, timely and responsible manner.

- **Having choices.** Patients and carers want to know what options are available to them from the NHS, voluntary and private sectors, including access to self-help and support groups, complementary therapies and information.
- **Continuity of care.** Good communication and coordination of services between health and social care professionals working across the NHS and social sectors is essential.
- **Equal access.** People want access to services of comparable quality wherever they are delivered.
- **Meeting physical needs.** Physical symptoms should be managed to a degree that is acceptable to patients and achievable in relation to the clinical situation and current knowledge and expertise.
- **Meeting psychological needs.** Patients and carers need emotional support from professionals who are prepared to listen to them and are capable of understanding their concerns.
- **Meeting social needs.** Support for carers, advice on financial and employment issues and provision of transport are necessary.
- **Meeting spiritual needs.** Patients and carers want support to help them explore the spiritual issues important to them.

A survey by the Commission for Health Improvement/Audit Commission revealed similar findings.[5] In addition it indicated that patients want to:

- have access to high quality information materials, such as leaflets, booklets, videos and the internet
- undergo only those interventions for which they have given informed consent
- die in the place of their choice
- be assured that their carers will be supported throughout the illness and in bereavement.

Current services

Many providers of supportive and palliative care in the public, voluntary and private sectors are offering highly effective services. There are however deficiencies in all parts of the country that affect the care of some patients. Among those reported are:

- patchy, inconsistent access to high quality information
- varied and inequitable access to rehabilitation services
- limited availability of people able to provide spiritual support
- variable provision of bereavement support
- insufficient numbers of psychological support specialists
- variability of provision of specialist palliative care services
- poor face-to-face communication.

The evidence from the survey on what patients want and the reports of deficiencies suggest that services need to provide:

- better organisation, coordination and integration of services
- improved assessment of the individual needs of people across the domains of physical, psychological, social and spiritual care and information needs
- improved training for all health and social care staff in providing good supportive and palliative care
- enhanced provision of services to meet currently unmet needs and to reduce inequalities in service provision and access
- active promotion of user involvement and of self-help and support groups.

Wellard's NHS Handbook 2006/07

Wellard's NHS Handbook 2006/07

Specialist palliative care services

The following tables set out the currently available services in the UK. Most inpatient, hospice at home and day care services are provided by hospices in the voluntary sector together with about half of the home care teams.

The voluntary services include 10 Marie Curie hospices with 236 beds and six Sue Ryder care units with 111 beds. The remainder are independent local charities including three services exclusively for HIV/AIDS with 50 beds.

There are 52 inpatient beds per million population and an estimated 58,000 admissions a year to inpatient units, including 41,000 new admissions. The mean length of stay in a hospice is 13 days.

Community palliative care services see an estimated 155,000 patients a year. Some 110,000 new patients are seen by home care nurses each year and home care teams care for 70 per cent of those dying from cancer.

Inpatient care

The function of inpatient care is to provide care for those whose distressing symptoms and other complex needs are not readily relieved in the home or other care setting. Its focus is on symptom management, short-term health assessment, rehabilitation and terminal care.

Day care

The function of day care is to enhance the independence and quality of life of patients through the provision of rehabilitation, physiotherapy, occupational therapy and psychological support in a social context.

Home care

The multiprofessional team's function is to provide specialist knowledge in symptom management, supplement the care of the dying, coordinate care, emotional and bereavement support and teaching to staff, carers and patients. The service should be available to patients at home, in care homes and in community hospitals.

Hospice at home

The aim of this service is to provide sufficient support to a patient to enable them to remain at home and to avoid admission to institutional care. It may involve practical nursing care for extended periods through the day and night. It may be provided in response to a crisis in the care of the patient at home or for the last few days of terminal care.

Hospital-based palliative care teams

The hospital-based palliative care team's

Table. UK palliative care provision at January 2005	
Inpatient units	
Adult units	220
Units:	
— NHS	64
— Voluntary	156
Beds:	
— NHS	667
— Voluntary	2,489
Total beds	**3,156**
Children:	
— Units	33
— Beds	255
Community and hospital support services	
Home care	358
Hospice-at-home	104
Day care	263
Hospital support nurses	68
Hospital support teams	293

function is to work with other
specialties in the hospital, giving advice
on symptom management, supporting
staff as well as patients and their
families/carers, and providing technical
expertise and sometimes a bereavement
support service. Additionally teams
provide both formal and informal
education.

Education and training in palliative care

Specialist palliative care services have a
lead role in developing a continuing
education and training programme that
is designed to enhance the palliative
care knowledge and skills of all health
and social care professionals in the area.

The cancer plan

Following publication of the NHS cancer
plan in 2000, the cancer networks have
established within their structures
supportive and palliative care networks.
These networks are taking on the
responsibility for developing palliative
care strategy for the cancer network.
They involve all local stakeholders
in the following:
• assessing local need
• assessing current service provision
• recommending priorities for
  development
• developing network-wide operational
  policies, care pathways and guidelines
• ensuring patient/user views are
  taken into account.
  The cancer plan provided an extra
£50m for specialist palliative care
services in England. In September 2003
the distribution of this across the
country was allocated. The principal
aims were to reduce inequalities in
access to services and to provide a more
realistic contribution to the costs of
voluntary hospices incurred in delivering services for NHS patients.

Building on the best

The *Building on the best: end of life
care initiative* commits the Department
of Health to take forward training
programmes so all adult patients
nearing the end of life have access to
high quality specialist palliative care to
be able to live and die in the place of
their choice.[6] The initiative is being
funded by £12m over three years from
April 2004. It is widening the pool of
staff trained in meeting the needs of
this patient group by adapting and
applying current cancer palliative care
models to other disease groups. Funding is being released on a weighted
capitation basis to strategic health
authorities over the period.

The long-term conditions national service framework

The national service framework for
long-term conditions, published in
March 2005, aims to transform the way
health and social care services support
people with long-term neurological
conditions to live as independently as
possible. Its principles are also being
applied to other long-term conditions.
It sets out a number of evidence-based
quality requirements for care from
diagnosis to the end of life.
  The ninth quality requirement
addresses the need for palliative care
services for people in the advanced
stages of neurological conditions and
the importance of enabling people to
make choices about end-of-life care.

References

1. NICE. *Improving supportive and
   palliative care for adults with cancer.*
   March 2004. www.nice.org.uk
2. NCPC. *Definitions of supportive and
   palliative care: briefing number 11.*
   London: NCPC (NCHSPCS), 2002
3. World Health Organisation. *Cancer*

pain relief and palliative care. Technical report series 804. Geneva: WHO, 1990.

4. Cancerlink. *Cancer supportive care services strategy: users priorities and perspectives.* London: Cancerlink, 2000.

5. Commission for Health Improvement/Audit Commission. *National service framework assessments No. 1: NHS cancer care in England and Wales.* London: CHI/AC, 2001.

6. Department of Health. *Building on the best: end of life care initiative.* July 2004.

National Council for Palliative Care. www.ncpc.org.uk

Help the Hospices. www.helpthehospices.org.uk

Dental services

In 2003 dental charges in the UK covered a little under 30 per cent of the total cost of NHS general dental services (GDS). In the same year, the gross cost of GDS in the UK was £2,173m.

Over the past 25 years the outlay on dental services has never accounted for more than 5 per cent of total NHS costs. Yet in the first years of the health service as much as 10 per cent of resources were devoted to GDS. Part of the reason for this fall is the improved dental health of the population. In 1968 in Great Britain, for example, over a third of the population had no natural teeth; in 2003 the proportion was 10 per cent. Also in 2003 across the UK, 62 per cent of 12 year olds and 50 per cent of 15 year olds were free from any obvious dental decay experience. In certain (fluoridated) areas of the country, the incidence of caries among children has dropped to an all-time low. According to the Office of Health

Economics, there were 20,304 dentists (excluding assistants) working in the GDS in the UK in 2003, 80 per cent more than in 1951. Among OECD countries, however, the UK has one of the lowest ratios of dentists to population.

A revised NHS dental contract in 1990 and a subsequent dispute over payments deterred dentists from undertaking NHS work — particularly in certain areas of the country.

Currently, 45 per cent of people aged 18 years and over and 61 per cent of children in England are registered with a dentist.

The dental strategy
In 2000 the government published a £100m strategy for modernising NHS dentistry. Important aims in *Modernising NHS dentistry: implementing the NHS Plan* are:

• ensuring that everyone who wants to can see an NHS dentist by phoning NHS Direct

• empowering patients by better and more accessible information to enable them to make informed choices about their oral health

• improving the safety and quality of NHS dentistry by improving clinical effectiveness and appropriateness of dental treatment

• tackling poor oral health, of children particularly, by improving the health of the worst off in society and narrowing the health gap.

Dental care in the NHS
Dental care, both preventive and curative, is an integral part of total healthcare. Dental services are provided in each sector of the NHS.

Dentists are concerned with the prevention, diagnosis and treatment of dental diseases, such as caries and gum disease; with bite problems which

New approaches to care — 7

disturb the jaw's normal functioning or distort appearance; with the effects of trauma and generally with oral conditions, which may indicate a local dental disorder or may be a manifestation of more general disease.

The General Dental Council (GDC) is responsible for the maintenance of educational and professional standards. Only dentists whose names are entered on the GDC's register are permitted to practise.

In the hospital service dentists follow the same career pathways as doctors, through the training grades up to consultant status.

In NHS general dental practice there is a one-year vocational training scheme.

The oral health plan for England

Choosing better oral health, published by the Department of Health in November 2005, sets out a number of measures primary care trusts can take to improve the oral health among their communities. The strategy identifies the following key areas for action in oral health:
• fluoride
• improving diet and reducing sugar intake
• encouraging preventive dental care
• reducing smoking
• increasing early detection of mouth cancer
• reducing dental injuries.

General dental services and the 2006 contract

Although general dental practitioners are in contract with primary care trusts, or health boards in Scotland and Northern Ireland, the assessment of fees for approved treatment has been undertaken by the Dental Practice Board (DPB) for dentists in England and Wales, the Scottish DPB in Edinburgh,

and the Central Services Agency in Belfast. The Dental Practice Board was absorbed into the NHS Business Services Authority in October 2005. The boards pay dentists direct, and they have powers to impose prior approval arrangements upon individual practitioners where statistical monitoring demonstrates an atypical prescribing pattern. This power is subject to the right of appeal. The DPB made statistical data about treatment available to health organisations on a regular basis

Under the Health and Social Care (Community Health and Standards) Act 2003, commissioning, including specialist services, and contracting for NHS dentistry will devolve from the Department of Health to PCTs from April 2006. From the same date, the budget for general dental services, which has been managed as a central non-discretionary budget, will be devolved to PCTs as part of their main allocations subject to a spending floor. The Department worked with the British Dental Association and the NHS to develop a robust base contract that all PCTs and dental practices are putting in place.

Under these arrangements from April 2006, unless local variations are agreed, the successor authority to the DPB will continue to pay practices broadly the same income. The cost of these payments will be recharged to PCTs. The fee structure for patients is being simplified and will use a banding system:
• band 1 £15.50
• band 2 £42.40
• band 3 £189.00
• urgent treatment £15.50.

Adult patients are charged for a dental examination. Those over 18 pay 80 per cent of the cost of their dental treatment up to a maximum of £189, unless they fall within the following

categories of exemption:
- full-time students under 19 years of age
- pregnant women
- women who have had a child within the past 12 months and members of families receiving income support or family credit. Patients who are on a low income but who do not fall into these categories may still get help with charges. There is no general exemption for pensioners.

The National Institute for Health and Clinical Excellence issued guidance in October 2004 on recall intervals. It recommended that dental patients should be recalled on the basis of clinical need with intervals varying from 3–18 months. These intervals will move away from the current practice of many dentists who recall patients every six months.

A number of personal dental services (PDS) pilots under the NHS (Primary Care) Act 1997 have been in progress. Over 30 per cent of dental practices have moved to PDS. The aim is for dentists and primary care trusts to take the lead in developing new ways of delivering services which target local oral health problems. Projects include mobile surgeries to provide domiciliary care for house bound people such as residents of care homes, and the appointment of dental therapists who are able to carry out simple dental procedures, and thus free up dentists' time.

NHS Direct is playing a part in telling people where to find an NHS dentist, and dental access centres are being established with the aim of providing fast and flexible access to NHS dentists. The centres are being set up in a number of locations, including high streets, clinics and in some of the primary care walk-in centres.

Patients do not need to be registered with a centre and can simply make an appointment by telephone.

The centres are providing both emergency and routine services.

Community dental services

Community dental services are generally located within NHS trusts. The service has a number of roles, to:
- screen the teeth of children in state-funded schools
- monitor the dental health of the population through screening and epidemiological programmes
- provide dental health promotion and preventive programmes
- provide dental care to patients who have experienced difficulty in obtaining treatment from the general dental services, or for whom there is evidence that they would not otherwise seek care from the general dental services
- provide services for special needs patients, to pregnant and nursing mothers and to the elderly.

There will also be close liaison with other healthcare workers and agencies. The extent to which each community dental service provides these services will depend on dental needs identified by the local health body. In many areas the purchasing authority will be advised on these matters by a consultant in dental public health.

The hospital dental services

Access to hospital dental services is usually by referral from either a general dental practitioner or a community dental practitioner, although patients may present themselves at dental hospitals for emergency treatment.

Ophthalmic services

Some 65 per cent of the population aged 16 years or over wear glasses or contact lenses, and the proportions rise to over 90 per cent for those aged over 45 years and

New approaches to care — 7

97 per cent for pensioners.

In April 1999 free NHS sight tests were restored for people over 60 years of age after 10 years of pensioners having to pay a charge for this service.

Ophthalmic services in the UK are divided into two sections. Primary eye care is provided by optometrists (ophthalmic opticians) and ophthalmic medical practitioners (OMPs), who provide contractor services for those eligible for examination under the general ophthalmic service (GOS) managed by health authorities/boards.

The hospital eye service (HES), which takes the form of specialist units in major hospitals, provides consultative, specialist medical and surgical services. The units are staffed by ophthalmologists and a team which may consist of doctors, optometrists, dispensing opticians, orthoptists and nursing staff.

Optometrists and OMPs provide private primary eye care services to those members of the public not eligible for GOS benefits. Many ophthalmologists also engage in private practice and carry out consultations and surgery through private healthcare and hospital arrangements.

While many in the population pay the full cost of sight tests and spectacles, those currently eligible for free NHS sight tests are:
• people over 60 years
• children under 16 (under 19 if in full-time education)
• those registered blind or partially sighted
• diabetics
• glaucoma sufferers (and their close relatives aged 40 and over)
• benefit claimants (income support, family credit, disability working allowance and income-based jobseekers allowance).

Those on a low income or needing complex lenses may also have entitlement.

NHS vouchers to help towards the cost of spectacles or contact lenses are available to children under 16 (under 19 in full-time education), those prescribed complex lenses, and benefits claimants (as above). Optical vouchers for 3.9m spectacles were reimbursed by primary care trusts and local health boards in England and Wales in 2004/05.

People who are eligible for GOS and who are housebound or have difficulty in travelling to a practice may receive financial help towards a home visit.

Certain low income groups are eligible for help towards private eye examinations (on certificate AG3).

Private and voucher-aided dispensing of spectacle appliances can be carried out by, or under the supervision of, optometrists, medical practitioners, dispensing opticians or unregistered sellers. However, this last category must dispense to a written prescription not more than two years old, and may not supply children under 16 years of age, nor, knowingly, a registered blind or partially sighted person. Unregistered sellers may not supply contact lenses or low vision aids.

The number of sight tests paid for by primary care trusts and local health boards in England and Wales in 2004/05 was 10.8m. This was a 3 per cent increase on 2003/04. Some 43 per cent of the tests were performed on patients aged 60 or over, and 22 per cent on children.

Consultations and treatment remain available to everyone under the hospital eye service, although the supply of optical appliances interacts with voucher arrangements in the GOS. The HES may refer patients to the GOS for refraction examination and the prescribing of any necessary optical appliances.

While the great majority of optical corrective appliances funded wholly or partially by the NHS consists of spectacles, contact lenses and solutions may be provided by the HES on clinical grounds. Vouchers, under GOS arrangements, may be applied towards the provision of contact lenses but without any commitment to solutions and aftercare. All such provision, however, forms only a small proportion of contact lens practice, which remains predominantly private.

Access to the general ophthalmic service by those members of the public who are eligible is direct. Access to the hospital eye service is essentially by referral by the patient's general medical practitioner but the majority of these referrals originate from optometrists/OMPs who detect eye disease during eye examinations. Hospital casualty departments may also refer patients. Some ophthalmologists will accept patients referred directly from optometrists where an emergency exists and urgent attention is necessary, and when the GP is kept informed. Some optometrists in the community also work in partnership with the HES and GPs to monitor some ophthalmic diseases, for example glaucoma, or general medical conditions which may cause ophthalmic complications, for example diabetes. Other areas of co-operation include children's eye care and the provision of special optical aids to visually handicapped people.

Other eye care services — such as those to industry to meet the requirements of the Personal Protection Equipment Regulations and to industry and commerce to provide for the needs of visual display unit users and others with visually demanding tasks — are predominantly provided by optometrists.

Drive to end long waits for eye surgery

In May 2003 the Department of Health pledged to end long waits for NHS cataract operations. At the time, at least 50,000 older patients were waiting over three months for cataract treatment. Some £73m was provided to primary care trusts to fund extra operations. A further £4m was used to fund the piloting of improvements to services to patients suffering from chronic eye disease and low vision.

By the end of January 2005 the Department of Health was able to announce that no one was waiting more than three months for their first cataract operation. Most cataract patients can now expect to be treated within six weeks. Alongside extra operations in NHS units, independent sector treatment centres have treated more than 13,000 cases.

Review of general ophthalmic services

August 2005 saw the announcement of a review of general ophthalmic services. The Department of Health wants to ensure that best use is being made of the services. It has suggested that some monitoring work currently done by hospitals might be undertaken by local optometrists. The review is looking at arrangements for achieving best value from the current £340m yearly spend on the services.

Distribution

At 31 December, 2004, there were 592 OMPs and 8,328 optometrists in England and Wales. In September 2001 there were 724 whole time equivalent ophthalmologist consultants in Great Britain. Ophthalmologists are concentrated in the eye departments of major hospitals. The other professions as GOS contractors and in private practice are reasonably well distributed throughout the country, although concern has been expressed at a lack of service available in some rural areas.

Training

Following registration as medical practitioners, ophthalmologists have to meet the requirements for training and experience which are required to qualify for consultant status, OMPs have to satisfy the conditions laid down in the GOS regulations.

Optometrists have to be registered by the General Optical Council, eligibility for which requires a degree in optometry, followed by one year's further clinical training in supervised practice and completion of the professional qualifying examination of the British College of Optometrists (BCO). Dispensing opticians are also registered by the General Optical Council following two years full-time training, completion of the Diploma of the Association of British Dispensing Opticians and a year working in practice with a qualified dispensing optician.

Continuing education and training for optometrists who are GOS contractors is funded by the Health Departments via a multi-representative body, the Directorate for Continuing Education and Training (DOCET). The secretariat is provided by the BCO.

Pathology services

The laboratory medicine services are integral to the diagnosis treatment and monitoring of disease states. Clinical decisions about patient management are informed by results and advice from laboratory investigations. Up to 70 per cent of all diagnoses depend on pathology.

Objectives and elements of the pathology service

The principal objectives of the services are to:
- deliver a comprehensive range of scientific investigations for patients in hospitals, outpatient departments and in primary care
- provide interpretation and clinical advice to the requesting clinician
- ensure that investigations are appropriate, timely and cost effective in patient care
- ensure that the quality of investigation and interpretation meets the needs of the patient.

Many of the elements of the laboratory medicine service are shown in figure 1. This demonstrates the wide range of services provided, many of which require direct links with patients and with other clinical specialists. The service operates 24 hours every day throughout the year to ensure optimum patient assessment and treatment.

Structure

Services comprise the laboratory disciplines of biochemistry, haematology, histopathology and microbiology. There are additional sub-disciplines including immunology, virology and cytopathology. These specialisms have been brought together within one pathology unit which is usually a directorate on its own, but in some organisations is linked to other diagnostic or clinical services. The four main disciplines are usually managed as separate departments within the unit, led by consultants or clinical scientists. Increasingly the disciplines share facilities such as specimen collection, reception and initial preparation. As techniques and technology across the disciplines converge, departments are developing the concept of a core automated laboratory where staff are trained to cover aspects of two or three disciplines operating within the same area.

Other clinical services

Figure 1 shows a range of clinical services in which the analytical processing and investigation of samples forms only a part of the total service. In haematology the consultants have inpatient beds and outpatient clinics to treat patients with certain cancers and other blood disorders. The haematologists are also responsible for the provision of a blood matching service for hospitals and for blood product control and issue. Clinical biochemists are directly involved in lipid, diabetes and endocrine clinics and microbiologists are responsible for the control of infection in hospitals and for developing information and policies on appropriate antibiotic treatment. Histopathologists, while providing a frozen section service to surgeons during operations for many years, are now often more closely involved in clinics where cytology specimens are investigated within the clinic. Histopathologists also have responsibility for the post-mortem and mortuary services in hospitals.

All the laboratory specialists make an important contribution to case conferences, to clinical audit and to clinical research where the interface between clinicians and laboratory specialists provides a forum for the development of guidelines and protocols and for review of appropriate use and development of the service.

Pathology services have close relationships with the public health service in England and Wales and public health medicine and local authorities in Scotland. They relate to NHS Blood and Transplant and to university departments. These organisations employ similar scientific and technical staff, undertake similar analytical work and are sometimes located on hospital sites.

Figure1

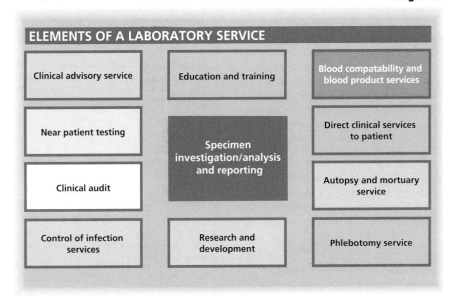

ELEMENTS OF A LABORATORY SERVICE

Clinical advisory service	Education and training	Blood compatability and blood product services
Near patient testing		Direct clinical services to patient
Clinical audit	Specimen investigation/analysis and reporting	Autopsy and mortuary service
Control of infection services	Research and development	Phlebotomy service

New approaches to care — 7

Professional staffing of laboratories

Consultants and clinical scientists of equivalent status are responsible for the professional direction of their specialty and one of their number is generally the director of pathology services with strategic and managerial responsibilities for service development. Such staff, which may represent between 10 and 20 per cent of the workforce, are responsible for ensuring efficient and effective use of the service and its resources in assisting diagnosis, management, early detection and prevention of disease.

The majority of the analytical work is undertaken by medical laboratory scientific officers (MLSOs), who must be state registered by the Health Professions Council. MLSO staff are largely recruited from graduates in biological sciences and only achieve state registration after one to two years training in a recognised laboratory.

Increasing workloads have resulted in increased levels of automatic analyses and computing. This has changed the levels and type of skills required from MLSO staff with a high degree of expertise required in these areas. Further consequences of greater workloads are the relatively increased proportion of non-analytical work associated with manual sample handling. Medical laboratory assistants (MLA) are employed to support MLSO staff in this work. Such staff do not work unsupervised and cannot work alone, for example in an emergency on-call situation.

Changes in demand and cost

Around 100m requests for investigation are received annually by pathology services in the UK. The range of investi-gations increase as new diagnostic tests are developed and evaluated. The adoption of clinical guidelines and protocols has increased the complexity of the work, for example, in histopathology. Hospital acquired infections have increased the length of stay for patients in hospitals throughout the UK. The development of the control of infection service in hospitals has increased significantly the workload in microbiology.

Changes in healthcare design have attempted to increase the efficiency of utilisation of beds by increasing the proportion of day case surgery, increasing the number of procedures carried out in outpatient departments and encouraging further investigation in primary care before referral to hospitals. These changes have increased laboratory workload and the proportion of investigations requiring rapid response. In some cases this has only been possible by establishing laboratory investigations close to the patient, for example, in outpatients departments or primary care centres.

Laboratory medicine services represent approximately 5 per cent of healthcare costs. Staff costs represent around 50 per cent of the total with consumable materials, capital equipment charges and overheads representing the remainder.

Revenue for the services is partly provided from secondary care and partly from primary care purchasers. Other smaller revenue streams vary but include environmental health work for local authorities, Crown Office autopsy work, pre-employment drug screening and clinical drug trials. Most laboratories undertake some research and development.

Current challenges within the services

Increases in workload of 50 per cent every five years, without significant changes in staff, has placed pressures on a service trying to maintain quality standards in the face of downward cost pressures. These quality standards have sometimes not been achieved with, in a number of cases, unacceptable patient outcomes.

The UK laboratory services has faced manpower recruitment and retention challenges specifically in the area of histopathology consultants and in the recruitment of MLSO staff, in all disciplines. In the latter, well-qualified graduates and existing state registered MLSO staff have been offered better rewards outside the NHS. Laboratories have been reviewing staff structure and skill mix to determine the range of duties which can be carried out by staff who are not state registered under the supervision of MLSO staff.

Laboratories are moving increasingly to extended working day and shift working. However this places further challenges on the ability to provide appropriate numbers of qualified staff for all shift periods.

The Department of Health's pathology modernisation programme, set up in 1999, is a 10-year strategy to modernise and rationalise pathology services. It seeks to develop standardised large-scale processes, advance technology (especially electronic information exchange), infrastructure consolidation, primary care linkages, and patient-centred and best use of scarce expertise.

In February 2004 guidance on modernising services was issued. It was backed by £9.1m revenue and £54m capital funding over the period 2003/04–2005/06, helping pathology services to expand. An implementation over-

sight group has been created. The main change proposed was that pathology services should be delivered through larger managed networks and the key focus was redesigning services to build pathology capacity. The networks would be managed by a lead trust on behalf of all trusts involved. Good practice guidance was also included on a range of issues, including standardisation, the pathology workforce, IT and technology.

As part of the funding, in 2005/06 each strategic health authority will receive £100,000 revenue funding for project management to support pathology network development locally.

The challenges for laboratory medicine services are twofold — firstly, senior laboratory staff and senior clinicians must manage demand to ensure that investigations carried out are cost effective in patient care and that guidelines and protocols are developed through an evidence-based medicine approach. Laboratory staff resources need to correlate with workload. Secondly, given the expectation of increased demand for laboratory investigations it is essential to ensure that investigations are carried out efficiently and in good time to meet the needs of the patient. In some specialties major automation and information technology in large capacity laboratories is an acceptable solution. In others, smaller laboratories close to the point of care are required to meet the demanded turnaround time. Examples are diagnostic testing on-site in one-stop clinics or intensive investigation of patients with chest pain to avoid or reduce inpatient stay.

Building a service responsive to patients, published in September 2005, details the work undertaken since the

New approaches to care — 7

launch of modernising pathology services drive, and outlines future challenges. Health minister Lord Warner announced a number of measures to keep up the momentum including an independent review of pathology services. The review panel is being chaired by Lord Carter of Coles.

Point of care testing

Near patient testing is routinely used for blood gases in intensive therapy units and many wards have blood glucose monitors. Since clinical decisions are taken on the basis of the results of these tests it is important that qualified staff provide quality control and training in the use of the equipment and this should be managed by the laboratory. More extensive and elaborate near patient testing requires careful evaluation, implementation and control. Who will take responsibility for the accuracy of the result? Who will operate the equipment and how will they be trained? Any necessity to repeat the test in the main laboratory means there is no saving in the number of requests. Test equipment placed in GP surgeries may not be well utilised.

However, the drivers for development of near patient testing are speed of service and ability to impact patient management rapidly. Changes in the balance of primary and secondary care, the need to decrease inpatient length of stay and the drive to reduce unnecessary outpatient return appointments are likely to increase point of care testing in acute inpatient areas, in outpatient clinics and in primary care centres. Outreach services providing such support will properly be managed, controlled and accredited through a core laboratory in the area. Although the unit cost of investigation will be much higher than a central laboratory the model may be cost effective in overall health cost terms.

Computer reporting to ward terminals and to GP surgeries, and links to the patient administration system (PAS) and other systems are already available and being installed rapidly. Well-managed information technology reduces the risk of human error in reporting and improves standards for turnaround times of results.

Risk management

A number of rare but highly publicised problems with misallocated results or poor standards of reporting point up the need to manage risk. All healthcare institutions should meet defined quality standards, and in July 2003 the Department of Health urged all NHS pathology laboratory services in England that had not already done so to enrol with an appropriate accreditation scheme. The principal accrediting body is the Clinical Pathology Accreditation (UK) Ltd. This was developed by the Royal College of Pathologists and other professional bodies with support from the Department. Laboratories seeking accreditation claim compliance with a number of standards; which compliance is assessed by a review and inspection process by trained professional inspectors.

Accreditation, membership of quality assessment schemes and the employment of sufficient qualified professional staff to direct and supervise work both in and out of normal hours all provide quality assurance within the laboratory. Managers have to address other aspects of risk including supporting clinical audit and the development of protocols, so that best practice can be seen to have been followed.

Inspector of microbiology

In January 2004, the Department of Health appointed Professor Brian Duerden as inspector of microbiology. His role is to promote and oversee standards in clinical and public health microbiology.

The need for such a post was identified in the chief medical officer's strategy for infectious diseases *Getting ahead of the curve* and is designed to ensure a high quality, integrated microbiology service across the country. Professor Duerden was formerly director of clinical quality for the Health Protection Agency and previously held senior posts within the public health laboratory service.

National pathology adviser

Dr Ian Barnes was appointed by the government in April 2004 as the first national pathology adviser to champion pathology modernisation across the country. He chairs the national modernisation group.

Conclusions

Laboratory medicine services are seen as a fundamental element of clinical medicine which should be consultant led. However clinical pathology is under pressure to contribute to the improvement in cost effectiveness and cost efficiency of the health service. This requires it to consider new ways in which it will finance and deliver the service. It must continually develop the service and maintain quality for a range of purchasers within primary, secondary and community care.

Efforts are being made to reconfigure services, to co-operate within geographical areas and to change working practices. Consultants are expected to lead by looking outwards and taking initiatives in clinical audit, the development of clinical protocols and by managing demand. Business process re-engineering and benchmarking techniques are likely to deliver improved cost effectiveness and ensure clinical effectiveness.

Further information

Modernising NHS pathology website. www.dh.gov.uk/PolicyAndGuidance/ OrganisationPolicy/SecondaryCare/ PathologyModernisationProgramme

Department of Health. *Making the change. A strategy for the professions in healthcare science.* February 2001.

Department of Health. *Modernising pathology services.* February 2004.

Department of Health. *Modernising pathology: building a service responsive to patients.* September 2005.

X-ray and imaging services

Hospital imaging departments employ numerous technologies and techniques to produce images of structures within the human body. These are collectively described as radiological techniques and include the use of ionising radiation, radioactive isotopes, ultrasound and magnetic fields. Images can be used to diagnose disease, provide treatment, as in interventional radiology, and monitor the response to treatment.

The complexity of technologies require ongoing specialist training of staff for effective and efficient use. The staff who deliver these services are multiprofessional, including doctors (radiologists, who are mostly consultants), technicians (radiographers, sonographers and sometimes physics technicians), nurses and those with secretarial and clerical skills.

There are health risks from ionising radiation, which means that its use must be likely to benefit the patient, by aiding diagnosis or treatment, and careful attention must be paid to radiation protection. These risks, and the choice of imaging techniques available, require radiologists to offer a proactive advisory service to clinical colleagues to allow the best technique to be selected for the clinical problem. A request by a clinician for a test seeks a radiological opinion or therapy, and is not a request for a photograph.

Many different patients are seen in radiology departments, including those from general practice, who are often attending hospital for the first time and who are anxious, not surprisingly. Increasingly, therefore, departments can be an important shop window for the hospital and its quality of service. Continuing front-of-house training for staff is likely to enhance this effect.

High quality radiological imaging services can greatly enhance both the effectiveness of medical services and the patient's perception of effectiveness and efficiency.

Technologies

X-rays. Early imaging relied on the use of X-rays, which were discovered by Röntgen in 1895. They enable the imaging of bones (for example, fractures), soft tissues of differing densities and metallic foreign bodies. The images obtained are two-dimensional, and traditionally have been recorded on film although a switch to electronic storage of digital images is underway.

Fluoroscopy. Other parts of the body can be imaged by X-rays when they are rendered radiopaque by the administration of, for example, barium into the gastrointestinal tract or iodine-containing contrast agents into arteries

and veins for vascular and renal studies. The images can be displayed on screens, allowing the demonstration of movement and the selection of representative images for recording on film.

Computerised tomography (CT scanning). In computerised tomography X-rays are used to measure the density of tissues across the patient from many different angles and allow a composite cross-sectional image to be derived by computer analysis. All parts of the body can be imaged in great detail. CT images are viewed on a video monitor and stored on film or optical disc. Newer spiral or helical scanners allow faster acquisition of thinner sections, data from which can be used to form an image in an alternative plane. This facility, and the frequent need to improve tissue contrast by giving iodinated contrast agents, result in CT being a high radiation dose examination.

Ultrasound scanning. Ultrasound scanning uses high frequency sound waves, and the principles are similar to those applied in nautical depth-sounding. Freedom from the hazards of ionising radiation means that ultrasound can be used repeatedly, and is particularly useful in pregnancy. All parts of the body can be imaged except those behind air (chest) or bone (adult skull). Scans are viewed on video monitors and may be stored on film, videotape or disc. Ultrasound equipment is inexpensive compared with other technologies, especially CT and magnetic resonance scanners.

Magnetic resonance imaging (MRI). A powerful magnetic field and radio waves are used to change the orientation of hydrogen ions in the body in magnetic resonance imaging. Computer analysis builds a cross-sectional image. Images can be obtained in any plane, and there is no ionising radiation.

Radioisotopes. Radioactive tracers aggregate in organs or bone which can then be imaged by detectors. Techniques employing a variety of radioisotopes are helpful in the diagnosis of disease in bones, lungs, kidneys, the heart and the thyroid gland. Some imaging and treatment using radioactive compounds takes place outside radiology departments in nuclear medicine units, headed by physicians.

Interventional radiology. Appropriately trained radiologists and others, including cardiologists, may perform surgical procedures which would previously have required general anaesthesia and an inpatient episode. These procedures include the dilatation of strictures in blood vessels and the bile ducts, insertion of stents or drainage catheters into the gastrointestinal and renal tracts, the obtaining of pathological specimens by biopsy and drainage of collections of body fluids and abscesses.

A national clinical lead

In February 2005, Erika Denton was appointed as the national clinical lead for diagnostic imaging. She is supporting the NHS in addressing workforce, technology and service changes needed to transform diagnostic services in order to meet the 18-week target from GP referral to treatment. She has joined three colleagues on the national diagnostics leadership group.

Current developments

In 2004, the Department of Health arranged a five-year deal for the provision of mobile MRI scanners and qualified staff from the independent sector. This is intended to cut waiting times across England by providing 120,000 more MRI scans a year from 12 mobile screening units, targeted at areas of greatest need. This constitutes a 15 per cent increase in NHS capacity.

Digital imaging and storage systems are presenting exciting possibilities for transmission of images within and without hospitals, with the benefit of fast access and remote working. Under the Department of Health's national programme for IT, picture archiving and communications systems (PACS) are being rolled out across the health service, making the concept of filmless hospitals achievable. Integration of PACS with hospital information systems facilitates electronic radiology practice.

In February 2005, a further £1bn procurement from the independent sector was announced. The scheme is intended to boost NHS capacity by providing quicker access to services such as MRI, CT and ultrasound scans. It is estimated that some two million extra procedures will be procured under this scheme. From November 2005, patients waiting longer than 20 weeks for MRI and CT scans were offered the choice of a scan at another hospital. The maximum wait for the majority of imaging scans, including MRI, CT, ultrasound or DEXA (dual-energy X-ray absorptiometry) scans, is expected to fall to 20 weeks.

In October 2005 the Department of Health announced £20m capital investment over two years from 2006/07 to build new positron emission tomography (PET)-CT scanning facilities for the diagnosis and staging of cancers. The scanners will be a mix of fixed site and mobile facilities. In 2005 there were seven fixed location scanners available to NHS patients mainly in the south east.

Management issues

The radiology department in a typical

district general hospital will process approximately 100,000 examinations annually. The workload is increasing at 5 per cent a year. This requires heavy expenditure on capital and revenue.

Demand can be contained by discouraging tests which do not contribute to the management of the patient. About 20 per cent of X-ray examinations have been found to be clinically unnecessary. These tests are expensive and hazardous. Unnecessary procedures can be reduced by offering guidance to referring doctors and monitoring compliance with such guidance, which purchasers should specify in contracts. The Royal College of Radiologists has produced guidelines which are regularly updated. At the least there should be vetting of high-cost and high volume procedures.

Service level agreements between departments can also serve to contain over-use of services. Finally, a system of internal trading by financial cross-charging between hospital directorates can be employed.

Staffing must be appropriate to workload in terms of numbers and skill mix. This will require a review of working patterns, including opening hours, out-of-hours systems, the proportions of part-time and support workers, and the extended roles of radiographers, sonographers and nurses. The costs of consumables can be contained by longer term contracts, which may also benefit equipment costs.

Departments need 10-year capital programmes, incorporating business case planning, which recognise the needs of users and purchasers. Partnerships with the private sector remain important for the provision of large capital schemes, and may involve aspects of service management. Directors and business managers will need to tread carefully in this area, and will benefit from shared experience and access to purchasing skills. Enthusiasm for income generation and innovative methods of service delivery will be needed.

Patient-centred delivery of services will develop further, leading to increasingly decentralised working in hospitals and in the community, facilitated by electronic transmission systems. This will create challenges for teams, but also opportunities to develop new roles and extended working.

Pharmacy services

Pharmacy services have an influence on many aspects of health service provision. Pharmacists are involved in all stages of the supply of medicines — from research in industry to dispensing and advising on the use of medicines in hospitals and the community.

Community pharmacy

In 2004 there were 12,120 community pharmacies and appliance contractors under contract to the NHS in the UK, 200 fewer than a decade earlier — that is one pharmacy for every 4,925 members of the population, employing about 22,500 pharmacists.

There has been a steady trend in recent years towards multiples, particularly with the major supermarkets opening pharmacies within their branches. The move to out-of-town shopping centres has also led to the closure of traditional high street pharmacies. While most pharmacies are still independent, the percentage in England and Wales belonging to chains of more than five rose to 54 per cent in 2004/05. A small proportion operate from NHS-owned primary care centres.

By law, all community pharmacy companies or individual pharmacies

Wellard's NHS Handbook 2006/07

must register their premises with the Royal Pharmaceutical Society of Great Britain (RPSGB) and, in the case of companies, appoint a superintendent pharmacist. All dispensing and sale of medicines in community pharmacies has to be supervised by a pharmacist. To dispense NHS prescriptions, the pharmacy must apply for a contract with the primary care trust.

Since 1987, pharmacy contracts have been controlled and applicants wishing to open premises have had to prove to the health authority/primary care trust that a new pharmacy is necessary or desirable. In January 2003 the Office of Fair Trading recommended that the regulations which controlled the distribution of pharmacies should be abolished but its proposal was rejected in Wales and Scotland and received a lukewarm reaction in England. Revised regulations came into force in England in April 2005.

Patients pay £6.50 per prescribed item, but 86 per cent of items are exempt from charges. Exemptions involve patients aged 60 and over, or under 16 (under 19 if still in full-time education), those suffering from certain long-term conditions, families receiving income support, pregnant women and nursing mothers. From April 2001 prescriptions written in Wales for patients under 25 years old have been free. Charges in Wales are being phased out and were being reduced to £3 from April 2006.

Remuneration and training

Pharmacists send monthly batches of dispensed prescriptions to the Prescription Pricing Authority for reimbursement. The pharmacist is paid the basic price of the drugs, with deductions made for discounts obtained from wholesalers, together with a profes-

sional fee and a container allowance. The Drug Tariff, compiled monthly by the Prescription Pricing Authority on behalf of the Department of Health, lists the drugs and appliances that pharmacists may dispense on the NHS and how much they will be reimbursed.

There are some 44,440 pharmacists registered with the RPSGB. They must first take a four-year pharmacy degree, complete one year's training in practice and then pass a further registration exam. The pharmacy course content has a broad science base, covering the chemistry of medicinal ingredients and how they are formulated into medicinal products, as well as their clinical use. As highly trained professionals, pharmacists have been an underutilised resource but there is a growing recognition that they can offer a major contribution to clinical and cost effectiveness in the NHS.

The government acknowledged this in a programme for pharmacy in England, launched in 2000 (*Pharmacy in the future — implementing the NHS Plan*). Similar initiatives have been introduced in Wales and Scotland.

The RPSGB sets professional standards under a code of ethics, and has disciplinary procedures in place should any pharmacist digress. The society also registers and inspects pharmacies under the Medicines Act 1968 and has enforcement responsibilities on the sale and supply of medicines.

The revised community pharmacy contract

Alongside the government's strategy for pharmacy is a revised contract for community pharmacists in England which was implemented from April 2005. The contract aims to improve the quality and range of services that community pharmacy offers to patients

New approaches to care — 7

and to support the integration of community pharmacy in the NHS. On top of the basic package of essential services, pharmacists have the option to offer additional services. Such services are commissioned by primary care organisations according to local needs. The specifications for these services, including the prices, are agreed nationally.

Payment to pharmacists are increasingly directed towards quality not dispensing volume, recognising that they need a fair return. The new arrangements need to preserve the position that every NHS prescription presented will be actioned promptly, competently and safely.

The contractual framework is set in the context of PCTs, who are responsible for planning local service provision to meet local needs and priorities within local development plans.

Similar plans have unfolded in Wales and Scotland.

Consultant pharmacists

Innovative posts are being created in the NHS for consultant pharmacists in both hospital-based services and primary care. A number of them are likely to be clinical specialist pharmacists, however they may be appointed in a number of areas of practice with posts structured around the four functions of:
• expert practice
• research, evaluation and service development
• education, mentoring and overview of practice
• professional leadership.

The Department of Health issued guidance in 2005 on developing consultant pharmacists and strategic health authorities are creating a system of approval of posts.

Structure of the new pharmacy contract

Services are categorised as follows:
• **essential.** These are dispensing, repeat dispensing, disposal of medication, promotion of healthy lifestyles, promotion of self care for patients with minor ailments and sign-posting for patients to other healthcare provision
• **advanced.** These require accreditation of the pharmacists concerned. Medicine use review is an example
• **enhanced.** Commissioned by the PCT, with actions and outcomes specified. Examples include: supervised administration schemes, supplementary prescribing, emergency hormonal contraception service, needle exchange, smoking cessation, minor ailment schemes, care home and intermediate care services and palliative care.

The electronic prescription service (EPS)

The electronic transfer of prescriptions between the prescriber, the dispensing pharmacy and the Prescription Pricing Authority is one of the main planks in the NHS programme for information technology. The first EPS pilot between a medical centre and pharmacy in Keighley, West Yorkshire, went live in February 2005. By the end of October 2005, 72 GP practices and six pharmacies were live on the system and some 70,000 prescriptions had been processed electronically. The aim is to make EPS available to all users by the end of 2007.

Medicines safety

In January 2004 a report on improving the safety of medication was published, written by Dr Jim Smith, the former chief pharmaceutical officer.

Building a safer NHS for patients — improving medication safety looks at the mistakes which arise in the prescribing, dispensing and administration of medicines and measures to minimise them. It provides guidance for health professionals and NHS organisations, drawing on experience and good practice within the NHS and worldwide.

With the developing work programme of the National Patient Safety Agency, and as part of the overall drive to improve quality and safety of care, the report's recommendations should help to make drug treatment safer for NHS patients.

The report explores the causes and frequency of medication errors, highlights drugs and clinical settings that carry particular risks, and identifies models of good practice to reduce risks.

Attention is often focused on the actions of individuals who are considered to be the cause of the error. But latent conditions within an organisation and triggering factors in clinical practice are important causes of error. Checks and error traps therefore need to built into all medication processes.

The direct cost of medication errors in NHS hospitals is estimated at £200–400m a year. To this must be added the unknown cost of errors in primary and community care, and also the indirect costs such as those arising from litigation. The potential savings from reducing serious medication errors are therefore substantial.

Medicines and value for money

The number of items dispensed, their net ingredient cost and the average number per head of population continues to increase. During 2003/04, pharmacies in England received 612m dispensing fees, an increase of 42.7 per cent from 1994/95. In Wales, pharmacies received 49m dispensing fees, an increase of 46.1 per cent from 1994/95. Across the UK each patient obtained an average of 13 prescriptions in 2003.

The net ingredient cost (cost of the drugs only, without discounts and fees) per prescription in the UK was £11.54 in 2004, compared to £11.33 in 2003. The proportion of prescriptions written for generic rather than branded medicines rose from 35 per cent to 79 per cent between 1985 and 2003.

Prescribing costs in general practice account for about 80 per cent of the overall NHS drugs bill (£8.556m in 2002 equivalent to an average of £145 per person). Medicines account for about 12.6 per cent of total NHS expenditure in 2002.

Successive governments have been looking for value for money in the supply and use of medicines in the NHS. The National Prescribing Centre was set up in 1996 as a centrally funded body to promote high quality, cost-effective

Number of community pharmacies and appliance contractors, 2004

England	9,759
Wales	703
Scotland	1,148
Northern Ireland	510
United Kingdom	**12,120**

Prescription items dispensed and total costs, 2003/04

England	639.5m	Total cost £7.6bn
Wales	51.3m	Total cost £550m
Scotland	71.4m	Total cost £933m
N Ireland	27.1m	Total cost £377m

New approaches to care — 7

prescribing. One of its activities is to publish the *MeReC Bulletin,* containing independent reviews of medicines, which is circulated to GPs and community pharmacists.

The centre works in conjunction with the National Institute for Health and Clinical Excellence (NICE). This acts as an appraisal body for new and existing treatments, including drugs, and disseminates advice on which treatments work best and those that are unsatisfactory.

A major source of independent information on drug therapy is the official *British National Formulary (BNF).* It details the actions, uses and side effects of medicines under different therapeutic categories.

Pharmacists are increasingly helping GPs to prescribe efficiently and cost-effectively by giving prescribing advice, developing local formularies and advising on prescription data. Some GPs have employed part-time pharmacists specifically to advise on their drugs budgets.

Pharmacists are also employed full-time by strategic health authorities and primary care trusts to advise on prescribing and make recommendations to GPs on the cost-effective use of medicines. The number of pharmacists working as prescribing advisers has grown tenfold.

In Wales, pharmacists play a significant part in the work of local health boards, and in Scotland, primary care requires pharmaceutical input at senior level to help manage capped drug budgets.

Community pharmacists have become more involved in medicines management, not just in supplying the medicines. They help to decide, jointly with the doctor, which medicines are best for individual patients and to monitor their progress.

Pharmacists' long-established role in giving advice to the public on over-the-counter medicines is another area in which the profession can make a major contribution to health services. The profession's promotion of pharmacies as the first port of call for minor ailments is being supported by governments wishing to encourage self-medication and decrease the burden on GP services. Pharmacists can detect serious illness at an early stage and refer patients to a doctor.

Changes in legislation in recent years have seen several medicines move from prescription only to pharmacy supply, enabling pharmacists to have more effective treatments at their disposal. In the NHS Plan the government has pledged to encourage medicines manufacturers to apply for non-prescription status for their products.

Pharmacy is also becoming more involved in health promotion. Pharmacists see people when they are fit, as well as when they are ill, so can give advice on staying healthy. Some offer smoking cessation programmes, cholesterol testing, blood pressure monitoring and diabetes screening. They may take part in needle and syringe exchange schemes to help prevent the spread of HIV.

Many of these extended roles are supported in the government's programme for pharmacy in the NHS.

The Department of Health report *Choosing health through pharmacy. A programme for pharmaceutical public health 2005–2015* sets out how the contribution of pharmacists to improving health might be maximised.

Standard coding

For the first time the NHS has developed a definitive dictionary of medicines and devices, known as dm+d, for

Wellard's NHS Handbook 2006/07

use across all sectors of healthcare delivery. It allows computer systems to exchange information about the specific medicines or devices used in the diagnosis and treatment of patients.

The dictionary provides a unique code for each product plus a text description and is integrated with SNOMED clinical terms, the standard clinical terminology for health information systems.

Repeat dispensing

A repeat dispensing scheme is being rolled out nationally in the context of the new contract for community pharmacists. The scheme makes it easier for patients with long-term conditions to obtain repeat prescriptions, relieving pressure on GP surgeries. In May 2003, 30 pathfinder sites started work and subsequently a further 40 sites were selected for a second wave.

The scheme involves the use of a master prescription, of up to a year's duration, and an associated batch of prescriptions used for dispensing and reimbursement.

Local pharmaceutical services

Following on from the development of personal medical services, some pharmacists have begun to work within a different employment framework in local pharmaceutical services (LPS). Pilot LPS schemes test new ways of contracting between community pharmacists and PCTs. In August 2002 the Department of Health approved a first wave of four LPS pilots and successive waves have been approved since.

Pharmacy input into
NHS Direct and NHS 24

Research indicates that 40 per cent of callers receive advice about medicines from NHS Direct nurses. Some 5 per cent of calls to NHS Direct and NHS 24

result in the caller being referred to a community pharmacist.

In England, Wales and Scotland pharmacists have been employed to advise the services on medicines and pharmacy issues. Guardian groups of pharmacists are responsible for the ongoing review of the clinical content of algorithms used in the NHS Direct and NHS 24 clinical assessment system.

Non-medical prescribing

The Health and Social Care Act 2001 allows supplementary and independent prescribing by nurses, pharmacists and other health professionals. Clauses in the Act enabled ministers to introduce a new type of prescriber, who are responsible for the continuing care of patients who have been clinically assessed by a doctor (supplementary prescribers). Suitably qualified pharmacists are also becoming independent prescribers in their own right.

Pharmacists might prescribe treatments that need regular monitoring and dose adjustment, such as anticoagulants. Or they might review patients on long-term medication and prescribe further supplies of prescription-only medicines as necessary. The Royal Pharmaceutical Society has set out what basic competencies and qualifications pharmacy prescribers should have.

Medicines matters is a guide produced by the Department of Health in March 2005 which describes the mechanisms for the prescribing, supply and administration of medicines to support the development of new roles or service redesign. It also outlines the continuing work on the non-medical prescribing programme and what it hopes to achieve.

In August 2000, legislation introduced patient group directions as an alternative method of prescribing.

Pharmacy in the NHS plan

The NHS Plan proposed a greater role for pharmacists in medicines management and prescribing.

The government wants pharmacists to spend more time on the clinical needs of individual patients, helping people to stay healthy, deal with minor illnesses and get the most out of their medicines. To do this, pharmacists need more support from technicians for routine dispensing work.

The proposals include:

- Supporting self-care. All NHS Direct sites should be able to refer callers to a pharmacy for advice on self-medication. There are more opportunities for pharmacists to become involved in health promotion, such as smoking cessation services. Pharmacists continue to play a major role in services for drug misusers, such as supervised consumption of methadone, which helps prevent overdose and keeps illicit supplies off the streets.
- Repeat dispensing schemes. Patients on long-term medication will be able to obtain their repeat supplies from a pharmacy without having to return to the doctor for a prescription.
- The government is investing £30m over three years to secure better use of medicines in the NHS. Much wastage and illness occurs because patients do not take their medicines correctly. Each primary care trust will have schemes in place enabling pharmacists to check if patients know how to take their medicine, if the dose is correct, if they are suffering adverse reactions and if the medicine is doing any

good. The Department of Health has set up a medicines management action team to promote such services. At the heart of this initiative is the concept of patient partnership in medicine taking, which aims to involve patients more in decision-making based on better knowledge of treatments.

- Electronic prescribing will be routine. GPs will send prescriptions electronically to pharmacies so the medicines will be ready by the time the patient arrives. Pharmacists will be connected to the Prescription Pricing Authority so pricing will take place automatically, without them having to send off bundles of prescriptions every month.
- The government is encouraging new agreements between the NHS, pharmacists and pharmacy owners. Local pharmaceutical services will be provided under locally tailored arrangements, free from the constraints of a national remuneration system. Many primary care trusts already contract locally for further services from community pharmacies, in addition to the basic dispensing services laid down in the national contract. For the first time, contracts are possible with individual pharmacists as well as pharmacy owners.

The programme for pharmacy in England is outlined in the document *Pharmacy in the future — implementing the NHS Plan.*

A Welsh pharmacy strategy, *Remedies for success: a strategy for pharmacy in Wales*, is also being implemented. In Scotland *The right*

Wellard's NHS Handbook 2006/07

medicine: a strategy for pharmaceutical care in Scotland was launched in February 2002 and patient care is being enhanced by making better use of pharmacists' expertise.

A vision for pharmacy

A vision for pharmacy in the new NHS, published in July 2003, builds on the programme for developing NHS pharmacy set out in *Pharmacy in the future.* It suggests that pharmacists could offer services traditionally only available at GP surgeries, including medication review and patient monitoring.

The document largely focuses on community pharmacy, but one chapter is devoted to hospital pharmacy.

Dr Jim Smith, former chief pharmaceutical officer for England, sets out what pharmacists should be able to offer in future. He describes 10 roles, to:
- provide convenient access to prescriptions and other medicines
- advise patients and other health professionals on the safe and effective use of medicines
- be a point of first contact with healthcare services for people in the community
- provide medicines management services, especially for people with enduring illness
- promote patient safety by preventing, detecting and reporting adverse drug reactions and medication errors
- contribute to seamless and safe

medicines management throughout the patient's journey
- support patients as partners in medicine taking
- prescribe medicines and monitor clinical outcomes
- be a public health resource and provide health promotion, improvement and harm reduction services
- promote value for money in the use of medicines to reduce wastage.

A wider role for pharmacists in public health is also proposed in the document. It says pharmacists are well placed to make an important contribution to improving public health and the wider promotion of health. It suggests areas such as smoking cessation, sexual health, reducing obesity and minimising health inequalities.

The report says the government would undertake discussions with the profession about independent prescribing by pharmacists.

The strategy also points to a potential role for the profession in using genetic tests to tailor medicines to individuals. It predicts that the range of medicines that pharmacies will be able to supply without a prescription will continue to increase.

Department of Health. *Pharmacy in the future — implementing the NHS Plan.* September 2000.

Department of Health. *A vision for pharmacy in the new NHS.* July 2003.

Named health professionals are able to supply medicines to specified groups of patients under strict protocols, without the need for individual prescriptions. The patient group directions are usually drawn up by a doctor and counter-signed by a pharmacist.

This method has been used by community pharmacists to supply free emergency contraception under stipulated conditions, for example, the woman must attend the pharmacy in

The Medicines and Healthcare Products Regulatory Agency

The Medicines and Healthcare Products Regulatory Agency (MHRA) was formed as an executive agency of the Department of Health in April 2003 from a merger of the Medicines Control Agency and the Medical Devices Agency. Its task is to protect the health of the public by ensuring that pharmaceutical and healthcare products and medical equipment are safe.

The main roles of the MHRA are to ensure that all medicines on the UK market meet appropriate standards of safety, quality and efficacy, and by working with users, manufacturers and legislators to ensure that medical devices meet appropriate standards of safety, quality and performance and that they comply with relevant directives of the European Union.

The MHRA works in partnership with the National Patient Safety Agency on, for instance, the direct system of electronic reporting of incidents from the health service.

Professor Sir Alasdair Breckenridge is the agency's chairman. The agency has a budget of £50m and a staff of some 700 people.

Medicines. The MHRA applies strict standards laid down by the Medicines Act 1968 and European Community legislation, but at the same time works to keep red tape to a minimum, so that treatments are licensed and made available to patients as quickly as possible. MHRA doctors, pharmacists and other scientists balance the benefits of medicines against any possible risks, before they are approved for use. All the research and test results for a medicine are examined in detail before a decision is made.

The MHRA seeks the advice of expert bodies such as the Commission on Human of Medicines. Only when the experts are satisfied that the medicine meets the standards of the legislation, is a marketing authorisation granted (previously a product licence). This is normally necessary before it can be prescribed or sold, and will stipulate the dosage, the format (tablets, creams and so on), the diseases to be treated by the medicine and the type of person for which it is suitable or unsuitable; for example, children.

There are three categories for the supply of medicines:
- **general sale list (GSL)** medicines are widely available for sale and use without the supervision of a pharmacist or doctor
- **pharmacy (P)** medicines can be obtained only from a pharmacy, where they are supplied under the supervision of a pharmacist, who may ask questions to ensure that if a medicine is necessary, the patient gets the best they need
- **prescription only medicines (POMs)** must be prescribed by a doctor, dentist or appropriately trained, other independent or supplementary prescriber. These medicines can be obtained from a pharmacy.

The MHRA monitors medicines while they are in use and keeps records of reported side effects. In a few cases, safety concerns may lead to a medicine being withdrawn.

The agency also has an inspectorate which is responsible for supervising and enforcing standards of pharmaceutical manufacture and wholesaling and of imported medicines. **Medical devices.** The term 'medical device' covers any product, other than a medicine, which is used in the healthcare environment for the diagnosis, prevention, monitoring or treatment of illness or disease. The definition encompasses a wide range of equipment; ranging from pacemakers to wheelchairs and from syringes to magnetic resonance imagers. The MHRA is responsible for regulating and advising on such devices for sale or use in the UK. The agency publishes device evaluation reports and guidance for both users and manufacturers as well as investigating device and equipment malfunction or misuse, issuing safety alerts where appropriate.

MHRA, Market Towers, 1 Nine Elms Lane, London SW8 5NQ. Tel: 020 7084 2000. www.mhra.gov.uk

The European Medicines Evaluation Agency

The European Medicines Evaluation Agency (EMEA) is situated in London and started work in January 1995. It handles licence applications for all biotechnology and high-technology medicines in Europe. Companies producing other medicines are able to apply either through a centralised licensing procedure via the EMEA, valid across the European Union, or through a decentralised procedure whereby authorisation granted in one member state can be recognised by others. The EMEA also has the roles of arbitrating in drug registration disputes between member states and of coordinating the monitoring of drugs in use.

EMEA, 7 Westferry Circus, Canary Wharf, London E14 4HB. Tel: 020 7418 8400. www.emea.eu.int

person and there must be no clinical reasons why she should not take the morning after pill.

Hospital pharmacy

Hospital pharmacy services aim to ensure the safe, effective and economic use of medicines. Many routine counting and pouring jobs in hospitals are done by technicians under pharmacist supervision, allowing pharmacists to develop their professional advisory roles. It is commonplace for clinical pharmacists to have an input into the choice of drug treatment as they accompany doctors and nurses on ward rounds.

Hospital pharmacists contribute significantly to cost-effectiveness by sitting on drug and therapeutics committees. These develop drug buying policies and formularies specifying which drugs should be used. The chief pharmacist usually has management responsibility for ensuring that prescribing complies with the formulary.

Dispensing services are available on all hospital sites where patients are cared for. Other more specialised services such as quality assurance, making up cytotoxic drugs and the supply of radiopharmaceuticals may be centralised. Pharmacists have also been instrumental in setting up comprehensive NHS drug information services.

Although the government, in its NHS Plan, wants hospital pharmacists to

New approaches to care — 7

extend their clinical role, there are concerns about staff shortages. The management structure in hospital pharmacy is determined by individual trusts. Pharmacy may be part of a clinical directorate or there may be a free-standing arrangement in which the pharmacy is a directorate in its own right.

The 2001 Audit Commission report *A*

spoonful of sugar. Medicines manage-ment in NHS hospitals* helped hospitals to identify how well they managed medicines, and where they needed to invest to match the levels of the best performers.

Medicines distribution

Community and hospital pharmacies obtain medicines mainly through wholesalers, rather than by direct buying from manufacturers.

The Medicines Act 1968 requires pharmaceutical wholesalers to possess a licence. In general they can supply only to registered community pharmacies, hospitals and primary care centres, plus UK-registered doctors, dentists and veterinary practitioners.

In hospitals, some direct buying takes place through NHS regional contracts or consortia arrangements between trusts, with deliveries from NHS and regional short-term stores.

The Prescription Pricing Authority

The principal functions of the Prescription Pricing Authority (PPA) are to calculate and make payments due to dispensing contractors in England for NHS prescriptions, and to provide information on prescrib-ing and dispensing on a monthly and quarterly basis to 27,000 general medical practitioners, strategic health authorities, primary care trusts and the Department of Health, through its PACT information services.

It also provides similar services for Jersey, Guernsey and the Isle of Man, as well as compiling the monthly issue of the *Drug tariff*. The PPA's other functions are to administer the NHS low income scheme and to detect prescription charge evasion, recovering unpaid charges and penalty charge payments from those who incorrectly claimed exemptions.

From its nine centres round England the PPA processes about 608m prescriptions a year, valued at about £6.6bn.

Under the Department of Health's review of arm's length bodies the PPA is due to become part of the NHS Business services Authority.

PPA, Bridge House, 152 Pilgrim Street, Newcastle upon Tyne NE1 6SN. Tel: 0191 232 5371. www.ppa.org.uk

Further information

Medicines, pharmacy and industry website. www.dh.gov.uk/mpi

Department of Health. *Review of prescribing, supply and administration of medicines. Final report* (Crown review). 1999.

Department of Health. *Building a safer NHS for patients. Improving medication safety.* January 2004.

Department of Health. *Making the best use of the pharmacy workforce — a consultation paper.* December 2004.

Department of Health. *Medicines matters: a guide to current mechanisms for the prescribing, supply and adminis-tration of medicines.* March 2005.

Department of Health. *Choosing health through pharmacy.* April 2005.

Ambulance services

Under the 1977 NHS Act, the Secretary of State for Health has responsibility for the provision of ambulance services to meet all reasonable requirements. Responsibility for the commissioning and provision of emergency and non-emergency patient transport services is delegated to health service commissioners and to ambulance service providers. Although there has been limited market testing, all emergency ambulance services continue to be provided by NHS ambulance trusts. Market testing of the non-emergency patient transport service has been much more widespread, but the majority of contracts have remained with NHS ambulance trusts.

There are 31 ambulance services in England, with single services each covering Wales, Northern Ireland and Scotland. Except in Scotland where the ambulance service is a special health board, all are NHS trusts or are an integral part of larger trusts.

Changes to ambulance services in England involving reducing the number of ambulance trusts from 31 to 11 were proposed in December 2005. The idea is to provide more investment for frontline services; savings in back room functions; greater capability to respond to major incidents, and more integrated services. The consultation process for the changes ended in March 2006.

Review of the ambulance service

In May 2004, Peter Bradley, chief executive of the London Ambulance Service, was appointed by the Department of Health to the part-time post of national advisor. At the same time he was invited to conduct a strategic review of services.

The findings of the review, *Taking healthcare to the patient*, were published in June 2005. The report sets out how ambulance services can be transformed from a service focusing on resuscitation, trauma and acute care towards becoming the mobile health resource for the NHS — taking healthcare to the patient in the community.

A number of changes are outlined:
• faster response times and revised targets
• better advice over the phone
• more care in the home — ambulance staff will be trained and equipped to carry out and interpret more diagnostic tests and undertake basic procedures in the home. They will also be able to refer patients to social services, directly admit patients to specialist units, and prescribe a wider range of medications
• more treatment at the scene — more patients with urgent, but not life-threatening, conditions will be treated at home rather than taken to hospital
• home visits for better health — routine assessments of patients with long-term conditions.

Assisting these changes is an increase in the number of emergency care practitioners. There are currently 630 working in England. So that resources can be used more efficiently Mr Bradley's review suggested the merger of ambulance trusts as described above.

Facts and figures

The number of category A (immediately life-threatening) emergency calls responded to within eight minutes rose by 10 per cent from 874,000 in 2003/04 to 965,000 in 2004/05. The total number of emergency calls rose by 5 per cent to 5.6m, and incidents attended rose by 6 per cent to 4.5m; 76.2 per cent of category A calls resulted in an emer-

New approaches to care — 7

gency response arriving at the scene of the incident within eight minutes (75.7 per cent in 2003/04).

In 2004/05 ambulance services in England undertook:

- 3.47m emergency journeys
- 0.85m urgent journeys
- 12.82m special/planned journeys.

The number of emergency journeys in 2004/05 was a 3.5 per cent increase over 2002/03, whereas the number of urgent journeys in 2004/05 decreased by 6.5 per cent compared to 2003/04.

Ambulance services in the UK:

- employ approximately 17,000 paramedics and technicians, 5,500 care assistants, and engaged over 5,000 voluntary drivers
- utilise 3,500 emergency and 3,000 non-emergency vehicles
- operate from over 900 ambulance stations
- work to over 100 emergency contracts and over 800 non-emergency contracts valued at a total of approximately £1bn.

Although the ambulance service remains firmly part of the NHS following a government initiative, active consideration is also being given to greater collaboration and co-operation with the other emergency services — that is, police and fire. A 1999 project piloted joint communications and control centres and other support facilities. Several ambulance services operate vehicles from joint ambulance/fire stations and many more use fire and police premises and facilities for the active standby of emergency ambulance vehicles.

Emergency and urgent services

The emergency ambulance service will provide the response to:

- emergency cases
- doctors' urgent admission requests

- requests for high dependency and urgent inter-hospital transfers
- major incidents.

Emergency cases are those arising from a 999 call, irrespective of source, or classified by a doctor as requiring an immediate response. *Urgent cases* are those where an ambulance is ordered by a doctor, dentist or midwife in order to admit a patient to hospital. This includes urgent inter-hospital transfers. The health professional ordering the transport must specify the time by which the patient should arrive at the hospital.

Patients with non-urgent conditions who dial 999 (category C) are not automatically sent an ambulance but can receive advice from NHS Direct, treatment at home or from other healthcare providers.

Performance standards

The NHS Plan emphasised the importance of improving the quality of care for patients. It highlighted a number of developments underway in the ambulance service. Ambulances in England have had to meet performance standards for responses to immediately life-threatening 999 calls.

Standards for ambulance services include:

- responding to 75 per cent of ambulance category A (life-threatening) calls within eight minutes or less
- responding to 95 per cent of category A calls within 14 minutes urban areas or 19 minutes rural areas
- responding to non-life threatening (category B) calls within 14 minutes in urban areas or 19 minutes in rural areas
- ensuring GP urgent calls arrive at hospital within 15 minutes of the time stipulated by the GP
- thrombolysis (clot busting drugs)

should be delivered within 60 minutes of the call for help. In 2004/05 55 per cent of patients were treated within this time.

Paramedics are allowed to administer a number of medicines, including a clot-busting thrombolytic, that had previously been restricted for use only by doctors. The use of new technology will improve care through telemetry links between ambulances and hospitals, the development of electronic patient records and the introduction of 12-lead ECGs within ambulances.

Research has shown the improvement to clinical outcomes of improved response times.

Prioritised despatch systems

Ambulance services use a system of telephone triage to determine the best response to a call. Two computer-based systems — Ambulance Medical Priority Despatch System and Criteria Based Despatch — have been developed to ensure that the triage is consistent and any risk of under-prioritisation is minimised. Both default to the highest priority if any information requested by the call taker is unavailable or ambiguous. The systems identify the urgency of response required for each call and classify them accordingly as category A, B or C.

Clinical effectiveness

Like many other healthcare providers, ambulance services are increasingly looking to use clinical audit tools for the assessment of the quality and effectiveness of the service, treatment and care they provide. Most ambulance services are involved individually or jointly at both local and national levels in clinical audit projects and many are collaborating with hospital clinicians

and commissioners. The Ambulance Service Association (ASA) and the joint royal colleges ambulance liaison committee have merged their clinical audit committees, and the ASA has a national clinical effectiveness programme manager to oversee this.

Training standards

Each frontline ambulance should be crewed by an ambulance paramedic and an ambulance technician. Both crew members will have completed various nationally recognised training courses at accredited training centres, and will have experience in the full range of accident and emergency services.

The highly trained ambulance crew assess the patient's needs and provide the most clinically appropriate package of care. Among other skills ambulance paramedics are able to intubate and defibrillate patients and to administer a range of life-saving drugs. Specific uses of drugs include pain relief, cardiac therapy, asthma therapy, diabetic stabilisation and fluid resuscitation.

Ambulance radio contract

In July 2005 the Department of Health signed a contract with the O_2 Airwave network to provide a new digital radio and communications system for NHS ambulance trusts in England. The contract is worth £390m over 13 years.

Replacing the existing analogue systems, the new system will deliver:
• improved communications with other emergency services
• better coverage for hand-held radios and in rural areas
• upgraded control room equipment, providing integrated dispatch systems.

Ambulance trusts will start taking delivery of the systems from mid-

2006, with full roll out planned for the end of 2008.

Air ambulances

Increasingly, helicopters are being used by ambulance services across the UK for air ambulance applications. Helicopter ambulances are deployed primarily for life-threatening cases and/or where accessibility by road is difficult or for long-distance hospital transfers for critically ill patients.

Non-emergency patient transport

Commissioners are required to contract the provision of non-emergency patient transport services for those patients for whom they are responsible and *who have a medical need for transport*. A non-emergency patient is one who, while requiring treatment provided by or through the NHS and which may or may not be of a specialist nature, does not require immediate or urgent ambulance transport.

The *medical need* for non-emergency transport must be determined by a doctor, dentist or midwife and will depend on the clinical condition of the individual and take account of social factors such as the availability of private or public transport and the distance to be travelled. The underlying rule is that each patient should be able to reach hospital in a reasonable time, in comfort and without detriment to their medical condition.

Non-NHS patients

Most NHS ambulance services will, subject to payment of appropriate charges, carry non-NHS patients. There is no charge for the provision of an emergency ambulance response. A patient initially carried as an NHS emergency case will only become liable for the cost of transport if the patient, or a person acting for that patient, opts for non-NHS treatment and gives a written undertaking to pay charges.

Further information

Department of Health. *Taking healthcare to the patient. Transforming NHS ambulance services.* June 2005.

Department of Health. *Configuration of NHS ambulance trusts in England.* Consultation document. December 2005.

Ambulances website. www.dh.gov.uk/PolicyAndGuidance/OrganisationPolicy/EmergencyCare/ModernisingEmergencyCare/ModernisingEmergencyCareArticle

The management of long-term conditions

In March 2004 former Health Secretary John Reid announced plans for a new deal in England for people suffering from long-term conditions like asthma and diabetes. A programme was launched to establish case-management demonstration sites within each of the strategic health authorities.

In the UK, there are some 17.5m people living with long-term conditions like diabetes and asthma. This often limits their ability to cope with day-to-day activities. For those patients with more than one condition, discomfort and stress is an everyday reality. For the most vulnerable, a lack of coordinated, personalised care can lead to a signifi-cant deterioration in health and often avoidable emergency hospital admis-sions. People with long-term conditions account for up to 80 per cent of

GP consultations — around 180m visits a year.

Chronic disease management schemes in the US have cut hospital admissions among the target group of patients by up to a half. These approaches were tested by the NHS. Specialist teams across the country provided advice, care and treatment for chronic disease — often cutting out the need for visits to GPs and hospitals.

The demonstrator sites introduced active management of high risk patients. They also provided coordinated patient centred care within a whole systems approach to keep patients with the greatest burden of illness healthy for longer.

The sites aimed to:
• develop data that enabled them to identify their target populations
• maintain health and promote wellbeing
• detect early changes in condition and prevent unnecessary admissions
• when admissions did occur, facilitate safe, early discharge.

The results of a pilot of active management of conditions at Castlefields Health Centre showed a 15 per cent reduction in admissions for older people and the average length of stay fell by 31 per cent, from 6.2 days to 4.3 days.

This success is mirrored in the US. An evaluation of the Evercare model of case-management for elderly patients found a 50 per cent reduction in unplanned admissions, without detriment to health. There was a significant reduction in the use of medication, with benefits to health and a 97 per cent family and carer satisfaction rate and high physician satisfaction.

Similarly, US provider Kaiser Permanente has, for example, an average length of stay of just four days for patients recovering from hip replacement surgery. This is in part due to its management of long-term conditions, facilitated by greater integration between generalist and specialist care.

The NHS improvement plan identified that 5 per cent of NHS patients who stay in hospital account for 42 per cent of hospital stays, and, eight of the top 11 causes of hospital admissions are long-term conditions.

The public service agreement (PSA) target for improving outcomes for people with long-term conditions involves offering a personalised care plan for vulnerable people most at risk, and reducing emergency bed days by 5 per cent by 2008. Linked to this is the older people's PSA target to increase the number of people over 65 supported to live at home by 1 per cent a year in 2007 and 2008.

In January 2005, the Department issued *Supporting people with long-term conditions* — an NHS and social care model to support local initiatives. The aim is to move away from reactive care based in hospitals, towards a systematic, patient-centred approach. Health and social care communities are being encouraged to adopt case management approaches as a means of ensuring these patients get joined-up health and social care.

Care needs to be rooted in primary care settings and underpinned by improved communications and partnerships across the whole local health economy.

The NHS and social care model reflects the learning from USA models such as Evercare and Kaiser Permanente, however, the values and structures of the NHS are different.

Along with the aim of treating patients sooner, nearer to their home,

New approaches to care — 7

the NHS and social care model seeks:
• early detection
• good control to minimise the effects of disease and reduce complications
• more effective medicines management
• reduction in the number of crises
• promoting independence, empowering patients and allowing them to take control of the lives
• prolonging and extending the quality of life.

The model is being implemented nationally by identifying all long-term conditions patients in a community and stratifying patients to match care to different needs of patients:

• **level 3: case management** — identify the most vulnerable people, those with highly complex multiple long-term conditions, and use a case management approach, to anticipate, coordinate and join up health and social care
• **level 2: disease-specific care management** — this involves providing people who have a complex single need or multiple conditions with responsive, specialist services using multidisciplinary teams and disease-specific protocols and pathways, such as the national service frameworks and the quality and outcomes framework
• **level 1: supported self care** — collaboratively help individuals and their carers to develop the knowledge, skills and confidence to care for themselves and their condition effectively.

Community matrons

The NHS is appointing 3,000 community matrons by March 2007 to spearhead the case management drive. The community matrons and other case managers are expected to have the authority to secure services for patients

at the time needed and to order investigations, make referrals and arrange admissions on behalf of patients.

The matrons are likely to have caseloads of around 50–80 patients with the most complex needs and who require clinical intervention as well as care coordination (level 3).

They will work across health and social care services and the voluntary sector, and develop a personalised care plan with the patient, carers and relatives. There will be more pooling of budgets.

District nurses are the largest group from which community matrons are being drawn, and they are expected to be independent and supplementary prescribers.

Good care management of the level 2 patients involves identifying their needs early and responding promptly with the right support with tailored programmes for individual patients. The challenge for PCTs is to extend strategies for improvement disease management locally.

In most cases, these patients will managed by multidisciplinary teams based in primary and community care, with the support of specialist advice, including from liaison workers such as a diabetic nurse.

Patients needing disease management will be identified and proactive care will be provided using clinical standards and protocols.

Patients will be recalled to ensure they get the care they need using prompts and reminders.

Patients will be reviewed regularly to ensure they receive the best evidence-based care and are supported to manage their condition.

To facilitate self care, all PCTs are being asked to make available the expert patient programme locally by

2008 (www.expertpatients.nhs.uk). With training and support, this encourages individual patients to be experts in the management of their own conditions and thus improve outcomes.

Around a half of patients with a long-term condition do not take their medicines as prescribed. For patients to take real control of their conditions, they need fast and convenient access to medicines, involvement in decisions about those medicines, advice about how to take them and information on any side effects which they may suffer. Pharmacists have an increasing role as a source of advice for patients and carers.

Further information
Department of Health. *Supporting people with long-term conditions. An NHS and social care model to support local innovation and integration.* January 2005.

Department of Health. *Improving chronic disease management.* March 2004.

www.dh.gov.uk/SelfCare

Genetic services

Advances in genetic science are expected to have a major impact on healthcare and the organisation of health services. With this in mind, the government published a White Paper in June 2003 entitled *Our inheritance, our future — realising the potential of genetics in the NHS*. It makes the point that the NHS must ensure that it has the expertise to make the best use of advances and must be ready to explain clearly to patients the new healthcare choices these will bring.

The Human Genetics Commission gives advice about human genetics and the social and ethical issues involved. The White Paper was backed with £50m investment over three years.

Former Health Secretary John Reid commented: 'Increasing understanding of genetics will bring more accurate diagnosis, more personalised prediction of risk and more targeted and effective use of existing drugs. It will give new gene based drugs and therapies as well as prevention and treatment regimes tailored according to a person's individual genetic profile.

'Our vision is for the NHS to lead the world in taking maximum advantage of the safe, effective and ethical application of new genetic knowledge and technologies for all patients as soon as they become available.'

Some £8m of the investment is being spent on upgrading genetics laboratories to prepare them for the expansion in genetic testing. Other sums are for introducing genetics based healthcare into mainstream NHS services, pharmacogenetics research and gene therapy research on inherited disorders such as cystic fibrosis.

The NHS Genetics Education and Development Centre, based in Birmingham Women's Healthcare NHS Trust, is receiving £600,000 a year for an initial three years to educate NHS staff about genetics and the role it plays in modern healthcare. The centre should mean that education in genetics becomes an integral part of all professional training programmes, not only for undergraduates but also for existing staff.

It is predicted that advances in genetics will soon impact on all branches of medicine.

New approaches to care — 7

Drug misuse

Around four million people use at least one illicit drug each year and around one million use at least one of the most dangerous Class A drugs (such as ecstasy, heroin and cocaine). Some 250,000 problematic drug users in England and Wales cause considerable harm to themselves and others.

Drug misuse gives rise to between £10bn and £18bn a year in social and economic costs, 99 per cent of which is accounted for by problematic drug users. There are strong links between problematic drug use and crime.

The government published its 10-year strategy for tackling drug misuse *Tackling drugs to build a better Britain* in 1998. It has four main aims:

• young people — to help young people resist drug misuse in order to achieve their full potential in society
• communities — to protect communities from drug-related antisocial and criminal behaviour
• treatment — to enable people with drug problems to overcome them and live healthy and crime free lives
• availability — to stifle the availability of illegal drugs on the streets.

The national strategy was updated in December 2002 with a range of interventions that concentrate on the most dangerous drugs, the most damaged communities and the individuals whose addiction and chaotic lifestyles are most harmful, both to themselves and others. This was backed with financial resources.

Strategic health authorities and primary care trusts receive a funding stream for drug prevention in vulnerable groups. Pooling of budgets for young people's substance misuse services between different local agencies is being piloted.

Overall responsibility for the delivery of the strategy lies with Home Secretary supported by the drug strategy directorate within the Home Office. Delivery of the treatment target is overseen by the National Treatment Agency (NTA) for substance misuse, a special health authority established by the Health Secretary in 2001.

Local delivery of the drug strategy is coordinated by drugs action teams. These are chief officer-level local coordinating and planning bodies supported by the NTA and drug teams based in the government offices for the regions.

The Department of Health's commitments to the drug strategy are:

• the public service agreement (PSA) target to: increase the participation of problem drug users in drug treatment programmes by 100 per cent by 2008, and increase year on year in the proportion of users successfully sustaining or completing treatment programmes
• providing local services in support of the Home Office PSA target to: reduce the proportion of people under the age of 25 reporting the use of Class A drugs and reduce frequent use of any illicit drug among young people, especially by the most vulnerable young people
• delivering the NHS Plan targets to: reduce levels of drug related death by 20 per cent and implement a national alcohol strategy.

The overall purpose of the National Treatment Agency is to:

• double the number of of people in effective, well-managed treatment from 100,000 in 1998 to 200,000 in 2008
• increase the proportion of people who successfully complete or, if

Wellard's NHS Handbook 2006/07

appropriate, continue treatment.

Parallel structures have been established with the Scottish Executive, the Welsh Assembly and in Northern Ireland.

Models of care sets out a national framework for the commissioning of an integrated drug treatment system for adult drug misusers in England. Published by the NTA and the Department of Health, it has similar status to a national service framework. The overriding concept behind *Models of care* is that drug action teams should seek to develop an integrated drug treatment system in their area, not just a series of separate services.

The national drug treatment monitoring system, introduced in April 2001, collects data on drug misusers presenting for treatment and those in treatment.

Further information

National Treatment Agency for Substance Misuse, 8th Floor, Hercules House, Hercules Road, London SE1 7DU. www.nta.nhs.uk

Department of Health substance misuse website. www.dh.gov.uk/ PolicyAndGuidance/ HealthAndSocialCareTopics/ SubstanceMisuse

The national Frank helpline (0800 776600) provides facts on drugs and refers callers to treatment and support organisations. www.talktofrank.com

Government website on the drugs strategy. www.drugs.gov.uk

Northern Ireland Assembly's website on drugs and drug strategy. www.healthpromotionagency.org.uk/ Work/Drugs/menu.htm

Sexual health

The Department of Health published the first national strategy on sexual health and HIV in July 2001, backed by investment to support a range of initiatives. The strategy aims to prevent the spread of sexually transmitted infections (STIs) and HIV and improve care and treatment for those who need it. It also signalled a national information campaign to promote safe sex and prevent STIs and HIV.

In recent years there have been significant increases in the prevalence of STIs, notably chlamydia, especially among young people. The Health Protection Agency records:

- an overall rise in the number of new diagnoses seen in genitourinary medicine clinics of 2 per cent in 2004 compared to 2003 (from 735,343 to 753,075)
- chlamydia increased by 8 per cent (from 95,879 in 2003 to 104,155 in 2004)
- syphilis increased by 37 per cent (from 1,641 in 2003 to 2,254 in 2004)
- genital warts increased by 4 per cent (from 76,457 in 2003 to 79,678 in 2004)
- gonorrhoea decreased by 10 per cent (from 24,915 in 2003 to 22,335 in 2004)
- genital herpes decreased by 1 per cent (from 19,180 in 2003 to 18,991 in 2004).

HIV/AIDS remains a threat to every generation of young adults and the wider population but disproportionately affects gay men and ethnic minority communities. At the end of 2004 an estimated 58,300 adults aged over 15 were living with HIV in the UK, 34 per cent of whom were unaware of their infection.

New approaches to care — 7

Elements of the national strategy include:
- targets to reduce the numbers of newly acquired HIV and gonorrhoea infections
- targeted screening for chlamydia
- a model for sexual health services that can be delivered by PCTs
- routine testing offered in sexual health clinics
- one-stop sexual health services
- a drive to reduce unintended pregnancy rates.

In March 2003 membership was announced of the independent advisory group which advises on implementation of the strategy.

Chlamydia. Genital *Chlamydia trachomatis* is the commonest STI in England, Wales and Northern Ireland, with 89,431 diagnoses in genitourinary medicine clinics in 2003. Highest rates are seen in young people, especially men and women under 24 years. Genital chlamydial infection is an important reproductive health problem, because 10–30 per cent of untreated infected women develop pelvic inflammatory disease (PID). A significant proportion of cases, particularly among women, are asymptomatic and so, are liable to remain undetected, putting women at risk of developing PID. Screening for genital chlamydia infection may reduce PID and ectopic pregnancy.

The phased implementation of the national chlamydia screening programme began in September 2002. The programme should cover the whole of England by March 2007, and in 2005 was well ahead in achieving the target. In November 2005 free chlamydia screening in Boots high street pharmacies across London became available as part of the Department of Health's initiative. Scotland, Wales, and North-

ern Ireland are also introducing chlamydia screening.

Teenage pregnancy. The government's teenage pregnancy strategy was launched in 1999 and has two goals:
- to halve the under-18 conception rate and establish a firm downward trend in the under-16 conception rate by 2010
- to increases the proportion of teenage parents in education, training and employment to reduce their long term risk of social exclusion.

A multi-faceted approach has been adopted. This includes helping young people resist pressure to have sex early through the development of easily accessible advice services and support for parents in talking to their children about sex and relationship issues.

Data for 2002 shows a reduction since 1998 in England's under 18 conception rate of 8.6 per cent. Data for 2001 shows the under 16 conception rate has fallen by 11.2 per cent since 1998.

The teenage pregnancy unit, located within the Department for Education and Skills, works across government departments to encourage a reduction in rates. Local authorities employ teenage pregnancy coordinators who work with the relevant local agencies, including primary care trusts.

Modernising services. A £300m programme over three years, to modernise and transform sexual health services in England, was announced in November 2004. The funding includes a £50m advertising campaign designed to tackle the rise in sexually transmitted infections. Some £130m is going to modernise genitourinary medicine clinics and £40m to upgrading preventive work such as contraceptive services.

Further information
Department of Health sexual health

website. www.dh.gov.uk/
PolicyAndGuidance/
HealthAndSocialCareTopics/
SexualHealth

Teenage pregnancy unit's website.
www.dfes.gov.uk/teenagepregnancy

Department of Health. *The national
strategy for sexual health and HIV.*
July 2001.

Department of Health. *The national
strategy for sexual health and HIV.
Implementation action plan.* June 2002.

Department of Health. *Effective
commissioning of sexual health and HIV
services: A sexual health and HIV
commissioning toolkit for primary care
trusts and local authorities.* June 2003.

Department of Health. *Screening for
infectious diseases in pregnancy:
standards to support the UK antenatal
screening programme.* August 2003.

Department of Health. *Recommended
standards for sexual health services.*
March 2005.

Transplant services

NHS transplant services started in the
UK in the 1960s, with kidney grafting.
Heart, liver, lung, pancreas, small bowel,
cornea, heart valve and bone transplants are now routine and skin is used
to treat severe burns. Well over one
million people worldwide have ben-
efited from a transplant.

Transplant is the primary treatment
for patients with major organ failure,
but is reliant on donor organs being
available and on potential donors being
identified. The success of transplant
surgery has led to increased waiting lists
as more patients are considered suitable
candidates, while at the same time the
number of organs available each year
has fallen as deaths from road traffic
accidents and from strokes decrease and
the techniques for managing critically ill
patients improve. Usually, people are
suitable as organ donors only if they die
from sudden brain injury yet are
receiving mechanical ventilation in an
intensive care unit. Only 1 per cent of
people die in these circumstances.

Many factors are taken into account
when allocating organs, such as blood
group compatibility, size, clinical
urgency and, in the case of kidneys,
donor and recipient tissue types. Once
the most suitable patients, and their
location, are identified, medical staff at
transplant units are alerted and asked
to confirm acceptance of the organ.

Around 2,800 transplant operations
and over 2,000 cornea transplants are
carried out each year in the UK and
Republic of Ireland, but at any one time
there are some 8,000 people in the UK
waiting for transplant.

Advances in surgical techniques and
better drugs mean that a year after
surgery 93 per cent of kidneys in living
donor transplants, 88 per cent of
kidneys from people who have died, 87
per cent of organs in liver transplants
and 85 per cent of organs in heart
transplants are still functioning well.

About 400 people die every year in
the UK while waiting for a kidney, lung,
heart or liver transplant and many more
will die before they even get on to the
transplant list.

In 2004/05, 2,375 people had
their sight restored through
corneal transplants.

Transplant framework for England
*Saving lives, valuing donors — a
transplant framework for England,*
published in 2003, sets out aims for

New approaches to care — 7

organ and tissue transplantation over ten years. It describes good practice based on national and international evidence which the government believes the NHS and society can use together to save lives and maximise the benefits of organ and tissue transplantation

It aims to encourage the NHS, commercial, voluntary organisations and the public to play their part in:

• ensuring at least 16m people are registered on the organ donor register by 2010
• developing a transplant service that respects the dignity of donors and is sensitive to the needs of donor families and friends and transplant recipients
• optimising the number of potential organ and tissue donors and the number of high quality, safe organs and tissues for transplantation
• increasing transplant rates to save lives and improve the quality of lives saved.

NHS Blood and Transplant

Following the results of the government's arm's length body review, NHS Blood and Transplant (NHSBT) was established in October 2005, combining the roles of UK Transplant and the National Blood Authority. NHSBT is statutorily responsible for providing a range of essential health services, including blood and tissue related services across England and transplant related services across the whole of the UK.

It is also responsible for commissioning and conducting research and development relating to some of its work. It is engaged in implementing relevant EU statutory frameworks and guidance and in broader international developments. NHSBT also provides expert advice to other NHS organisations and the Department of Health.

NHSBT provides a 24-hour support service for the matching, allocation and distribution of donor organs for transplant in the UK and Republic of Ireland. It is also responsible for maintaining records of all patients awaiting organ transplant.

It also:

• maintains and analyses the national database of transplant information to provide activity and outcome audit and to inform clinical practice
• monitors transplant and donor activity and the use of transplant facilities nationwide
• provide a communications focus and network for the transplant community in the UK, Republic of Ireland and abroad.

NHSBT's facilities are also used by the UK health departments to:

• maintain the NHS Organ Donor Register, a computerised database for recording the wishes, regarding organ donation, of members of the public (currently over 12.4m)
• maintain the Human Organ Transplants Act Register
• support the Cornea Transplant Service Eye Banks in Bristol and Manchester.

The government undertakes organ donation publicity campaigns to maintain and raise public approval of organ and tissue donation and attract new potential donors. People are able to join the organ donor register through their GPs or through the Driver Vehicle Licensing Agency. Some retailers, credit card companies and financial institutions also actively promote organ donation to their customers.

The NHS Organ Donor website — www.nhs.uk/organdonor — provides facts and figures relating to organ donation.

The Human Tissue Authority

The Human Tissue Authority (HTA) was established on 1 April 2005 to oversee the implementation of the Human Tissue Act from 1 April 2006. This is to ensure that consent is obtained for the removal and use of human tissue and organs for research and other purposes. The HTA is a non-departmental public body covering England, Wales and Northern Ireland. It is chaired by Baroness Hayman.

NHS Blood and Transplant.
www.nhsbt.nhs.uk

NHS organ donor line: 0845 6060400

Department of Health. *Saving lives, valuing donors — a transplant framework for England*. July 2003.

Blood transfusion services

Following the results of the government's arm's length body review, NHS Blood and Transplant (NHSBT) was established in October 2005, combining the roles of UK Transplant and the National Blood Authority. NHSBT is statutorily responsible for providing a range of essential health services, including blood and tissue related services across England and transplant related services across the whole of the UK. The organisation's first chairman is Bill Fullagar and its chief executive Martin Gorham.

It is also responsible for commissioning and conducting research and development relating to some of its work. It is actively engaged in implementing relevant EU statutory frame-

works and guidance and involved in broader international developments. NHSBT also provides expert advice to other NHS organisations, the Department of Health and to ministers; and appropriate advice and support to health services in other countries.

Prior to the establishment of NHSBT, the National Blood Authority (NBA) managed blood services and the regional blood centres in England and north Wales. Their core purpose was: 'To save and improve lives by meeting patients' needs for blood products, tissues and related services.'

The objectives continue to be to:
• provide sufficient blood, blood products, tissues and related services to current quality standards
• explore opportunities for continuous improvements in efficiency and quality
• develop safer and more effective products and services to new, improved quality standards
• promote the appropriate and efficacious use of blood, blood products, tissues and services
• modernise donor recruitment, donor session and donor retention processes
• recruit, develop and retain an appropriately skilled, educated and motivated workforce.

There is a guarantee to deliver blood, blood components, blood products and tissues from the 15 blood centres to anywhere in England and north Wales.

Blood collection

The National Blood Service is entirely dependent on voluntary donors. Some 1.3m such donors contribute blood donations each year.

Efforts are made continually to recruit more donors from all walks of life. TV advertising has been used

New approaches to care — 7

successfully to boost recruitment. A national call centre has also been set up to provide a 24-hour helpline for donors (08457 711 711). However, retaining existing donors and encouraging them to keep their appointments can be more important.

In collection sessions, donors are asked a series of questions about their health and a simple test is performed to ensure that they are not suffering from anaemia.

At the blood centre the blood group of a donation is determined and other tests are designed to ensure the safety of blood with respect to the transmission of infectious agents.

Some blood centres are also able to collect platelets using automated machines which return the red cells to the donor's circulation. This procedure can be carried out more frequently than whole blood collection.

Funding

Hospitals reimburse the blood centres according to the services and products they use. There is a national price list for blood components. The service agreements involved encourage the National Blood Service to maintain high standards of quality and supply and to adopt cost effective practices.

Modern transfusion therapy

Almost all blood is separated into its main components and this enables patients to be supplied with just the product(s) they require.

Cellular components of blood (red cells and platelets) can be separated out as well as the plasma in which they are suspended. Whole blood is used only rarely, usually in the treatment of massive haemorrhage.

Bio Products Laboratory (BPL) uses plasma (imported from the USA) for fractionation into purified plasma products; notably, these are the coagulation factors VIII and IX used in haemophilia A and B, albumin products required for much support therapy, and immunoglobulins. Synthetic clotting factors are being used for haemophiliacs to replace those from donated blood plasma.

Blood centres also perform specialist services, such as tissue typing for organ and bone marrow transplantation and antenatal serological tests.

NHS Blood and Transplant.
www.nhsbt.nhs.uk

Blood website. www.dh.gov.uk/
PolicyAndGuidance/
HealthAndSocialCareTopics/BloodSafety/
fs/en

To drive up standards in the health service, the Department of Health introduced a national performance assessment framework (PAF). The framework was designed comprehensively to measure and encourage the improvement of performance, efficiency and patient care.

Health authority indicators covered action to be taken in six areas:
• health improvement
• fair access to services
• effective delivery of appropriate healthcare
• efficiency
• patient and carers' experience of healthcare
• health outcome.

NHS trust indicators covered action to be taken in four areas:
• clinical effectiveness and outcomes
• efficiency
• patient and carers experience of healthcare
• capacity and capability.

There were also three interface indicators, common to both NHS and personal social services frameworks, which supported joint performance assessment by the NHS and social services.

Healthcare commissioners and providers have used the indicators to assess local services and ensure that they meet set standards. They are not direct measures of quality, but highlight areas where action or investigation may be required. Indicators are used in drawing up local delivery plans.

Targets for progress against these areas have been built into the accountability arrangements that run through all aspects of the way the NHS is managed. Use of the framework from 2001 led to the issuing of star ratings for acute NHS trusts. Highest scoring hospitals were awarded three stars while the lowest no stars. The rating carried funding implications and affected the degree of autonomy a trust had. Managers of under-performing hospitals were given a deadline to improve performance.

From 2002, the assessment applied to all NHS organisations and, from July 2002, performance ratings and indicators were published together (www.dh.gov.uk).

From 2003, the Commission for Health Improvement took over the DH's performance assessment role, and in April 2004 this role was handed to the the successor body the Healthcare Commission, which had plans to change the star ratings system.

A new set of standards — fewer in number and with a strong emphasis on the quality of patient care — were introduced from April 2005.

Standards for better health covers every aspect of NHS work and is divided into two categories. Firstly a set of core standards sets the level of quality of care which every patient should expect, wherever they are treated in the NHS.

For example:
• patients must be able to access emergency care promptly
• patients must be provided with information on the care and treatment they receive, and know what to expect during and after treatment
• measures must be put in place to improve patient safety by, for example, minimising the risk of infection and making sure medicines are handled safely
• hospitals and surgeries should be safe and secure, and meet national levels of cleanliness
• healthcare organisations must have disease prevention and health promotion programmes in place.

Secondly, the core standards are supported by developmental standards which set out what the NHS should aspire to deliver for patients. For example, the NHS's role in educating patients in order to manage their own long-term conditions or by devising action plans to tackle health inequalities between different communities.

The document sets out 24 core standards and 10 developmental standards covering seven key areas: safety, clinical cost effectiveness, governance, patient focus, accessible and responsive care, healthcare environment and amenities and public health.

Further information

Department of Health. *Standards for better health*. March 2005.

Department of Health. *National standards, local action: health and social care standards and planning framework 2005/06–2007/08*. July 2004.

Healthcare Commission. *Assessment for improvement. The annual health check*. March 2005.

Performance assessment in the NHS and social care
www.dh.gov.uk/PolicyAndGuidance/Performance

Health Care Standards Unit.
www.hcsu.org.uk

The Healthcare Commission

The Healthcare Commission (legal name: the Commission for Healthcare Audit and Inspection) is the independent inspection body for the NHS and private and voluntary healthcare. It was launched in April 2004 under the Health and Social Care (Community Health and Standards) Act 2003 and succeeded the Commission for Health Improvement.

The Healthcare Commission has brought together:
• the work of Commission for Health Improvement (CHI)
• the health value for money work of the Audit Commission
• the private healthcare role of the National Care Standards Commission.

The functions of the Mental Health Act Commission are also expected to be integrated with those of the commission, subject to legislative changes.

The commission also has a range of new responsibilities and activities including assessing the arrangements in place to promote public health and an independent stage of the NHS complaints procedure. In this work it has taken over the role of NHS trust convenors, whose task had been to determine whether an independent review of a complaint was necessary.

The commission promotes improvement in the quality of healthcare in England and Wales. In England only this includes regulation of the independent healthcare sector. The commission undertakes national improvement reviews in both England and Wales and is developing a distinctive Welsh programme. The Healthcare Inspectorate Wales is responsible for local inspection and investigation of Welsh NHS bodies. The independent healthcare sector in Wales is regulated by the Care Standards Inspectorate for Wales.

The commission is independent of the NHS and government and reports annually direct to Parliament on the state of healthcare in England and Wales. It is designed to offer an independent guarantee that systems to monitor, assure and improve clinical quality are in place in hospitals, primary care and community services. Its aims are to reduce variations in clinical quality across the country and rapidly to eliminate malpractice.

The commission's functions can be summarised as:

- assessing the performance of NHS organisations by reference to standards published by government
- seeking to promote improvements in the provision of healthcare
- identification of where, and how well, public resources are used to provide healthcare
- publishing annual ratings of all NHS organisations in England and an annual report to Parliament on the state of healthcare
- working with the Commission for Social Care Inspection to ensure integration of healthcare and social care inspection (by 2008 both commissions are expected to merge into one body)
- carrying out independent reviews of complaints about NHS services in England
- acting as the leading inspectorate in relation to healthcare — coordinating the activities of other bodies involved in inspection
- investigation of serious failures in health services
- reporting to the Health Secretary any serious concerns about the quality of public services or how they are run

The commission is chaired by Professor Sir Ian Kennedy and there are 13 other commissioners. Its chief executive is Anna Walker.

In June 2004, the commission published an agreement between the main healthcare inspection, review and audit bodies in England, aimed at reducing the burden of inspection on frontline healthcare staff. The concordat commits each organisation to a set of principles which aim to support improvement in health services minimising disruption and duplication, ensure that information is shared appropriately and encourage joint inspections.

The commission unveiled in April 2005 — the annual health check — the new system for assessing public and private healthcare in England. It aims to reduce regulatory burdens while giving the public a more accurate picture of performance. It offers patient and public representatives a formal role in judging the quality of services, and instead of routinely subjecting all NHS trusts to week-long visits every three years, it targets such inspections where there is evidence of a problem. It aims to keep the scale of inspections proportionate to the issue of concern.

The commission expects to make more intelligent use of the wide range of information that is available to it on NHS organisations and to use it for continuous surveillance. It has a statutory duty to take account of the Department of Health's *Standards for better health* in its assessments of performance.

The star rating system is ending, but health service providers are required to publish annual declarations of their performance and introduce improvement reviews, which focus on priority areas.

The commission says: 'We aim to paint a richer picture than ever before of what is happening in healthcare — putting the onus on healthcare organisations to make sure that they are meeting the expected standards of performance, while also checking their assessments with others in the local community'.

The commission checks that declarations made by trusts are accurate by:
- obtaining corroboration from patient and public involvement forums,

strategic health authorities and local councils
- checking declarations against data collected by other regulators and other publicly available information
- compiling independent surveys of patients and staff, as well as carrying out random and unannounced spot checks
- using intelligence gathered by the commission when handling NHS complaints and investigations into serious failures in service.

Each September, the commission says to what extent organisations are meeting the standards, as well as existing and new government targets. It gives an annual performance rating on a four-point scale, ranging from excellent to weak.

As part of its work on developmental standards, the commission is carrying out improvement reviews on priority areas of healthcare. Initially, these cover substance misuse, tobacco control and services for children in hospital services. The results of these reviews will be used to drive up performance in organisations that are doing less well, typically the bottom 10 per cent. They will also show how patients fare when moving between health and social care organisations. In 2006 reviews will also be undertaken on heart failure and adult mental health services, and reviews are being developed on chronic obstructive pulmonary disease and diabetes.

The system has been introduced in two stages. The first stage was in October 2005 when NHS trusts published draft declarations. In April 2006, trusts published a final declaration. The commission will publish its first assessments of performance in September 2006.

Healthcare Commission. *Assessment for improvement. The annual health check.* April 2005.

Healthcare Commission. *State of healthcare 2005.* July 2005.

Healthcare Commission. www.healthcarecommission.org.uk

Commission for Social Care Inspection www.csci.org.uk

Audit Commission www.audit-commission.gov.uk

Healthcare Inspectorate Wales. www.hiw.wales.gov.uk

Care Standards Inspectorate for Wales. www.csiw.wales.gov.uk

The national patient and user survey

Another mechanism for monitoring standards is patient and user surveys. The NHS Plan requires each NHS trust in England annually to obtain feedback from patients about their experiences of care.

The NHS patient survey programme covers all types of trust. In addition, other surveys focus on implementation of the national service frameworks.

The survey results are used in the annual performance indicators published by the Healthcare Commission. In February 2005 the commission published the findings from its 2004 outpatients and A&E patient surveys. They revealed high levels of satisfaction, with more than eight of ten people feeling positive about the care they had received. All 169 acute trusts with outpatient facilities and all 153 trusts with an A&E department participated. The trusts randomly selected 850 patients from those who attended the hospitals between June and August 2004. These patients received questionnaires by post, responses to which made up the findings.

September 2005 saw the publication of the primary care trust survey of patients. Responses were received from some 117,000 patients. With regard to the quality of care that patients receive from GPs, the survey found:

- 76 per cent reported definitely having confidence and trust in the doctor whom they saw
- 69 per cent said that they were involved as much as they wanted to be in decisions about their treatment.

On the other hand:

- 12 per cent said they were unable to see a GP within two working days
- 30 per cent said that they could not book an appointment three or more working days in advance.

In 2006 the Healthcare Commission plans for surveys to be conducted on maternity services and inpatient hospital care.

This work is supplemented by many other local surveys by NHS organisations.

The advice centre for the NHS patient survey programme is funded by the Healthcare Commission and is based at the charity Picker Institute Europe.

In April 2005, the Picker Institute drew together the views of nearly one million people who have participated in the national patient survey programme. *Is the NHS getting better or worse?* revealed that patients want more information, more involvement in decisions about their care, more help when transferring from hospital to home, and easier access to their GPs at more convenient times.

Picker Institute Europe. *Is the NHS getting better or worse?* April 2005. www.pickereurope.org

Healthcare Commission. www.healthcarecommission.org.uk/ NationalFindings/Surveys

NHS surveys advice centre: 01865 208127. www.nhssurveys.org

Corporate governance statements and assurance

The 1994 *Code of conduct and code of accountability* document laid down the need for boards to ensure that they delivered the necessary standards of accountability, probity and openness. Corporate governance is the system by which an organisation is directed and controlled, at its most senior level, in order to deliver those standards and to meet its objectives.

It is based on the premise that if sound systems are in place at the top of an organisation then the chances of failure to deliver key standards will be reduced. Corporate governance is therefore designed to provide reason-able, but not absolute, assurances of effectiveness. A parallel can be seen in clinical governance, which is based on the premise that if good clinical systems are in place then the chances are greater that patients will receive good quality care.

The assurance framework

During 2004/05 much effort was expended by bodies such as external auditors to encourage NHS organisa-tions to develop an effective assurance framework and to embed it into the heart of the organisations decision-making processes.

The framework needs to provide the supporting evidence for the chief executive's annual statement of internal control.

The following steps are important to establishing a robust system of assurance:

- establish principal strategic objectives for the organisation
- identify principal risks that may threaten the achievement of those objectives
- evaluate the key controls intended to manage those risks
- set out the arrangements for obtaining assurances on the effectiveness of key controls across all areas of principal risk
- identify positive assurance and areas where there are gaps in control of those assurances
- implement plans to take corrective action where risks have been identified.

To support all of these processes it is important to maintain dynamic assurance framework arrangements, and, importantly, a well-founded and evolving risk register.

Statement on internal control

Each year the chief executive of boards is required to sign the annual statutory statement on internal control (SIC). This statement sets out the extent to which the organisation complies with good corporate governance practice. It can either confirm that sound systems of internal control have been and continue to be in place throughout the year, or, can indicate areas where more time is required to comply and the action being taken to fulfil the standards.

Standards for better health

From August 2004 the former NHS controls assurance regime was halted. This listed the main systems that an organisation needed to have in place, it broke each system down into constituent parts and gave a way of assessing progress in implementing best practice. It assisted boards and chief executives in the process of implementing and checking internal controls. Important

elements of the controls assurance standards were incorporated into the core performance standards for the NHS set out in *Standards for better health*. NHS organisations now have to make an annual declaration to the Healthcare Commission about whether or not they believe they are conforming to the standards.

Annual reports and meetings

Each NHS organisation is required to produce an annual report and to hold an annual public meeting. These are essential elements in the process of public accountability. The main elements of the annual report are laid down as mandatory but there are also optional elements. The layout and format of the annual report is not prescribed and there is considerable variation from one organisation to another.

The annual report and meeting are intended to demonstrate that matters of governance, probity and openness have been properly addressed by the board/authority. They are analogous to the requirements placed on directors under the Companies Acts.

In addition, annual reports provide important documentation of historical value when the issues facing the NHS and action taken to bring about improvements are subsequently reviewed.

Contents of annual reports

The required content of annual reports for trusts is set out in the *NHS trusts manual for accounts* (January 2002). Periodically changes are made to the required contents to reflect public concern on particular issues. The report must cover the 12 months up to the preceding 30 March.

The current requirements are, in summary, as follows:

- Background Information — a brief history of the organisation, its range of responsibilities, the names of the directors during the year and the main aims and objectives including spending plans.
- Companies Act requirements — the main activities and changes during the year, business activity during the year and the end of year position, important planned developments, research and development activity, financial reserves, policy in relation to disabled employees and consultation with staff.
- Operating and financial review — the reason for and effect of any changes in accounting policies, and a discussion on trends and factors that have affected results.
- Codes of conduct and accountability — details of senior managers' remuneration and how it was determined including the composition of the remuneration committee, a compliance statement in line with the NHS chief executive's requirements on senior managers pay (or a justification if there has been non-compliance), and details of the directors' register of interests.
- Better payments practice guide — evidence of compliance with the Confederation of British Industry code on prompt payment of invoices.
- Management and administration costs — information on the management costs as defined nationally, including where appropriate a description of efforts to reduce them or explanations of any significant increases.
- Service quality improvements — progress on meeting inpatient and outpatient waiting list targets and a description of complaints handling

arrangements, including numbers of complaints, speed of response and numbers referred for independent review.

- Equal opportunities — an equality statement showing how the organisation has taken forward the national and local equality priorities and targets in line with the national policy document *Positively diverse*.
- Partnership working — examples of joint action with local authorities for the benefit of patients, including sources of funding.
- Other — there are a range of other requirements including the names of the external auditors, private finance arrangements, local pay bargaining, statement on internal control, clinical governance arrangements and income generation activities.

There are other recommended but not mandatory topics which can be included in the annual report. These include descriptions on service improvements, progress towards tackling inequalities, response to staff surveys, contributions to public health initiatives, value for money activities, information on health and safety and occupational health.

Issuing annual reports

Either the annual accounts or the summary financial statements must be published with the annual report. They must be made available free of charge to members of the public and must be available for distribution at least seven days prior to the annual meeting.

The quantitative elements of the annual report have to be reviewed and agreed by the auditors. This is an important step to ensure consistency with the annual accounts. Time has to be allowed for this stage to ensure that

Performance management — 8

the documents are still available in advance of the annual meeting.

The chief executive as the accountable officer must formally sign off the annual report.

A copy of the annual report and annual accounts has to be submitted to the strategic health authority. This is an important step in the process of accountability from the board through to the NHS chief executive, Secretary of State and Parliament.

There are limited requirements on trusts about the distribution of the annual report. It must be available on request in advance of the annual meeting, but many trusts arrange for it to be widely distributed to NHS premises, public libraries and to health-related voluntary organisations. Often annual reports in newspaper format are distributed to all households in the locality perhaps as a supplement to a local free newspaper.

The annual report is also a crucial document in delivering local accountability to the public. While there may be a handful of interested individuals who wish to pore over the report and the annual accounts in detail, the majority of the public are interested in a more superficial way. Annual reports and certainly annual accounts in their prescribed format are far from user friendly. A challenge facing trusts is how to comply with the national requirements on content while also making them readable and accessible to the public and staff.

Different formats are used ranging from glossy publications, to newspapers, poster displays and even calendars. Extensive use of photographs and the addition of human interest stories are usually included to bring the report to life.

Annual meetings

The annual public meeting must be held before the end of September in order to adopt and discuss the annual report for the preceding financial year. The meeting must be publicised via the local media and be held at a time and place that makes it accessible to the general public. In practice the level of public attendance tends to be low and may be limited to those closely associated with other local health service organisations and from staff. There can however be exceptions when the attendance is in the hundreds if the organisation has been at the centre of a local controversy.

A typical format for an annual meeting might be a formal adoption of the annual report and accounts by the board, brief illustrated presentation on its main contents followed by an opportunity for members of the public to question the board. The annual meeting must be a public meeting as opposed to a meeting in public so the question time is an important part of the proceedings. Some trusts employ independent facilitators, perhaps TV or radio journalists, to chair the question time to ensure that questions are thoroughly dealt with and that members of the public are encouraged to challenge the board.

To generate interest in attending annual meetings when there is no burning issue the formal business is often supplemented by a presentation from a clinician and/or an exhibition displaying the work of the organisation.

National service frameworks

National service frameworks are evidence-based ten-year programmes spelling out the standards the health service must meet in major care areas and disease groups. As well as setting explicit standards and principles for services, they specify the type of services that should be available in primary care settings, local hospitals and specialist centres. They are issued in England and Wales by the Department of Health and the National Assembly of Wales, in conjunction with the National Institute for Health and Clinical Excellence. Scottish NSFs come under the auspices of NHS Quality Improvement Scotland, in conjunction with the Scottish Health Department.

NSFs provide target milestones with the aim of improving levels of care and removing unacceptable regional and local variations in services. The intention is to ensure major health issues and disease areas are tackled effectively and consistently across the NHS. Locally, NSFs are implemented within the framework of the three-year local delivery plan, with progress monitored by the Healthcare Commission. Central programmes support their implementation.

The government has introduced NSFs for paediatric intensive care, mental health, coronary heart disease (CHD), cancer, older people, diabetes, children, young people and maternity services, renal services, and long-term conditions. The mental health framework was published in September 1999, that for coronary heart disease in March 2000, the cancer plan in September 2000, and the framework for older people in March 2001. The full diabetes framework was available from November 2002 and that for the children's NSF in October 2004. The complete renal services NSF was published by February 2005 and the long-term conditions NSF was published in March 2005.

The cancer plan, an NSF by effect if not by name, consolidated and expanded upon the Calman-Hine report (1995). There are also national standards for paediatric intensive care services.

The frameworks are an important part of the government's drive to improve quality in the NHS, which also includes the clinical governance initiative and the work of the National Institute for Health and Clinical Excellence (NICE) and the Healthcare Commission.

The principles of each framework incorporate evidence of clinical and cost effectiveness and the views of health service users. The frameworks are drafted by independent external reference groups, comprising clinicians, managers and users.

Frameworks:
• set national standards and define service models for a specific service or care group
• put in place programmes to support implementation
• establish performance measures against which progress within an agreed timescale will be measured.

Each framework includes:
• a definition of the scope of the framework
• an evidence base, including needs assessment, present performance, and clinical and cost effectiveness
• timescales for delivery
• key interventions and associated costs
• commissioned work to support implementation, such as research and development, appraisal, benchmarks and outcome indicators
• supporting programmes, including workforce planning, education and

training, personal and organisational development, and information development

- a performance management framework.

National service frameworks are an important blueprint for health and social care professionals to help them provide more consistent services. While NSFs are likely to raise standards, give professionals a new focus and encourage successful interagency working, they are ambitious and place fresh demands on staff to reach the gold standard in a short space of time. The mental health NSF, for example, contained a long list of national milestones that health organisations and other local agencies were expected to implement locally over a two-year period. The NHS and local partner agencies welcomed the government's acknowledgement that it would take longer to implement the mental health NSF in full.

Management of medicines. A resource to support implementation of the wider aspects of medicines management for the national service frameworks for diabetes, renal services and long-term conditions. July 2004.

The national service framework programme

The following NSFs have been published:

- paediatric intensive care frame work (1997) (It describes a planned service with appropriate staffing and equipment)
- mental health (September 1999)
- coronary heart disease (March 2000)
- the cancer plan (September 2000)
- older people (March 2001)
- diabetes (standards — December 2001, delivery strategy — January 2003)
- children, young people and maternity services (standard for hospital services — April 2003, remainder — October 2004).
- renal services (dialysis and trans plantation — January 2004, chronic kidney disease, acute renal failure and end of life care — February 2005)
- long-term conditions (March 2005).

The NHS cancer plan

The NHS cancer plan. A plan for investment. A plan for reform (September 2000), brings together all aspects of cancer care, including research, prevention, screening, diagnosis and treatment, as well as securing further investment in cancer services.

Central to the plan are three commitments to:

- address the variation in smoking rates

that exists between different social groups
- reduce waiting times for diagnosis and treatment
- invest an extra £50m in hospices and specialist palliative care.

The *Cancer plan* takes forward commitments in the NHS Plan and builds upon *A policy framework for commissioning cancer services: guidance for purchasers and providers of cancer services* (the Calman-Hine report, 1995) — a strategic framework for commissioning cancer services. Following implementation of this report, cancer services have to be provided at three levels — primary care, cancer units (in local hospitals) and cancer centres (in larger designated hospitals) — and these are linked together with the aim that each patient receives the most appropriate level of care at any time according to the progression of the disease and other factors.

The primary aims of the *Cancer plan* are to:
• save lives
• ensure people with cancer get professional support and care as well as the best treatments
• tackle health inequalities
• invest in the cancer workforce, in research and to prepare for the effects of research into genetics.

In England, more than one in three people will develop cancer at some stage in their lives and one in four will die of cancer. Yet new technologies and treatment pathways, lifestyle changes (most significantly reduced smoking) and national screening programmes have reduced the overall impact of cancer — death rates from lung cancer among men have fallen, as have death rates from breast cancer and cervical cancer. Equally, survival rates for certain cancers have improved dramatically — almost two thirds of children with cancer are now cured, as are over 90 per cent of men with testicular tumours.

There remain, however, inequalities in respect of both the incidence of certain cancers and treatment received following diagnosis. A strong socioeconomic factor is apparent, as people from deprived backgrounds are more likely to get and die from certain cancers than their more affluent contemporaries. Demographics too, play a part, as patients in different parts of the country receive varying quality and types of treatment.

To address these problems the *Cancer plan* sets out actions and milestones to deliver improvements in cancer services — by 2010, NHS five-year survival rates for cancer should compare with the highest in Europe. To address the variation in smoking rates that exists between different social groups (and the resulting cancer and heart disease), smoking rates among manual groups are to be reduced from 32 per cent in 1998 to 26 per cent by 2010. Specific local targets have also been set for the 20 areas with the highest smoking rates.

The NHS has too few cancer specialists of every type. To address inadequacies in numbers the plan proposes an additional 20,000 nurses, 500 radiographers and 1,000 cancer specialists.

Hospices and specialist palliative care services have received an extra £50m NHS investment a year. NHS investment in specialist palliative care services will match that of the voluntary sector.

An infrastructure problem has also been recognised, as much equipment is outdated and inadequate. More scanners and other equipment used to diagnose and treat cancer are to be bought and £93m from the New Opportunities Fund (National Lottery money) will fund over 300 pieces of equipment for the breast screening programme.

A cancer research network has been set up, to improve the quality, speed and coordination of clinical research, and the Department of Health is partnering Macmillan Cancer Relief to develop services to improve genetic risk assessment for cancer.

The cancer task force, led by Professor Mike Richards, the national

Performance management — 8

cancer director, is leading the national implementation to ensure that nationally, within regions, and in local cancer networks, clinicians, managers, patients and other partners will be able to realise the objectives of the plan.

Ultimately, the maximum wait from an urgent referral for suspected cancer to the beginning of treatment should be a month. Milestones towards achieving this target are:

2001. A maximum wait of one month from urgent GP referral to treatment for children's cancers, testicular cancers and acute leukaemia.

A maximum wait of one month from diagnosis to treatment for breast cancer.

2002. A maximum wait of two months from urgent GP referral to treatment for breast cancer.

2005. A maximum one month wait from diagnosis to treatment for all cancers.

A maximum wait of two months from urgent GP referral to treatment for all cancers.

The Cancer Services Collaborative

The Cancer Services Collaborative (launched in 1999) reported that teams across the country halved the time taken to receive first treatment and reduced waiting times for radiology by nearly two-thirds. From April 2001 the programme was rolled out nationwide, involving every cancer network in England.

There are four main aims for the programme, to:
• take out delays and reduce the time to first treatment
• increase the proportion of patients whose care is pre-booked
• ensure that patients have their treatment reviewed by all of the team involved in providing the care

• improve patient and carer experiences of cancer services.

Service guides and evidence-based improving outcomes guidelines help facilitate the programme. Other guides cover linked services. A toolkit service guide also underpins the modernisation of cancer services.

Support initiatives

Various initiatives have been funded to help meet the objectives of the plan, including:
• smoking cessation services in primary care — £53m specific funding over three years, rolled out across the NHS from 2000/01
• school fruit (£42m) and 'five a day' schemes (£10m) to increase consumption of fruit and vegetables over two years, from the New Opportunities Fund
• a £165m investment programme, announced in May 2003, to replace over three years all MRI scanners, CT scanners and linear accelerators in use in the NHS before 1997.

Programmes to reduce cancer will often have a beneficial impact upon other key disease areas, for example, coronary heart disease.

Extending cancer screening. Targets for improved screening include:
• testing to detect prostate cancer
• pilots for colorectal screening completed
• breast-screening programme for all women aged 65–70
• upgrading the cervical screening programme.

The national cancer director. Professor Mike Richards is national cancer director, appointed to work with health professionals and drive through the national programme for improving cancer services.

Progress report. In a October 2004

progress report Health Secretary John Reid said that cancer deaths had fallen by more than 12 per cent in six years. He also announced that from April 2006 there would be a phased roll out of the national bowel cancer screening programme. Research had shown that the faecal occult blood test method of screening could reduce deaths from bowel cancer by around 15 per cent. Speeding up the diagnosis and treatment of cancer would be one of the main focuses

in the coming months.

The NHS cancer plan. A plan for invest-ment. A plan for reform. September 2000.

The NHS cancer plan : three year progress report — maintaining the momentum. October 2003.

The NHS cancer plan and the new NHS. Providing a patient-centred service. October 2004.

The national service framework for children

The national service framework for children, young people and maternity services establishes standards for promoting the health and wellbeing of children, young people and mothers; and for providing high quality services which meet their needs.

There are 11 standards covering the following areas:

Standard 1 Promoting health and wellbeing, identifying needs and intervening early
Standard 2 Supporting parenting
Standard 3 Child, young person and family centred services
Standard 4 Growing up into adulthood
Standard 5 Safeguarding and promoting the welfare of children and young people
Standard 6 Children and young people who are ill
Standard 7 Children in hospital
Standard 8 Disabled children young people and those with complex health needs
Standard 9 The mental health and psychological wellbeing of children and

young people
Standard 10 Medicines for children and young people
Standard 11 Maternity services.

Most sections of the national service framework (NSF) were published by the Department of Health and the Depart-ment for Education and Skills in September 2004 but standard 7 on children in hospital was released earlier in April 2003.

The 10-year programme is intended to stimulate long-term and sustained improvement in children's health. The NSF aims to ensure fair, high quality and integrated health and social care from pregnancy, right through to adulthood.

The NSF needs to be implemented by NHS trusts, primary care trusts and local authorities over the ten years although the timing and planning of implementation are local matters.

The NSF standards will be delivered locally and monitored by independent bodies including the Healthcare Com-mission and OFSTED.

In April 2003 an extra £70m was committed over three years to neonatal intensive care services. Over the three years from 2003/04 to 2005/06 the

Performance management — 8

government invested over £300m in child and adolescent mental health services provided by the NHS and local authorities.

The children's NSF is composed of a number of documents including an executive summary and an information technology strategy to support the NSF.

Part one is the core standards document which sets out the first five standards designed to achieve high quality service provision for all children and young people and their parents or carers.

Part two encompasses standards six to 10, which address children and young people and their parents who have particular needs. These standards are to be implemented in conjunction with the standards in the core document.

Part three of the NSF addresses the particular needs and choices of women and their babies before or during pregnancy, throughout birth, and for the first three months of parenthood.

A primary care strategy has been produced to help all those in the primary care team to implement the parts of the NSF's standards that are relevant to their daily work.

Exemplars are based around a child's journey through care, and illustrate how the standards and key themes of the NSF can be put into practice. Exemplars have been published on:
• complex disability
• maternity services
• asthma
• autistic spectrum disorders
• chronic fatigue syndrome
• acquired brain injury
• discharge and support of children requiring long-term ventilation in the community.

The NSF standards require services to:

• give children, young people and their parents increased information, power and choice over the support and treatment they receive, and involve them in planning their care and services
• introduce a new child health promotion programme designed to promote the health and wellbeing of children pre-birth to adulthood
• promote physical health, mental health and emotional wellbeing by encouraging children and their families to develop healthy lifestyles
• focus on early intervention, based on timely and comprehensive assessment of a child and their family's needs
• improve access to services for all children according to their needs, particularly by co-locating services and developing managed local children's clinical networks for children who are ill or injured
• tackle health inequalities, addressing the particular needs of communities, and children and their families who are likely to achieve poor outcomes
• promote and safeguard the welfare of children and ensure all staff are suitably trained and aware of action to take if they have concerns about a child's welfare
• ensure that pregnant women receive high quality care throughout their pregnancy, have a normal childbirth wherever possible, are involved in decisions about what is best for them and their babies, and have choices about how and where they give birth.

The government is also promoting the development of children's trusts which will have an important role to play in coordinating and integrating the planning and delivery of health, social care and education services.

Other components of the agenda to improve delivery of services are the development of information-sharing arrangements, a common assessment framework, lead professional and a common core of training for the workforce.

Starting in the most disadvantaged areas, the government is also establishing children's centres, offering integrated early years education, family and parenting support, and health support.

In the NSF, children and young people are defined as under 19 years. However, the age ranges for service provision vary according to the different agencies' statutory obligations.

The national clinical director for children is Dr Sheila Shribman.

The local delivery document, published in December 2004, identifies how the NSF fits into the *Every child matters — change for children* programme, and what it means for health organisations.

Getting the right start: national service framework for children, young people and maternity services. April 2003.

Improving the patient experience: friendly healthcare environments for children and young people, Better hospital food: catering services for children and young adults. April 2003

The national service framework for children, young people and maternity services. September 2004.

National service framework for children, young people and maternity services. Supporting local delivery. December 2004.

Every child matters — change for children programme.
www.everychildmatters.gov.uk

The national service framework for coronary heart disease

The coronary heart disease (CHD) national service framework (NSF) is the government's blueprint for the prevention, diagnosis and treatment of the disease. Currently in the UK more than 1.4m people suffer from angina and 300,000 have heart attacks each year. In England more than 110,000 die of heart problems (of whom more than 41,000 are under the age of 75). Among unskilled men the death rate is almost three times higher than it is among professionals. Heart disease is more common in deprived areas, yet treatment and care is often better in more prosperous areas.

The framework was prepared by an expert group led by Professor Sir George Alberti, former president of the Royal College of Physicians, and sets out standards and services which should be available throughout England. It recognises the importance of prevention and primary care as well as the contribution of more specialised services.

The ten-year programme is intended to reduce premature deaths from CHD, and promote faster, fairer access to high quality services. The NSF establishes 12 standards which cover:
• reducing heart disease in the population
• preventing CHD in high-risk groups in primary care
• treating heart attack and other acute coronary syndromes
• investigating and treating stable angina

Performance management — 8

- revascularisation
- managing heart failure
- cardiac rehabilitation.

CHD targets. People with a suspected heart attack should receive professional assessment and, where appropriate, be treated with thrombolytic drugs within an hour of calling for medical help or of dialling 999. This involves:

- improving ambulance response times so that 75 per cent of life-threatening emergencies receive a response within 8 minutes
- increasing to at least 75 per cent the proportion of emergency departments able to provide thrombolysis, leading to 75 per cent of eligible patients receiving it within 30 minutes of hospital arrival by April 2002 and within 20 minutes by April 2003.

From April 2002, 80–90 per cent of people discharged from hospital following a heart attack should have been prescribed aspirin, beta-blockers or statins.

GPs have been working to identify people with established CHD or those at risk. People developing symptoms of angina should be assessed by a specialist within two weeks of referral.

Implementation. Local delivery plans for implementing the NSF are in place.

Specialist smoking cessation clinics and rapid-access chest pain clinics have been set up in some locations.

The 2001 cardiac investment and reform programme committed additional funds to the treatment of CHD,

Summary of progress in CHD services

	Then	Now
Adult smoking prevalence	28% (2000)	25% (2003)
Number of children receiving fruit at school	0 (2000)	over 2m
Estimated number of lives saved with statins	2,900 (2000)	9,000 (2004)
Number of patients waiting over 12 months for heart surgery	1,093 (Mar 2000)	0 (Dec 2002)
Number of patients waiting over 9 months for heart surgery	2,694 (Mar 2000)	0 (Mar 2003)
Number of patients waiting over 6 months for heart surgery	2,766 (Apr 2002)	0 (Nov 2004)
Number of patients waiting over 3 months for heart surgery	Expected to be zero by end March 05	
Percentage of heart attack victims given thrombolysis within 30 minutes of arrival at hospital	38%(2000)	84% (Dec 2004)
Consultant cardiologists	467 (1999)	694 (June 2004)
Heart surgeons	182 (1999)	240 (June 2004)

Source: *Coronary heart disease national service framework: leading the way — progress report 2005.* March 2005.

including heart operations in both NHS and private hospitals and improved diagnosis, treatment and rehabilitation.

The NHS Plan target of 6,000 extra heart operations by April 2003 has been exceeded.

The national director for CHD. Consultant cardiologist Dr Roger Boyle is national director for CHD and works with health professionals to drive through the national programme for improving CHD services.

Progress report. *Winning the war on heart disease*, published in March 2004, revealed that deaths from cardio-vascular disease fell by more than 23 per cent between 1995/97 and 2000/02.

It said that the treatment of heart attack patients had been revolutionised in four years. Eight in 10 heart attack patients received life-saving thrombolysis treatment within 30 minutes of hospital arrival in 2003 — compared to less than four in 10 in 2000.

It was expected there would be no heart patients waiting over six months for an operation by the end of March 2004 — compared to over 2,700 waiting

that long in 2002.

Half way through the ten-year NSF programme in March 2005 a further progress report was published alongside a new chapter for the NSF on arrhythmias, or irregular heart beats, which affect over 700,000 people and cause up to 400 sudden and unexplained cardiac deaths a year. The chapter outlines recent improvements in the diagnosis and treatment of the condition.

Progress in CHD services in the past five years are summarised in the table.

National service framework for coronary heart disease. DH, March 2000.

The national service framework for coronary heart disease: winning the war on heart disease. Progress report 2004. March 2004.

New NSF chapter on arrhythmias and sudden cardiac death. March 2005.

Coronary heart disease national service framework: leading the way — progress report 2005. March 2005.

The national service framework for mental health

The national service framework for mental health — published September 1999 — targets the mental health of working age adults, its treatment in primary and specialist care and also the role of partner agencies.

It details mental health:
• promotion
• assessment
• diagnosis
• treatment
• rehabilitation.

The standards. The NSF sets

national standards and defines service models in the five areas of:
• mental health promotion
• primary care and access to services
• effective services for people with severe mental illness
• supporting carers of people with mental health problems
• preventing suicide.

Implementing the NSF. Local delivery plans for implementing the NSF have been in place since April 2000.

Elements of the NSF are included in local delivery plans, long-term service agreements and clinical governance arrangements.

The national director of mental

Performance management — 8

health. Professor Louis Appleby, the national director of mental health, leads the mental health taskforce. Its role is to work with health professionals and drive through the national programme for improving mental health services.

Identified areas for action include the phasing out of mixed-sex psychiatric accommodation and 24-hour access to mental health services for patients and carers.

Implementation is backed by targeted funding which, for instance, is leading to the greater use of modern drug therapies.

In a progress report in December 2004, Professor Appleby noted that:

• suicide levels were at their lowest recorded levels
• most users of services reported that

their experience of mental healthcare had been positive
• staff numbers had substantially increased and modern treatments were in widespread use
• specialist community mental health teams had ben set up across the country, offering home treatment, early intervention or intensive support for people with complex needs.

At the time of this report health minister Rosie Winterton announced an extra £30m for 2004/05 to improve local, general psychiatric intensive care units.

National service framework for mental health. September 1999.

The national service framework for mental health — five years on. December 2004.

The national service framework for older people

The national service framework for older people (March 2001) aims to drive up the quality of care for older people across England and to tackle age discrimination. It affects older people whether they live at home, in residential care or are being cared for in hospital.

Funding made available to implement the NSF included £1.4bn a year by 2004 — across health and social care — announced as part of the NHS Plan and investment of £120m to provide single sex accommodation, reduce noise, improve privacy and provide on-site rehabilitation equipment. In addition £105m is being spent on community equipment such as hoists, grab rails, chair lifts and other aids to provide help at home.

Developed with the advice of an external reference group which brought together healthcare agency practitioners, partner agencies, older people and their carers, the NSF is founded on knowledge-based practice and partnership working between those who use and those who provide services. It lists eight standards (below) which are designed to have a major impact on those working in primary and secondary care and social services and on the care they provide.

The NSF contains specific measures to reduce disability from stroke and falls, to improve the use of medicines by ensuring that people have effective treatment, and to provide support for older people with mental health problems, emphasising earlier diagnosis and fairer access to drugs for conditions such as Alzheimer's disease. Care pathways are set out for stroke care, falls, confusional state, depression and dementia. Healthy living is also actively promoted, with access to advice and

244

support, and an emphasis is placed upon preventing health problems arising, for example, by immunisation against 'flu, or through advice to reduce the risks of falls.

Decisions on treatment should be based upon clinical need — not age. More investment is going towards those conditions specifically affecting the elderly, for example, reducing delays for joint replacements and cataract operations. Action is targeted on A&E and throughout hospitals ensuring that older people receive quicker and better care.

More specialist staff are provided for in the NHS Plan, including over 200 more consultants specialising in treating older people. A planned additional 7,800 nurses, 2,500 therapists, and other health professionals are involved in the care and support of older people. Care which requires the skills of a qualified nurse is free of charge, whether it is provided at home or in a care home. New teams and services enable more older people each year to be cared for and treated at home and so prevent unnecessary hospital admissions.

Where required, each elderly person receive a one-stop assessment service and have their own individual health and social care plan agreed and decisions on long-term care are not taken without a proper assessment of the chances of rehabilitation. Rehabilitation services are being expanded and improved, with the provision of 5,000 more intermediate care beds and more respite care available for carers.

Service models are described in the NSF, as are local and national underpinning programmes for implementation. A series of rolling national milestones aim to ensure progress, with performance measures to support performance improvement. Guidance has been issued to NHS organisations and local councils, setting out action to be taken to improve the provision of community equipment services and their development — particularly in conjunction with intermediate care initiatives.

Summary of progress in implementing the NSF

Changing attitudes	Then	Now
Tackling age discrimination in heart procedures Proportion of cardiac surgery patients aged 75 and over	2.2%(1993)	10%(2003)
Personal care records Councils that have implemented the single assessment process	0%(2000)	80%(Oct 2004)
Direct payments Number of older people aged 65 and over receiving direct payments	500 (2000/01)	2,700 (2002/03)
Adult protection protocols Proportion of localities that have established adult protection policies	0%(2000)	70%(2004)

Source: Philp, Ian. *Better health in older age.* November 2004.

Performance management — 8

The national director for older people's services, who is leading implementation of the NSF, is Professor Ian Philp.

The eight national service framework standards are:

Standard one: rooting out age discrimination. NHS services will be provided, regardless of age, based on clinical need alone. Social care services will not use age in their eligibility criteria or policies, to restrict access to available services.

Standard two: person-centred care. NHS and social care services treat older people as individuals and enable them to make choices about their own care. This is achieved through the single assessment process, integrated commissioning arrangements and provision of services, including community equipment and continence services.

Standard three: intermediate care. Older people will have access to a new range of intermediate care services at home or in designated care settings. These will promote their independence by providing enhanced services from the NHS and councils to prevent unnecessary hospital admission. Effective rehabilitation services will enable early discharge from hospital and prevent premature or unnecessary admission to long-term residential care.

Standard four: general hospital care. Older people's care in hospital is delivered through appropriate specialist care and by hospital staff who have the right set of skills to meet their needs.

Standard five: stroke. The NHS will take action to prevent strokes, working in partnership with other agencies where appropriate.

People who are thought to have had a stroke have access to diagnostic services, are treated appropriately by a specialist stroke service, and subsequently, with their carers, participate in a multidisciplinary programme of secondary prevention and rehabilitation.

Standard six: falls. The NHS, working in partnership with councils, takes action to prevent falls and reduce resultant fractures or other injuries in their populations of older people.

Older people who have fallen receive effective treatment and rehabilitation and, with their carers, receive advice on prevention through a specialised falls service.

Standard seven: mental health in older people. Older people who have mental health problems have access to integrated mental health services, provided by the NHS and councils to ensure effective diagnosis, treatment and support, for them and for their carers.

Standard eight: promoting an active healthy life in older age. The health and wellbeing of older people is promoted through a coordinated programme of action led by the NHS with support from councils.

At the time of publication of the NSF an additional report was produced specifically looking at how the use of medicines for and by older people can be improved.

Progress reports on the NSF have been published in 2003 and 2004.

National service framework for older people. March 2001.

Medicines and older people. Implementing medicines-related aspects of the NSF for older people. March 2001.

National service framework for older people. Report of progress and future challenges. March 2003.

Better health in older age. November 2004.

The national service framework for renal services

There are more than 30,000 people in England with established renal failure either receiving kidney dialysis or living with a transplanted kidney. About half of these patients have had a transplant and the rest are on dialysis to remove toxins and excess water from the blood. There are fewer than 700 patients under 18 years.

While services for kidney patients have grown over the past 40 years, problems remain with variation in access to services and the quality of those services. Established renal failure is irreversible, and is fatal within a few weeks if not treated.

The renal services national service framework is designed to drive out inconsistencies in standards.

Dialysis is the main form of treatment but can involve people spending up to four hours on a kidney machine, three times a week. Kidney transplants — the best option for most patients — can free people from this regime, but demand outstrips supply.

There are a number of modules:
• effective delivery of dialysis
• transplantation
• chronic kidney disease
• acute renal failure
• end of life care.

The first two of these modules were published in part one of the NSF in January 2004 and the other modules in part two in February 2005. Part one sets five standards to improve the quality of care for people with established renal failure. It identifies 30 markers of good practice which will help the NHS and its partners manage demand, increase fairness of access and improve choice and quality in dialysis and kidney

transplant services. The NSF aims to help patients make informed choices and prevent them from developing the complications of the disease.

The five standards set for 2014 are:
• access to information
• early preparation for dialysis
• to ensure patients commence dialysis in a planned way
• dialysis to best suit the needs and preferences of the individual patient
• improve the access to, and outcome of renal transplants for all those who will benefit from this treatment.

Early action has focused on the following steps to be achieved by 2006:
• a national survey
• expanding haemodialysis capacity in both the home and centres
• renal units participating in a national comparative audit
• every patient having the choice of the type of dialysis they receive, including home haemodialysis dialysis where appropriate
• to achieve NICE recommendations on immunosuppressive therapy.

The government has a £60m capital investment programme to increase capacity for haemodialysis patients over 2000–06. A 2002 survey indicated that there were 2,539 haemodialysis stations for adults in England.

Peritoneal dialysis is a home-based treatment in which fluid is introduced into the abdomen, where it draws waste products and excess water out of the blood using the peritoneal membrane as a filter.

Implementation of part two of the national service framework should ensure that healthcare professional offer the best possible treatment to people with kidney disease. It is designed to help primary care staff spot the early signs of chronic kidney disease, which affects an estimated

2.5m people, and thus reduce the need for dialysis or transplant. It encourages the NHS to use all opportunities to reduce the incidence of acute renal failure and cut the number of deaths by reinforcing NICE guidelines on pre-operative testing.

National service framework for renal services. Part one: dialysis

and transplantation. January 2004.

National service framework for renal services. Part two: chronic kidney diseases, acute renal failure and end of life care. February 2005.

Delivering the national service framework for renal services. September 2005.

The national service framework for long-term conditions

This national service framework sets 11 quality requirements to transform the way health and social care services support people with long-term neuro-logical conditions to live as independ-ently as possible. Although the NSF focuses on people with neurological conditions, much of the guidance it offers can apply to anyone living with a long-term condition. NSF themes are:
• independent living
• care planned around the needs and choices of the individual
• easier, timely access to services
• joint working across all agencies.
   The NSF covers conditions such as Parkinson's disease, motor neurone disease, epilepsy, multiple sclerosis and acquired brain and spinal cord injuries. About 10m people across the UK have a neurological condition. These account for 20 per cent of acute hospital admissions and are the third most common reason for seeing a GP. Over a million people attend accident and emergency departments each year with a head injury, which can lead to long-term neurological damage.
   Services in the NSF include:
• comprehensive assessment and regular review of their needs
• joint health and social care plans that

change over time (especially for those with rapidly progressing conditions) and take other needs into account such as housing, transport, benefits, education, careers advice, employ-ment and leisure
• a single point of access to services via a named contact
• self referral, allowing individuals to refer themselves quickly back to services as their care needs change
• access to a broad range of services including rehabilitation, equipment, accommodation and personal care to help them live as independently as possible at home
• support to help people to work.
   Important to implemention are:
• partnerships between statutory services and voluntary and independ-ent sector organisations
• closer links between GPs, local hospitals and specialist neuroscience and spinal cord injury centres
• more education about neurological conditions for staff in all settings.
   The NSF is supported by web-based good practice guidance which includes examples of innovative services illustrat-ing each quality requirement.

The national service framework for long-term conditions. DH, March 2005.

Supporting people with long term conditions. An NHS and social care model to support local innovation and integration. DH, January 2005.

Wellard's NHS Handbook 2006/07

The national service framework for diabetes

Diabetes can affect people of all ages in every population. Socially disadvantaged groups in affluent societies and people from ethnic minority groups are particularly vulnerable. There are 1.4m people with diagnosed diabetes in England and every year the number of people living with diabetes increases. Up to a million people may have diabetes and remain undiagnosed, and prevalence is expected to double over the next ten years.

Diabetes has a major impact on the wellbeing of individuals, yet evidence shows that the onset of type 2 diabetes can be delayed or prevented by effective self-management and care. Unless the disease is managed effectively, it can lead to heart disease, stroke, kidney failure, blindness and foot amputation. An estimated 5 per cent of NHS expenditure goes on diabetes.

National standards to improve the care for people with diabetes in England were published in December 2001 and the delivery strategy for the NSF in January 2003. The goal is to make the best practice offered in some places the norm.

The NSF was the first to focus on a chronic disease and outlines a care plan for people with diabetes and methods of preventing the disease.

Aims. The NSF aims to:
• minimise the risk of diabetes developing
• improve self-management of insulin
• improve blood glucose/pressure control in diabetics
• target foot care for people at high risk
• provide community-based diabetes clinics
• ensure ward nurses work to reduce hospital stays
• target communities at greatest risk.

The NSF builds on the programme of published NSFs, especially those for coronary heart disease and older people, as well as linking to the NSFs for renal services and children.

The 12 standards cover:
• prevention of type 2 diabetes
• identification of people with diabetes
• empowering people with diabetes
• clinical care of adults with diabetes
• clinical care of children and young people with diabetes
• management of diabetic emergencies
• care of people with diabetes during admission to hospital
• diabetes and pregnancy
• detection and management of long-term complications.

The delivery strategy. The strategy, published in January 2003, calls for PCTs to set up diabetes networks, review local baseline assessments, ensure systematic treatment regimes, participate in audit and develop training programmes.

By 2006, a minimum of 80 per cent of people with diabetes are to be offered screening for the early detection of retinopathy, and practice-based registers should be updated.

The national clinical director for diabetes is Dr Sue Roberts.

National service framework for diabetes: standards. December 2001.

National service framework for diabetes: delivery strategy. January 2003.

National service framework for diabetes: one year on. April 2004.

Improving diabetes services — the NSF two years on. March 2005.

Structured patient education in diabetes: report from the patient education working group. June 2005.

At the last count, around 5,500 partnerships existed in the UK, accounting for some £4bn of public expenditure, according to the Audit Commission. Successful partnership between health and social care providers, government departments and agencies is central to the reforms of the NHS, the implementation of patient-centred care and the delivery of improved quality and efficiencies.

Health Act flexibilities are already in place, enabling the NHS to work with local authorities to improve services. Pooled budgets, lead commissioning and integrated provision allow providers to respond to local circumstances rather than organisational boundaries. Since May 2001 the Health and Social Care Act has allowed for the creation of care trusts, which focus care on patient needs and promote closer integration between healthcare providers and local authorities.

The NHS Plan contains commitments to embrace direct health concerns and factors such as environment, transport and investment. Progress builds on delivery systems already in existence within the NHS, local authority health and social care units and voluntary groups. The priorities and planning framework 2003–06, published in October 2002, again gave a joint lead to health and social services for mental health and older people's services.

Local NHS organisations are expected to work as part of the local strategic partnership to ensure coordination of planning and community engagement, integration of service delivery and input to the wider government agenda. Local strategic partnerships are non-statutory bodies which bring together different parts of the public sector, as well as private, community and voluntary organisations. They are intended to be multisectoral umbrella partnerships to improve quality and governance.

In September 2004, the first strategic agreement between the Department of Health, the NHS and the voluntary and community sector was published. It is designed to benefit patients, carers and services users by providing them with alternatives so that they can choose services that best suit their needs.

Spearhead primary care trusts, the former health action zones and other local action zones can be integrated into local strategic partnerships to strengthen links between services. The partnerships are responsible, in areas of deprivation, for developing a local strategy for renewal. In the 70 most deprived local authority areas a neighbourhood renewal fund has been available to implement the improvement of services. A *new commitment to neighbourhood renewal: a national strategy action plan* (2001) aims to narrow the gap between deprived neighbourhoods and the rest of the country. Its main objective is to remove serious social disadvantage through inadequate housing within the next 10 to 20 years.

In October 2002, the integrated care network was launched, which supports those wishing to integrate working between the NHS and local authorities. The local partnerships developed focus on many groups, including children, older people and the disabled, who have experienced problems in receiving joined up services. The users of the network may be frontline organisations or those with a responsibility to support frontline organisations such as strategic health authorities. The network coordinates existing initiatives and helps to develop appropriate resources where these are limited.

The care services improvement partnership (CSIP) became operational on 1 April 2005. Its main goal is to support positive changes in services and in the wellbeing of:
• people with mental health problems
• people with learning disabilities
• people with physical disabilities
• older people with health and social care needs
• children and families with health and social care needs, and
• people with health and social care needs in the criminal justice system.

CSIP is made up of some new teams and some teams that used to be part of the Department of Health centrally or the NHS Modernisation Agency.

An interdepartmental group has been working to implement health impact assessment in key areas of government policy. The group has produced a screening tool to enable policy-makers to make an informed judgement about the health impact of any proposals. The Office of the Deputy Prime Minister (ODPM) piloted the tool in relation to its road safety programme and other departments are incorporating it into policy-making.

The Social Exclusion Unit — located within ODPM — works to coordinate and advise on the government response to social exclusion.

The Department for Education and Skills is responsible for a number of initiatives addressing unemployment/poverty and therefore affecting public health. The New Deal is a key part of the government's Welfare to Work strategy, targeting particular groups. It aims to develop work skills and experience, thereby improving employment prospects. The Sure Start programme, which aims to increase opportunities for approximately 450,000 children (0–4 year olds), is expected to affect one third of children under four, currently living in poverty.

The Home Office is responsible for the Drug Prevention Advisory Service, established to promote effective drug prevention at local, regional and national level, in line with the government's national drugs strategy *Tackling drugs to build a better Britain*. The Home Office is also responsible for the community safety strategy, which involves local health organisations.

Environmental protection is the responsibility of the Department for Environment, Food and Rural Affairs, which aims to protect and improve the environment, and to integrate environmental concerns across government. A principal concern is the protection of individuals from the effects of poor air quality or toxic chemicals.

Non-governmental public health organisations also contribute to improving health.

Department of Health. *Making partnership work for patients, carers and service users.* September 2004.

Audit Commission. *Governing partnerships: bridging the accountability gap.* October 2005.

Care services improvement partnership, Room 8E46, Quarry House, Quarry Hill, Leeds LS2 7UE. Tel: 0113 254 5127. www.csip.org.uk

Integrated care network. www.integratedcarenetwork.gov.uk

National Treatment Agency (for substance misuse). www.nta.nhs.uk

Neighbourhood Renewal Unit. www.neighbourhood.gov.uk

Social Exclusion Unit. www.socialexclusionunit.gov.uk

Wellard's NHS Handbook 2006/07

Local authorities and healthcare

The government has placed great emphasis on the benefits of the health service and local authorities working together. A number of White Papers and other central initiatives give guidance on how different agencies should be working in partnership so as to provide seamless services for the benefit of patients and carers. The Department of Health issues joint national priorities for health and social services.

The NHS has powers to pool budgets and resources, introduce lead commissioning and establish integrated provision. It is achieving these through local partnerships with other agencies, notably social services.

At the local level, the NHS and local government is coming together through membership of primary care trusts.

The NHS Plan sought to remove many of the barriers between the NHS and social services. It set out incentives for joint working, making use of flexibilities provided by the Health Act 1999. Much of the collaborative working is taking place in the context of intermediate care services which aim to provide alternative settings to the acute hospital for mainly older people returning from medical and social dependence back to day-to-day independence.

The Plan also introduced the concept of care trusts. These are responsible for both local health and social care. Care trusts commission and deliver primary and community healthcare as well as social care for older people or other client groups, such as children. Social services is

delivered in such trusts under delegated authority from local councils.

In order to improve outcomes for children and young people set out in the 2003 Green Paper *Every child matters — change for children* there needs to be whole system reform and more effective integration of services. The Children Act 2004 strengthens this through a duty to co-operate and a leadership role for local authorities in bringing together local partners through children's trusts.

Another change in the relationship between the health service and local government has arisen in the area of public involvement. From January 2003 local authority overview and scrutiny committees have been able to scrutinise the NHS and call local NHS chief executives and other managers to account, based on the needs, interest and concerns of the local population. The process provides another route for the public to raise issues about local health services and have them examined by councillors.

The scrutiny committees have formal powers to refer public concerns over major changes to health services or inadequately consulted upon decision-making to the Health Secretary.

The Commission for Social Care Inspection

Two independent inspectorates, the Commission for Social Care Inspection (CSCI) and the Healthcare Commission, strengthen the system for inspecting health and social care. CSCI was developed in parallel with the Healthcare Commission and works closely with it — there is a legal duty for the two inspectorates to co-operate and by 2008

Wellard's NHS Handbook 2006/07

both commissions are expected to merge into one body.

From April 2004, the Commission for Social Care Inspection became the inspectorate for social care, encompassing the work of the Social Services Inspectorate (SSI), the joint review team of the SSI/Audit Commission, and the functions of the National Care Standards Commission in relation to social care.

The inspectorate is independent and its commissioners are appointed by an independent process. It reports annually to Parliament and ministers on the state of social services, the performance of social services and the use to which social services resources have been put.

The inspectorate:

• carries out local inspections of all social care organisations — public, private, and voluntary — against national standards and publishes reports

• registers services that meet national minimum standards

• carries out inspections of local social service authorities

• reports nationally on social care provision and resource allocation

• provides independent scrutiny of complaints

• publishes an annual report to Parliament on national progress on social care and an analysis of where resources have been spent

• validates all published performance assessment statistics on social care

• publishes the star ratings for social services authorities.

The chair of the commission is Dame Denise Platt and she is supported by five commissioners. The commission's chief inspector is David Behan.

Commission for Social Care Inspection, 33 Greycoat Street, London SW1P 2QF. Tel: 020 7979 2000. www.csci.org.uk

While one-fifth of elective surgery is performed in the independent sector, virtually the whole population relies on the NHS for accident and emergency care. A&E work, very complex cases and the provision of chronic care are more difficult for private hospitals to offer because of the resource and staffing levels needed.

During the Labour government's second term of office, from 1997–2005, new working principles were developed for the NHS whereby healthcare for the UK's population was still largely paid for by the Exchequer and provided on the basis of need and not the ability to pay, but the government encouraged non-NHS organisations to provide a greater proportion of that care. To tackle lengthy NHS waiting times and to introduce a greater degree of competition, the Department of Health created over capacity by establishing independent sector treatment centres (ISTCs) for elective surgery and diagnostic procedures. There are 14 independent treatment sites delivering a full service and three sites delivering an interim service. There are also 44 NHS-run treatment centres and another two are expected to open in 2006. By October 2005, over 223,000 had been treated in NHS treatment centres since the start of the programme in April 2003.

In February 2005, the Department of Health also announced a £1bn procurement from the independent sector of diagnostic tests to boost NHS capacity and provide quicker access for patients to services such as MRI, CT and ultrasound scans.

The government has also created a new route for providing NHS personal medical services. Alternative personal medical services (APMS) contracts can be with a variety of bodies, including independent sector, not-for-profit and voluntary organisations. Such alternative providers could have a marked effect on the traditional patterns of general practice and primary care in the NHS.

The NHS and the independent healthcare sector have always been intertwined. Hospital consultants frequently provide private care for patients on NHS premises, with the patients using some 3,000 pay beds, and in independent sector facilities. There are important rules governing how consultants divide their time between NHS and private work and these were reviewed for the revised consultants' contract. Healthcare is sometimes contracted out to independent hospitals by the NHS locally and this been a feature of the recent drive to reduce waiting times in the health service.

The NHS's relationship with the independent healthcare sector has been put on a formal footing in a concordat announced in the NHS Plan. Entitled *For the better of patients*, it encourages the NHS to use spare capacity in the private sector to have patients treated more quickly. The concordat lays down that local arrangements between the NHS and private sector must assure high standards of care for the patient and good value for money for the taxpayer. It calls for the NHS and private sector to transfer critical care patients to and from each other wherever clinically appropriate, reducing the number of cancelled operations. It expects the two sectors jointly to develop intermediate care facilities and to share information on workforce supply and demand, adverse clinical incidents and patient details.

NHS trusts received an estimated £408m in income from private patients in 2003/04, according to Laing and Buisson.

At the end of 2003 some 7.5m people were covered by private medical insurance and through schemes offered by employers — 12.7 per cent of the population. Revenues of independent hospitals and clinics in the UK (excluding NHS pay beds) reached an estimated £2,846m in 2003.

Nursing and residential care
Independent organisations provide three quarters of long-term nursing and residential care.

The Commission for Social Care Inspection carries out local inspections of all social care organisations — public, private, and voluntary — against national standards and publishes reports.

Laing and Buisson estimate the total value of the care home market for elderly and physically disabled people at April 2003 was £10.2bn, of which private sector operators accounted for £6.9bn. At April 2003, there were an estimated 501,900 places in residential settings for long stay care of elderly and physically disabled people across all sectors (private, public and voluntary) in the UK. Overall UK capacity has de-creased by some 13,400 places in the 15 months to April 2003, a similar annual rate of closure to the previous year. Total capacity is now some 73,700 (13 per cent) lower than the 1996 peak of 575,600.

The fee survey in March 2003 found average weekly fees of £455 for private nursing care for elderly people and £329 for private residential care in the UK.

For the benefit of patients. A concordat with the private and voluntary healthcare provider sector. DH/Independent Healthcare Association, October 2000.

Royal Pharmaceutical Society of GB. *The administration and control of medicines in care homes.* August 2001.

A code of conduct for private practice. Guidance for NHS medical staff. DH, April 2003.

English Community Care Association, 145 Cannon Street, London EC4N 5BQ. Tel: 020 7220 9595. www.ecca.org.uk

Financing the system — 11

The NHS is estimated to have spent £94bn across the United Kingdom in 2005. The NHS budget is planned to reach £105.6bn by 2007/08 and which point the rate of increase is predicted to tail off. UK health spending as a proportion of gross domestic product is projected to reach 9.4 per cent by 2007/08. The plans include substantial increases in capital investment in IT, buildings and equipment.

The government undertakes comprehensive spending reviews involving all government departments and sets a fixed public spending programme for three years at a time. The latest review occurred in the summer of 2004 but the 2006 review has been postponed for 12 months. The Budget statements from March 2000 have produced extra funding for the NHS which has created the financial platform for implementing the NHS Plan.

Scotland, Wales and Northern Ireland have traditionally spent more than England on the NHS but the predicted average growth for these parts of the UK is still 6 per cent.

Government expenditure on health and personal social services is the second largest after social services and the NHS has been given priority relative to other public services. The largest element of NHS expenditure goes on staff. This runs at about 75 per cent of total revenue.

The proportion of gross domestic product (about 8.3 per cent) going on total healthcare (public and private) is lower than many other Western countries partly because of the relative efficiency of the NHS system and partly through the relatively low earnings of its staff. The NHS does not have to bear the administrative costs and individual billing associated with insurance-based systems. The government aims to bring expenditure up to the European Union average (about 9 per cent of GDP).

NHS funding per country (2003/04)

England	— £53.5bn
Wales	— £3.4bn
Scotland	— £6.7bn
Northern Ireland	— £2.5bn*

* Social services are included in the Northern Ireland budget

The Gershon review of public sector efficiency

In July 2004 Sir Peter Gershon reported on the results of his independent review of public sector efficiency. The review

NHS spending (£bn)

	2003/04	2004/05	2005/06	2006/07	2007/08	Average real growth (%)
UK	72.1	79.3	87.2	95.9	105.6	7.4
England	53.5	59.0	65.0	71.6	78.9	7.5

Source: Comprehensive spending review and Budget 2002

focused on releasing resources for frontline services. Some £20bn of efficiency gains in 2007/08 were identified across the public sector.

In response and as part of a wide programme to improve efficiency and cut bureaucracy in the management of the NHS, the Department of Health has undergone restructuring and a reduction in staff numbers. At the same time, predicted savings of £150m are being made as a result of the Department's review of its arm's length bodies (ALBs). The Department believes it is on course to halve the number of ALBs by 2008.

Following publication of the Gershon report, the Department

committed to annual efficiency gains of £6.5bn by March 2008. In November 2005, Health Secretary Patricia Hewitt announced that savings of £1.7bn had been achieved since March 2004 — £200m ahead of target.

Cost pressures and inflation

Increases in expenditure traditionally also include annual assumptions on efficiency savings which have to be found from the resources of the NHS. The DH's priorities and planning framework for 2003–06 lays down that NHS organisations should demonstrate added value by securing a minimum 1 per cent increase in cost efficiency and a

The Wanless review

The first evidence-based assessment of the long-term resource requirements of the NHS, conducted by a team led by Derek Wanless, former group chief executive of NatWest Bank, concluded that the UK must expect to devote a considerably larger share of its national income to healthcare over the next 20 years. The government accepted this conclusion.

Securing our future health: taking a long-term view, published in April 2002, welcomed the intention of extending national service frameworks to other disease areas. It recommended that the National Institute for (Health and) Clinical Excellence had a major role to play in examining older technologies which might no longer be appropriate or cost effective.

Wanless recommended that there should be regular and rigorous independent audit of all healthcare spending. It recorded that exemp-

tions for prescription charges were not logical, nor rooted in the principles of the NHS. The review's projections included a doubling on spending on information technology.

The report noted the vital interface between health and social care and the need for quality improvements in social care to parallel those in health.

In April 2003, the Chancellor of the Exchequer asked Derek Wanless and his team to to provide an update with a particular focus on preventive health measures and the wider determinants of health in England. The second report, *Securing good health for the whole population,* published in February 2004, recommended that the government should set a clear national framework of objectives for all the key risk factors such as smoking and obesity. PCTs and local authorities should agree local targets based on the national objectives.

Financing the system — 11

minimum increase in quality equivalent to 1 per cent of its budget.

The revenue spending allocated in cash terms has to meet the effects of inflation over the three-year period. The NHS traditionally has higher inflation than the general economy, mainly because of the cost of the specialist goods and services it purchases. Increases above inflation have to be met from within the agreed spending totals, and as this inflation usually exceeds Treasury estimates it eats into the funding set aside for service development.

Where the money comes from

Some 95 per cent of NHS funding comes from general taxation and national insurance contributions. Patient charges account for 2 per cent and there are other smaller sources, including the proceeds of asset sales.

Distribution of funds

The total amount of NHS resources consist of three main elements:
• Department of Health expenditure
• expenditure on centrally purchased services, for example NHS Blood and Transplant
• a unified allocation for hospital, community health and family health services with a cash limit attached to it. This third item includes payments to general practitioners, dentists, pharmacists and optometrists. The annual budget is top-sliced at national level to fund central initiatives and special services.

Funding formulae are used to make the allocations to primary care trusts and health boards. The formulae vary slightly between the constituent parts of the UK and can take into account factors such as population, age, gender structure, geographic and social problems, and morbidity and mortality rates.

NHS organisations receiving revenue allocations have a statutory duty not to overdraw their approved cash-limited amount.

Primary care trusts

By April 2003, 80 per cent of NHS revenue was being channelled through primary care trusts. The Department of Health has allocated to PCTs in England £64.3bn for 2006/07

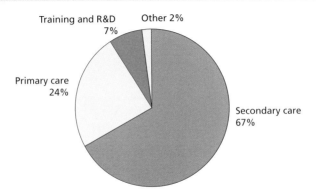

Chart 2: Breakdown of NHS expenditure in 2002-03 (total £54.5bn)

Training and R&D 7%

Other 2%

Primary care 24%

Secondary care 67%

and £70.4bn for 2007/08.

This is the first time allocations have been made directly to the PCTs in England and the first time also that three-year allocations have been made, rather than annual ones. A new funding formula was used, which aimed to give a better measure of the health needs of each local community. Ever PCT budget is to grow by a minimum of 28 per cent

over the three years.

Each PCT receives a unified budget. The budget is cash limited — meaning that an overspend in one area has to be made up by a cutback in another. PCTs have a statutory duty not to exceed their cash limit.

Four distinct areas must be funded:
• commissioning hospital, mental health and learning disability

Chart1: Breakdown of NHS expenditure in 2002-03 (total £54.5bn)

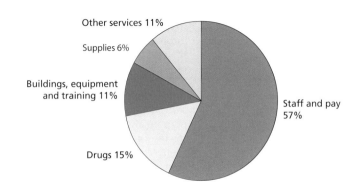

Other services 11%

Supplies 6%

Buildings, equipment and training 11%

Drugs 15%

Staff and pay 57%

Chart 3: Breakdown of additional spend in 2002-03 (total £5.2bn)

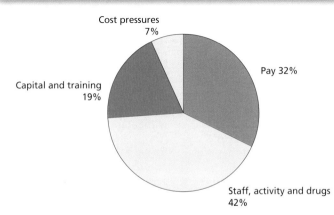

Cost pressures 7%

Capital and training 19%

Pay 32%

Staff, activity and drugs 42%

Source: *Delivering the NHS Plan — expenditure report.* DH, April 2003.

Financing the system — 11

services (up to 75 per cent)
- primary care infrastructure — GP staff, computer and premises (4 per cent of the budget), and prescribing (15 per cent)
- providing community services — health visitors and district nurses, etc (5 per cent)
- running and management costs (about 1 per cent).

Allocations are set for PCTs based on healthcare need using a national formula but with some local flexibility. The allocation is based on the number of patients registered with the PCT's GPs plus an estimate of the number of unregistered patients.

PCTs may also receive additional funds through:
- providing services for other PCTs
- their ability to develop income generation schemes.

The majority of commissioning of healthcare has been done by primary care trusts. Commissioning includes:
- assessing the health needs of communities and people
- specifying the services and performances needed from each provider to meet these needs within the resources available
- entering into service agreements with providers to set performance targets
- transferring money to them for the services they actually provide
- managing their performance against the targets to seek improvements and developments.

Within national guidance on priorities and service frameworks, PCTs are free to deploy their resources as they see fit, provided only that they are delivering on targets and outputs agreed in the local delivery plan and that they reserve the appropriate amount to remunerate GPs for the provision of general medical services.

Primary care trusts pay capital charges on their assets.

Care trusts also include local social services teams and resources, relying on pooled budgets.

NHS trust income

NHS trusts derive their income from:
- service agreements to provide hospital services for primary care trusts
- provision of education and training of healthcare professionals, including undergraduate and postgraduate medical and dental research and education
- support for NHS sanctioned R&D
- income-generating schemes, such as the sale of land and services, for example, shops and car parking.

Financial control in trusts is complex. This creates a demanding role for trust boards. They must:
- prepare and publish a five-year strategy every three years
- prepare a three-year business plan every year
- prepare annual income and expenditure budgets to set out the plan to achieve the three financial objectives
- ensure adequate budget provision is made for inflation, cost pressures, cost improvement targets and contingencies
- review monthly financial reports on the state and forecasts of the trust's financial position
- maintain financial performance in line with similar trusts
- contain management costs within targets.

Stewardship

Non-executive directors on NHS trusts and primary care trusts have a prime role in effective stewardship of each organisation. To succeed, they must be:
- well informed of the financial position

- have a clear grasp of financial issues facing the NHS
- seek high standards of financial management
- have the capacity to influence decisions
- be sure that actions have been taken as agreed
- be able to seek modifications to any decisions that have not succeeded
- be able to achieve such changes and yet remain apart from executive activities
- have excellent relations with executive directors
- have excellent relations with the appointed auditors.

It is a demanding role. Each chairman has a responsibility to empower the non-executive directors to succeed.

Local delivery plans
PCTs draw up three-year local delivery plans which are combined to form the strategic health authority local delivery plan. Financial plans are linked to these local delivery plans.

Individual service level agreements, within the financial plans, are usually based on care groups or clinical conditions. To be finalised the agreements require the involvement of GPs, other health professionals and local interests to collate commissioning intentions.

Service level agreements
Service level agreements (SLAs) for the delivery of health services set out the responsibilities of both parties on issues such as the cost, volume, quality, efficiency and effectiveness of the services to be provided. Typically these agreements between purchasers and providers of healthcare last for three years.

Primary care trusts and NHS trusts draw up service level agreements, which

cover all treatments and services.

One-off treatments not covered by specific agreements are funded by non-recurrent adjustments to allocations. For example, if a patient away from home is admitted as an emergency they will be treated in the nearest hospital. The primary care trust in which the patient is treated receives an extra allocation to take account of the costs of the treatment while the patient's home PCT has its allocation reduced by the same amount.

National schedule of reference costs
NHS trusts and PCTs are required to publish their costs on a consistent basis. Aggregated in a programme the figures provide a national schedule of reference costs which itemises the costs of individual treatments across the NHS. The reference cost index is being published on a regional as well as a national basis. All hospital and community health expenditure has been included from 2004. The aim is to provide:

- a benchmark for improvement
- a means to identify good practice and sources of inefficiency
- evidence to inform the negotiation of service agreements.

Over time the variability of costs for the same treatments across the country has reduced. The reference costs form part of the efficiency component of the NHS performance assessment framework.

Payment by results (PbR)
In October 2002 the Department of Health published *Reforming financial flows. Introducing payment by results.* Important changes include moving to a nationally agreed set of prices for healthcare procedures. Commissioners

will base their decisions on the quality and type of care they wish to purchase, not price. The move to a national tariff is being phased in over five years and will advance the government's concepts of patients' choice and of a variety of providers delivering healthcare to NHS patients. The aim is also to take the focus away from disputes over prices and place more emphasis on the volume, outcome and mix of services that meets a population's needs and the desired pathway of care for patients.

The NHS is moving from being a universal service provider to a service specifier, with a national price and quality standard, delivered by a plurality of providers who can meet the quality standards at that price.

The financial flows document calls for commissioning by PCTs at specialty level based on volumes adjusted for casemix using healthcare resource groups (HRGs).

When the payment by results system is fully operational, providers will be funded for their activity at a national tariff rate. There will be an adjustment for regional variations in cost, but not for provider-specific cost differences. Activity will be measured in inpatient spells, rather than finished consultant episodes.

As well as more stringent agreements with NHS providers, commissioners will enter legally binding agreements with foundation trusts, independent sector treatment centres and other independent providers.

For 2003/04, the Department asked that service level agreements for at least six surgical specialties should be set at specialty level. It called for a move away from block contracts (where funding is fixed regardless of the activity provided) and explicit links

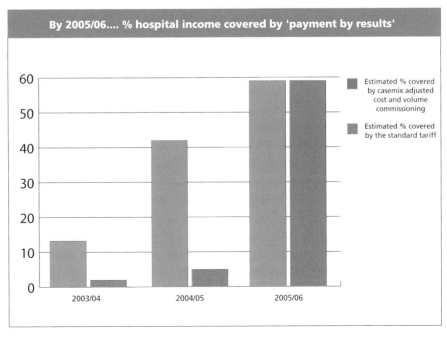

By 2005/06.... % hospital income covered by 'payment by results'

Estimated % covered by casemix adjusted cost and volume commissioning

Estimated % covered by the standard tariff

between funding and the volume of services. Prices continued to be determined locally but national reference costs were used as a guide. For 15 HRGs, the DH proposed commissioning should be at the level of the individual HRG.

As increased activity may not be enough to reduce waiting times, PCTs and NHS trusts were also advised to manage referral and admission thresholds and priorities for admitting patients.

In 2004/05, the number of HRGs included in the scheme was increased to 48 and health communities were asked to use HRGs to casemix adjust their cost and volume service level agreements for all surgical specialties.

From 2005/06 the new system covered all elective procedures. And for 2006/07 it was extended to cover admitted patient care, outpatient and accident and emergency services. To share the overall financial risk between providers and commissioners, a reduced rate tariff of 50 per cent applies to emergency activity above a threshold. This is set at the level of the 2005/06

outturn plus 3.2 per cent. There is also a combined tariff for minor injuries, and short-stay tariffs specific to HRGs. Critical care is excluded from the tariff, and PbR will be piloted for mental health trusts from 2007/08.

By 2008 it is anticipated that tariff prices will be used for almost all activity. Foundation trusts began the phased introduction of payment by results (PbR) from 1 April 2004.

To minimise as well as guide the resolution of disputes under PbR between commissioners and providers of services, a code of conduct was published in January 2006.

Under payment by results, a trust can make and keep a surplus, or can reinvest it to increase activity volume or improve quality. Providers who underperform compared to the commissioning agreement will have funding reduced during the year.

A choice of provider has been routinely offered to patients at the point of booking from December 2005.

Programme budgeting

In 2002, the Department of Health initiated the national programme budgeting project. The aim has been to develop a primary source of information, which can be used by all bodies, to give a greater understanding of where additional NHS funds are going and what is being obtained for the money invested.

All PCT (and strategic health

What are healthcare resource groups?

Healthcare resource groups (HRGs) are a tool classifying patients into a manageable number of groups of cases that are clinically similar and that require similar levels of healthcare resources for diagnosis, treatment and care.

HRGs were developed in the UK by the NHS Information Authority, with input from clinicians, to reflect clinical practice and patterns of delivery. Other countries have developed similar tools, often called diagnostic related groups (DRGs).

Some elective tariffs in use in 2004/05	
Cataract extraction (B02/3)	£786
Bilateral hip (H01)	£7,319
Primary knee (H04)	£6,182
Varicose vein (Q11)	£1,063
Major breast surgery (J02)	£2,386

Financing the system — 11

authority) expenditure, including that on primary care services, is mapped to programmes of care based on medical conditions.

Analysis of expenditure in this way should help PCTs examine the health gain that is obtained from investment.

Shared services initiative

Started in 1999, the shared services initiative is based on the tried and tested idea of pooling expertise and leveraging buying power to secure a better deal for trusts than they could achieve on their own. This type of approach is now feasible across a wider range of service activities, such as finance, that can be joined together by computer networks. The aim is not only to bring down the cost of administration, but also to provide services and information more efficiently and make better use of scarce skills.

The shared services development project, revealed that the NHS had 600 finance services using a wide range of computer systems and processes of varying quality. A feasibility study concluded that the NHS could provide financial services for all primary care trusts and NHS trusts from between 10 and 25 centres. South Leeds and Bristol were chosen as two pilot centres. In

The Audit Commission

The Audit Commission is responsible for ensuring that public money is spent economically, efficiently and effectively in the areas of local government, housing, health, criminal justice and fire and rescue services in England. It appoints external auditors to all local government authorities and NHS bodies within England. It also inspects public services and reports back to the public on the results.

The commission is an independent public body sponsored by the Office of the Deputy Prime Minister with the Department of Health and the National Assembly for Wales.

It has a chairman and up to 15 commissioners drawn from a wide range of fields, including industry, local government, the health service, the accountancy profession and the trades unions. Members are appointed by the Deputy Prime Minister, the Secretaries of State for Health and by the National Assembly for Wales. The commission's chief executive has the title of controller.

The commission is required to be self-financing, and its income comes almost entirely from the fees charged to clients for audit work.

District auditors, appointed by the commission, carry the responsibility for the statutory audit of the authorities' accounts. This includes taking a view of the arrangements an authority has in place to secure economy, efficiency and effectiveness.

District auditors are either partners in accountancy firms or employed by the commission's operations directorate.

National value for money studies the commission used to conduct on the NHS are now performed by the Healthcare Commission.

Audit Commission, 1st Floor, Millbank Tower, Millbank, London SW1P 4HQ. Tel: 020 7828 1212. www.audit-commission.gov.uk

November 2004, the Department of Health announced a joint venture with the IT services company Xansa. It is predicted that NHS Shared Business Services Ltd, the company formed, will save the NHS over £220m over ten years by encouraging NHS trusts to use centralised services.

The other project in progress under the initiative is the electronic staff record. The opportunity in human resource management is clear: data inputting time can be saved and faster access to HR and payroll information can be given to employers when staff change jobs within the service. Other benefits include: better information to support workforce planning; accurate and consistent management information which can be used locally and centrally to support performance management and potential links with

The National Audit Office

The National Audit Office (NAO), headed by the comptroller and auditor general is the external auditor of central government spending in the UK. The comptroller and auditor general, Sir John Bourn, and his staff are independent of government. Established under the National Audit Act 1983, the NAO's role is to ensure accountability to Parliament and the taxpayer for all monies voted by Parliament. The comptroller and auditor general has statutory responsibility for certifying a wide range of public sector accounts, including the appropriation accounts of the Department of Health, and the summarised accounts of the NHS.

The comptroller and auditor general, who is an officer of the House of Commons, also has statutory powers to report to Parliament on the economy, efficiency and effectiveness with which departments and other bodies have used their resources. This means that the NAO has statutory access to all NHS bodies, including NHS trusts and primary care trusts, and can examine the appointed auditors' reports and records. The NAO publishes 50 of these value for money reports each year, including some five covering the work of the Department of Health and the NHS. Recent NAO reports have looked at: stroke care, patient safety, the Norwich and Norfolk public finance initiative hospital, the NHS cancer plan, tackling cancer — improving the patient's journey, and patient choice at the point of GP referral.

The results of NAO's work are reported to Parliament and are usually considered by the Committee of Public Accounts (PAC). The PAC takes evidence on health issues by questioning the chief executive of the NHS.

The PAC publishes its own report based on the NAO's findings and the evidence heard. It makes recommendations for further action to improve value for money. The government formally responds in a Treasury minute by providing information on the steps taken to implement the PAC's recommendations and the wider lessons learned.

NAO, 157 Buckingham Palace Road, London SW1W 9SP. Tel: 020 7798 7000. www.nao.gov.uk

Financing the system — 11

other systems such as e-learning.

The NHS Bank

The informal system of brokerage between NHS organisations in which surpluses were lent to those with a deficit has been replaced by the NHS Bank. It offers loans and grants to NHS organisations for investment in reformed working practices and innovative service delivery.

The bank is at arm's length from the Department of Health and provides risk reserves for PCTs and overdraft facilities for NHS trusts. It is also plays a role in financing capital investment for the NHS.

The bank's board of governors are managers from the NHS, and the bank is responsible for administering:
- a special assistance fund of £100m, providing planned support via strategic health authorities
- public capital brokerage — managing the profile of capital expenditure across the NHS
- cash only brokerage within a nationally determined control total.

Audit Scotland

Audit Scotland, set up in April 2000, provides services to the Accounts Commission and the auditor general for Scotland. Both offices help ensure that the Scottish Executive and public sector bodies in Scotland are accountable for the proper, efficient and effective use of public funds.

The Accounts Commission has secured the statutory external audit of all Scottish health service bodies and councils.

Audit Scotland, 110 George Street, Edinburgh EH2 4LH. Tel: 0131 477 1234. www.audit-scotland.gov.uk

Capital and private finance

Capital for NHS projects is obtained either as a government-funded grant with associated capital charges or from private sector investment through the private finance initiative (PFI) with a subsequent flow of revenue costs. For PFI schemes NHS trusts invite bids to design, finance, build and operate new NHS facilities.

It is the norm that all capital schemes should be tested to establish if there is a viable private sector investment opportunity. There are strict conditions on the nature of the contracts between the private sector and the NHS, the principal of these being

Northern Ireland Audit Office

The Northern Ireland Audit Office (NIAO) provides independent assurance, information and advice to Parliament and the Northern Ireland Assembly on:
- the proper accounting for and regularity and propriety of Northern Ireland Departmental and other expenditure, income, assets and liabilities
- the economy, efficiency and effectiveness with which public sector bodies use their resources.

In November 2004, NIAO published a report showing that proportionately more people were having to wait longer for NHS treatment in Northern Ireland compared with elsewhere. It made recommendations to the Department of Health, Social Services and Public Safety on how the situation might be improved.

Northern Ireland Audit Office, 106 University Street, Belfast BT7 1EU. Tel: 028 9025 1000. www.niauditoffice.gov.uk

the proper transfer of risk to the private sector and improved value for money to the NHS over the life of the asset.

A successful PFI project will be managed with a long-term contract, usually in the form of a lease, with the private partner. This can often be with a special purpose vehicle (SPV) where a private sector consortia is involved.

A PFI project has major implications for a trust's cost structure. Expenditure will be against an ongoing lease payment instead of the conventional approach of borrowing capital monies and financing the ongoing running costs as internal costs, especially capital charges. This changes the cost structure and balance sheet of a trust. These are major corporate issues, and must only be pursued with the full engagement and understanding of the trust board.

PFI projects include:
• hospital building, maintenance and sometimes hotel services
• new GP premises
• hotel services
• information and IT services, especially for care records development and provision.

Trusts also put in business cases to obtain discretionary capital from the Department of Health via strategic health authorities for new build and

The Wales Audit Office

The Wales Audit Office (WAO), under the direction of the auditor general for Wales, Jeremy Colman, provides the country with a comprehensive audit and inspection service across a wide range of public services.

The WAO provides assurance about the proper stewardship of and accounting for the publics' money, while also contributing to the improved delivery of public services in Wales.

The WAO, created on 1 April 2005, brings together the Audit Commission in Wales with the National Audit Office in Wales. Previously the role of the NAO in Wales was to audit the financial statements of all Welsh government departments and agencies, and many other public bodies. The Audit Commission in Wales was responsible for auditing and inspecting local Welsh public health services. Both bodies carried out value for money studies.

The new body has new and enhanced powers.

The then auditor general for Wales, Sir John Bourn, reported on two issues concerning the NHS early in 2005. In January 2005, Sir John commented that although Wales spent more on health per head of population than England, people living in Wales had to wait significantly longer for elective health treatment than those in England. There were also substantial regional variations in waiting times within Wales in which the length of wait depended on where patients lived. Long waiting times were worst in south east Wales. Particular specialties also experienced disproportionately long waiting times.

Wales Audit Office, Deri House, 2 Park Grove, Cardiff CF10 3PA. Tel: 02920 260260. www.wao.gov.uk

major refurbishment schemes. Bids are prioritised.

Capital spending for an NHS trust is limited by its external financing limit (EFL). This is set by the Department of Health and based on a trust's business plan. PFI schemes do not have an impact on a trust's EFL. This allows trusts to take on capital projects beyond the limit financed by the Department.

The NHS is given allocations of capital funding for three years. Allocations are made to the NHS in two parts. Operational capital (formerly block capital) is for the purpose of maintaining and enhancing existing capital stock. Strategic capital, which is allocated direct to strategic health authorities, is for distribution at their own discretion for larger scale investments.

The Department of Health says NHS trusts and PCTs in England have on average received an increase of 10 per cent for operational capital (totals: 2003/04, £684m, 2004/05, £763m, 2005/06, £866m). The growth in strategic capital in the strategic health authorities is given as 13 per cent, 11 per cent and 14 per cent for each of the three years. The residue of the capital is being held centrally with by far the largest part being for IT (2003/04, £400m, 2004/05, £700m, 2005/06, £1.2bn).

A £100m access fund forms part of the three-year capital allocations. This offers rewards to NHS trusts and PCTs who make rapid progress in improving access to services for patients, including reducing waiting times in A&E and for planned operations and outpatient clinics. The money can be spent on equipment and refurbishments, and consultants and their teams within NHS trusts are able to decide how at least half of any payment is spent.

NHS LIFT

The NHS Local Improvement Finance Trust (NHS LIFT) delivers improved primary care facilities in England by batching together a number of primary care developments within an area. The schemes are focused in poor areas, usually inner cities. They have been established as public–private partnerships.

In excess of £700m has been earmarked for NHS LIFT. By the end of 2005, 54 new buildings were open and in 2006, a new building is expected to be open every week.

Joint finance and pooled budgets

Joint finance is a relatively small NHS budget. It can be used for projects that promote more effective joint working between health and local authority services. It is best used as a catalyst for change, with sponsoring organisations committed to the responsibility for collaborative working as projects come to fruition.

Pooled budgets are more prevalent. PCTs working closely with social and education services have been developing innovative types of pooled budgets for projects such as:
• Sure Start
• older persons care agencies
• joint commissioning.

Positive, collaborative attitudes, with health and social services teams pooling their budgets offer benefits to communities. This is the aim of joined up services. It is also the financial platform for care trusts.

Devolution

In Scotland and Wales, the devolved governmental bodies have a major say in health and healthcare policies and priorities and how funds are distributed. There is much scope for different:

• health strategies for the population
• structural arrangements
• innovations.

Devolution is enabling different approaches to be tried, and important lessons to be learnt in different parts of the UK. As well as benchmarking with EU member states, the NHS may be able to benchmark more productively within the UK.

Further information

Department of Health finance and accounting web pages www.dh.gov.uk/PolicyAndGuidance/OrganisationPolicy/FinanceAndPlanning/fs/en

NHS shared financial services. www.sharedfinancialservices.co.uk

HM Treasury www.hm-treasury.gov.uk

National schedule of reference costs. www.dh.gov.uk/PolicyAndGuidance/OrganisationPolicy/FinanceAndPlanning/NHSReferenceCosts/fs/en

Department of Health. *Extending choice for patients.* December 2001.

HM Treasury. *Securing our future health: taking a long-term view. Final report.* Derek Wanless. April 2002. www.hm-treasury.gov.uk/wanless

Investment and reform. Wanless, Budget 2002, Comprehensive spending review. Briefing no. 59. NHS Confederation, May 2002.

Department of Health. *Reforming financial flows. Introducing payment by results.* October 2002.

HM Treasury. *Securing good health for the whole population. Final report.* Derek Wanless. February 2004. www.hm-treasury.gov.uk/wanless

HSC 2005/001. *Primary care trust recurrent revenue allocations 2006–07 and 2007–08.* 9 February 2005.

Richard Douglas, Department of Health. *Payment by results: 2005/06.* 4 August 2005.

Communications — 12

Openness and accountability

The NHS is a major employer of staff, major spender of taxpayers' money and directly influences the lives of those who look to it for services. Within each of these areas there is scope for systems and individuals to take advantage of the powers of the NHS for their own gain or to disadvantage users of the service. Over the years there have been examples of corruption, favouritism and fraud. These have included misappropriating funds, making appointments to posts not based on equality of opportunity, dishonestly representing information on financial and waiting list positions, and withholding information from patients about their treatment or condition, including for example their resuscitation status.

Code of conduct and code of accountability

When these incidents come to light they undermine the public's confidence in the NHS and question the extent to which public service values are carried out in practice. In 1994 the government published a *Code of conduct and code of accountability* which described the corporate governance arrangements in the NHS. It began by stressing the importance of public service values being at the heart of the NHS. It stated that those working in the NHS have 'a responsibility to respond to staff, patients and suppliers impartially, to achieve value for money from the public funds with which they are entrusted and to demonstrate high ethical standards of personal conduct'.

The code stressed three crucial public service values:
• accountability
• probity
• openness.

The code amplifies on these stating

that there should be a willingness to be open with the public, patients and staff, that business should be conducted in a socially responsible way and that public funds should be properly safeguarded with business conducted as efficiently and effectively as possible. The code reiterated the importance of avoiding conflicts of interest by declaring such interests in a register available for public scrutiny. Similarly there is a section on the dangers of accepting hospitality from potential suppliers and the importance of complying with guidance on standards of business conduct. Boards are also required to ensure staff have a proper and widely publicised procedure for voicing complaints or concerns about misadministration, breaches of the code and other concerns of an ethical nature.

Freedom of Information Act

The requirements for openness in the NHS have been tightened up as a result of the Freedom of Information Act 2000. Under the Act individuals have the right to be told whether information exists on them and the right to receive information in the form of a copy, summary or by inspection. Non-compliance with a reasonable request can lead to a fine or imprisonment for a contempt of court.

In addition to responding to individual requests public bodies are required to produce a publication scheme. For the NHS there are 17 classifications of type of information, and the publication scheme must state in what form the information exists and whether a charge will be made to access it. The publication scheme has had to be active from October 2003. The right of access to information for individuals came into force in January 2005.

The right of access applies to all

types of recorded information held by NHS organisations regardless of the date of the information. The Act does, however, set out some exemptions to this right, such as court records and commercial interests. It also places a number of obligations on public authorities about the way in which they provide this information. Requests for information must be in writing. Subject to exemptions, anyone making a request must be informed whether the organisation holds the information and, if so, be supplied with it — generally within 20 working days. There is also a duty to provide advice or assistance to anyone seeking information (for example to explain what is readily available or to clarify what is wanted).

In a case where a request for information is denied there is a right of appeal to the Information Commissioner. As well as approving publication schemes and promoting compliance with the Act, the commissioner has powers of enforcement.

Accountability

Statutory accountability of health bodies and trusts is to the Health Secretary and to Parliament. The formal responsibilities of health bodies are set out in the 1994 *Code of accountability.* Health boards have six functions for which they are held accountable to:

- set the strategic direction of the organisation within the overall policies and priorities of the government and the NHS, define its annual and longer-term objectives and agree plans to achieve them
- oversee the delivery of planned results by monitoring performance against objectives and ensuring corrective action is taken when necessary
- ensure effective financial stewardship through value for money,

financial control and financial planning and strategy
- ensure that high standards of corporate governance and personal behaviour are maintained in the conduct of the business of the whole organisation
- appoint, appraise and remunerate senior executives
- ensure that there is effective dialogue between the organisation and the local community on its plans and performance and that these are responsive to the community's needs.

While a health organisation is held responsible as a corporate statutory body, the chief executive has specific responsibilities as the accountable officer. This role places individual responsibility on the chief executive to ensure that the board operates within the corporate governance requirements.

In practice health organisations are set specific targets on a wide range of topics against which they are performance managed. At any one time there may be many national targets against which a board is being monitored. The importance placed on particular targets shifts according to the political agenda. Delivering financial balance, hitting waiting list and access targets, controlling management costs, implementing national service frameworks, complying with NICE guidelines, and delivering the clinical governance agenda will all be high priorities for a board. The overall performance of each board against the national targets is assessed in the national standards monitored by the Healthcare Commission.

Boards and in particular their chief executive and senior executives know that their tenure of office will be jeopardised if they consistently fail to deliver to required performance levels.

Communications — 12

Overview and scrutiny committees

From January 2003, local authorities with social services departments were given powers to carry out an overview and scrutiny role of local health services. This is one of the arrangements to replace community health councils, which ceased to exist in September 2003. Each local authority has determined its own approach to this role. The health overview and scrutiny committees have been established in accordance with the regulations to consist of a mix of elected members together with representatives of voluntary organisations and patients' forums. Their emphasis is more on issues of health service changes, health inequalities, and strategic direction rather than operational deliver against targets.

The press and the NHS

The NHS is never far from the headlines. The public has a deep commitment and interest in the NHS. Every year most people will make several visits to their GP and at least one visit to their local hospital — either as a patient or visitor — so most people have a personal interest in hearing about the NHS. As the major employer in most areas many readers of local papers will be employees of the NHS. It is always high on any political agenda with daily stories being run in the press about the NHS's performance and its suitability to meet the demands of the future. Human interest stories emerging from reports of inquests or dissatisfied patients, or from the successes of medical care, ensure that the NHS will always attract keen media attention.

Local media

At a local level NHS trusts and primary care trusts will have a continuing and close relationship with local editors and reporters. The local weekly and daily papers and the local radio stations will depend on the local hospital and primary care staff to provide them with prompt information about breaking news stories and on issues of local concern. It is important that clear links are established at an appropriate level to ensure that reporters know whom to approach for an informed and prompt reply. The reporters will be working to tight deadlines, which will not permit them to wait for the NHS representative to become available. Authority to release information to the press on routine matters will need to be delegated while it is important that comment on more serious matters is handled by the communications manager, chief executive or other senior manager. A system needs to be in place to deal with press enquiries at any time of the day or night.

Senior health service staff and chairmen will often know and have established a working relationship with the editors of local newspapers. Many of the larger regional papers will also have a specialist health reporter. Provision should be made to look after reporters at public trust and health authority meetings, although their attendance will be dependant on the level of interest in the topics under discussion. There is a requirement on public bodies to make announcements notifying the public of the time and place of their formal meetings. Many health organisations recognise that reporters do not have the time to attend lengthy meetings and instead offer a press briefing once a month, perhaps the day before the formal meeting, to explain issues under debate and to issue topical press releases.

Even where good working relationships have been established with the press, there will be occasions when press coverage is seen as hostile by NHS bodies. This is particularly the case when service changes are under consideration. The press reflect public concern and can be expected to support a public that is vehemently opposed to seeing local hospitals or services closed or centralised. Sustained press campaigns have on occasions led to the removal of a chair or chief executive, and they can have enormous repercussions for local politicians. A campaign to save Kidderminster Hospital led to the establishment of a health campaigning pressure group that successfully put forward a candidate, Dr Richard Taylor, to fight the general election. His election and the ousting of the sitting MP went to emphasise the potential power of campaigns run with local press support.

In line with policy on openness and accountability, health organisations are encouraged to co-operate with the media. They are required to do so through public consultation prior to decisions to make significant service change. A time when the policy on openness has to be tempered is during general and local election campaigns. Advice is then issued to public bodies not to make significant announcements or launch major campaigns, which might compete with politicians for editorial space or jeopardise the neutrality of the NHS.

National media
The national media, television, radio and newspapers, will have specialist staff that concentrate on health issues. Their links are mainly with the Depart-

ment of Health communications department and national health-related organisations. They do however illustrate national debates with local examples. Their relationship with local health organisations will be infrequent and not based on any need to maintain good longer-term relationships. Handling enquiries from national reporters needs special care especially because of its potential impact on national politics. Ministers operate on a rule of 'no surprises' and trusts are expected to alert the Department of Health if they are dealing with issues that could potentially attract national publicity. This is usually done initially via the communications staff at the strategic health authority.

An important source of information for staff and for promoting the spread of news and good practice throughout the NHS is the professional press. All professional staff are likely to read their own professional journal. Examples are the *Lancet, British Medical Journal, Hospital Doctor, Nursing Times*, and the *Health Service Journal*.

Communications specialists
A few years ago it would have been unusual for trusts and health authorities to have their own professional press and public relations officers. But an increased awareness of the importance of communicating well with the public and employees has led to most organisations having their own or easy access to a communications department. These are staffed by professional staff often with a journalistic background. They take responsibility for press and public relationships, the organisation of special events, for the production of patient and staff literature and for internal communications including newsletters. Their seniority and influ-

Communications — 12

ence continues to grow with them now often being influential in policy making rather than, as in the past, just available try to sort out or explain the consequences of decisions. The have their own national organisation, the Association of Healthcare Communicators and that holds its own annual conference.

Each NHS organisation will wish to develop its own communications strategy. This will set out how communications will support the organisation's corporate objectives. It will set out the policy for both internal and external communications identifying the main target groups, for example, staff, patient groups, health and social service partners, local authorities, public and press. It will describe the consistent messages that the organisation wishes to convey to each stakeholder group. It will recognise the wide range of communication techniques at its disposal from leaflets and literature, through to websites and focus groups. A good communications strategy will enable an organisation to be clear about what it wishes to say, to whom and by what means. It will be set out in specific and measurable terms enabling the organisation subsequently to evaluate its success and amend it accordingly.

Major news stories

From time to time, local NHS organisations are likely to become the focus of intense media interest. It can be overwhelming if appropriate and timely arrangements are not in place. There are planned or predictable events, like official openings, royal visits, and celebrity births. Unplanned events like major incidents, outbreaks of infection, or the admission of high profile personalities can put organisations under great pressure. Within minutes hundreds of reporters, television crews and radio journalists can descend on a hospital or locality. Plans need to be in place that enable security arrangements, press facilities and interviewees to be activated rapidly. This should be part of every organisation's emergency planning process. Failure to do so can lead to switchboards, clinical staff and managers being totally overwhelmed. Journalists and photographers will go to great lengths to gain access to the story of the day and breaches of privacy and disruption to patient services will easily occur if plans are not well rehearsed and ready to be implemented at any time.

Importance of good press relations

The relationship between the NHS and the press will never be free of tension but the most successful organisations have recognised that a proactive, positive approach reaps the greatest benefits. It does not guarantee good press coverage but it increases the chances of being treated fairly when problems arise and of attracting publicity for positive service developments. The press are an invaluable means of getting key messages across to patients, staff and the general public.

Good information facilitates effective clinical care and management of the health service. Effective information systems have been identified as the enabler for many of the NHS reforms set out in the NHS Plan and the modernisation agenda. The purpose of the NHS's strategy *Information for health* (1998) and its update *Building the information core* (2001) were to ensure that information was used to help patients receive the best possible care.

The strategy aimed to enable professionals to have timely information to provide that care and play their part in improving the public's health. It also aimed to ensure that patients, carers and the public had the information to make decisions about their own treatment and care, and to influence the shape of health services generally.

For healthcare professionals and managers, the emphasis has been on delivering information to support day-to-day clinical practice. As a consequence, the strategy was based around five major principles:
• information should be person-based
• systems should be integrated
• management information should be derived from operational systems
• information should be secure and confidential
• information should be shared across the NHS.

The strategy aimed to deliver:
• lifelong electronic records for every person in the country
• 24-hour online access to patient records and information about clinical best practice for all NHS clinicians
• seamless care for patients through GPs, hospitals and community services by the sharing of information across the NHS information highway
• fast and convenient public access to information and care through online information services and telemedicine
• effective use of NHS resources by providing health planners and managers with the information they need.

The NHS Information Authority was set up in 1999 to deliver the information strategy. Its work programme was commissioned by the Department of Health. It was tasked with:
• acting as the driving force behind the development of an information-enabled NHS
• developing the NHS's capacity to manage information management and technology risks.

In April 2005 it was succeeded by Connecting for Health and the Health and Social Care Information Centre. Connecting for Health is responsible for delivering the national programme for information technology (NPfIT) in England.

Connecting for Health

The £6.2bn programme NPfIT was launched in June 2002 to ensure delivery of the information strategy. The programme took over the specification, procurement, resource management, performance management and implementation of the IT strategy. In addition to the central funds, there is local investment from baseline allocations to NHS organisations to ensure local buy-in.

The procurement strategy was designed to accelerate the impact of IT across the NHS. Richard Granger was appointed director general of NHS IT in September 2002 and is responsible for implementing the national programme. Strategic health authorities each have a chief information officer to support the coordination of IT plans across health communities and performance manage implementation.

In terms of procurement, major components of the programme such as networks have been outsourced. The various elements of the programme have also been outsourced to local service providers (LSPs). They are ultimately responsible for the delivery of a full range of IT services in a specified locality. This may be the geographical area that covers a single strategic health authority or a cluster of SHAs. National infrastructure service providers (NISPs) have been contracted to deliver the enabling infrastructure across the NHS that supports improved broadband capacity, completes connectivity for healthcare professionals and supports staff and delivers e-mail and directory services for all staff. National application service providers (NASPs) have been contracted to deliver discrete applications services.

There are a number of elements in the programme:

• the NHS care records service (NHS CRS) — with an individual electronic record for every patient in England, securely accessible by patients and those caring for them
• the electronic booking service (choose and book) — offering patients a choice of hospitals or clinics and more convenience in the date and time of their appointment
• electronic prescription service (EPS) — providing a service for safe generation and transfer of prescriptions from primary care to the pharmacy of the patient's choice
• a new national network (N3) — providing IT infrastructure and broadband connectivity for the NHS so patient information can be shared between organisations

• contact — a central e-mail and directory service for the NHS, to enable staff to transfer patient information, swiftly and securely
• picture archiving and communications systems (PACS) — to capture, store, display and distribute static and moving digital medical images, providing clearer X-rays and scans and faster, more accurate diagnosis
• IT supporting GPs, including the quality management and analysis system (QMAS), support for the quality and outcomes framework and a system for GP to GP patient record transfer.

To develop the patient-based records at the heart of the next generation of NHS information systems, common record structures, terminology and protocols for the capture of clinical data have been developed.

Telemedicine will allow patients to receive treatment or healthcare professionals to seek advice from colleagues and specialists over short or long distances. An advantage should be the

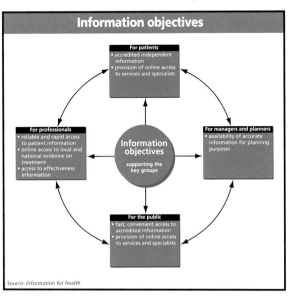

Information objectives

For patients
• accredited independent information
• provision of online access to services and specialists

For professionals
• reliable and rapid access to patient information
• online access to local and national evidence on treatment
• access to effectiveness information

Information objectives
supporting the key groups

For managers and planners
• availability of accurate information for planning purposes

For the public
• fast, convenient access to accredited information
• provision of online access to services and specialists

Source: *Information for health*

elimination of long waits and inconvenient journeys for some patients.

Local implementation strategies

Strategic health authorities have local implementation strategies (LISs) in place. Primary care trusts take an active part in determining priorities, targets and the use of resources. Investments to support the information requirements of PCTs have to be planned and implemented in the context of the LIS and be reflected in primary care investment plans (PCIPs).

The NHS care records service

Each person's electronic NHS care record will comprise both demographic information, such as name, address, date of birth and NHS number, and medical information, such as previous treatments, ongoing conditions, medication, allergies and the next appointment. The personal demographics service (PDS) is the national, electronic database of demographic details. It will enable a patient to be readily identified by NHS staff and associated, quickly and accurately, with their correct medical details.

The PDS is a component part of the spine, which is the national data store for elements of the NHS care records service. Information on the PDS is held nationally on the spine and accessed by authorised NHS staff through their organisation's local system.

The design and roll-out of the NHS care records service has been organised into two parts. Services that are common to all users nationally are the responsibility of British Telecom, the national service provider. Services delivered at a more local level are the responsibility of five local service providers. The contracts have been awarded to the following LSPs:
• Eastern — Accenture

• London — BT
• North East — Accenture
• North West and West Midlands — CSC
• Southern — Fujitsu

Choose and book

The electronic booking of outpatient appointments and admission dates is being extended across the NHS. This gives patients more choice in the timing of their contact with an NHS service and reduces the number of patients who do not attend. Booking should replace waiting lists, with the intention of reducing waiting times to no more than three months for a routine outpatient appointment and six months for inpatients, and ultimately falling to three months for inpatients.

The contract for the electronic booking system has been awarded to Atos Origin and its implementation is expected to gain momentum during 2006.

Conclusion

Successful implementation of the NHS information strategy should mean that timely information is available for all those involved in the healthcare process, including, of course, the public.

Further information

Department of Health information policy. www.dh.gov.uk/PolicyAndGuidance/InformationPolicy/fs/en

Connecting for Health. www.connectingforhealth.nhs.uk

Information for health. NHS Executive, 1998.

Building the information core: implementing the NHS Plan. DH, 2001.

Delivering 21st-century IT support for the NHS. DH, June 2002.

Making IT happen. Information about the national programme for IT. DH. January 2004.

Clinical decision support systems

An important mechanism for achieving clinical governance and ensuring high standards of care across the UK is clinical decision support systems (DSSs) that provide point of care information resources to assist clinicians in their treatment and diagnosis of patients.

DSSs provide a form of electronic clinical knowledge management, designed to support the clinical process and use of knowledge, from diagnosis and investigation through treatment and long-term care.

Typically, clinical DSSs are based on standardised algorithms or decision trees, and integrate a medical knowledge base, patient data and generate case specific advice.

Such systems have the advantage of being able to synthesise patient specific information, perform complex evaluations, and rapidly present the results to health professionals. Evidence also indicates they can enhance clinical performance in terms of drug dosing and preventive care.

Clinical protocols and guidelines are being developed at the national level by NICE and through national service frameworks, which set out the standards the NHS must meet in common conditions such as coronary heart disease, stroke, mental health problems and cancer. Increasingly, national and locally developed guidelines and care protocols are being incorporated into clinical information systems. The requirements for accreditation (RFA) for GP practice clinical systems already require all practice systems to support the GP DSS system PRODIGY, which deals with the choice of medicines for prescribing.

As electronic records develop it will become possible to incorporate guidelines and protocols directly into care delivery systems so, for example, junior doctors are guided through an organisation's standard protocols.

A standardised clinical decision support system also underpins NHS Direct. When a call is made to the service the nurse asks questions and offers advice following a standardised set of on-screen algorithms.

The system used by NHS Direct is also being used to support face-to-face nurse assessments in NHS walk-in centres, emergency departments and out-of-hours primary care services.

Similar systems are also increasingly being used by ambulance services to prioritise calls and determine appropriate responses.

Clinical coding

To develop the patient-based records which lie at the heart of the next generation of NHS information systems, the health service is developing common record structures, terminology and protocols for the capture and communication of clinical information. A clinical information management programme (CIMP) is coordinating work at both national and local level.

In 1999, the Read Codes were made mandatory throughout the relevant parts of the NHS. However, during 2000, the NHS agreed to collaborate with the College of American Pathologists (CAP) to merge the Read Codes with the college's systematized nomenclature of medicine (SNOMED). End-users and suppliers were supported in making the transition to the new terms and clinical codes.

Reliable and timely coding of clinical activity in the NHS is an essential element of the payment by results (chapter 11) system.

Confidentiality

Patients are entitled to expect that information given by them to their GP or health professional will be used only for their treatment and care and for no other purpose without their permission.

Only authorised NHS professionals involved in a patient's care will be able to access their record. Access will be on a need to know basis according to job role.

State of the art authentication processes are being used. All NHS staff must be authorised as users. Once authorised, they use a smartcard and PIN to access the systems. An audit trail of when, where and by whom patient records were accessed, will help to assure confidentiality.

All health professionals and NHS organisations have a duty to preserve patient confidentiality. In acute trusts the health records manager should ensure that there are written policies on confidentiality and disclosure within the department. All staff working in health records must sign an undertaking to protect the confidentiality of the patient. A breach of this undertaking will result in serious disciplinary action and possible dismissal. Following the implementation of the Data Protection Act 1998 there is also the possibility of criminal sanction.

Particular attention should be paid to:
• defining who can release what information
• the positioning of computer screens and wall charts and the use of pass-words and access levels
• physical security of health records
• controlled use of fax machines and, particularly, not passing on information by telephone either internally or externally without checking the identity of the caller.

Departments have experienced many bogus calls to hospitals and these callers can become abusive if they are not given the information they request. All requests should be challenged vigorously.

In November 2003 the Department of Health issued a revised NHS confidentiality code of practice. It replaced previous 1996 guidance and is an important component of emerging information governance arrangements for the NHS.

The document:
• introduces the concept of confidentiality
• describes what a confidential service should look like
• provides a description of the main legal requirements
• recommends a generic decision support tool for sharing/disclosing information
• lists examples of particular information disclosure scenarios.

The Department points out it is in an evolving document because the standards and practice covered continue to change. Where appropriate it is supplemented by additional guidance on the DH website.

Caldicott guardians

Dame Fiona Caldicott's review of the use of patient-identifiable information, published in 1997, recommended the creation of guardians (known as Caldicott guardians). Their role is to safeguard and govern the usage of confidential patient information within NHS and social services organisations.

Healthcare information — 13

Since 1999 chief executives of NHS organisations have each appointed a senior health professional as guardian. Their duties (set out in HSC 1999/012) are to:
- manage audit of current practice and procedures
- produce annual plans for improvement (monitored as part of clinical governance)
- introduce registered access authorisation to the NHS strategic tracing service (and similar data)
- develop protocols governing the disclosure of patient information.

Data Protection Act 1998
The Data Protection Act 1998 came into force on 1 March 2000, bringing new rights for individuals and responsibilities. The Act relates to records from which living individuals may be identified — regardless of the medium in which they are held. It supersedes the Access to Health Records Act 1990 in respect of subject access. (This latter Act covers records of deceased persons only.)

The list of health records that apply to the Act is numerous. It includes computerised and manual records, hand-written clinical notes, health professionals' correspondence, laboratory reports, radiographs, X-rays, printouts from monitoring equipment, photographs, videos and even tape-recordings of telephone conversations.

Access to records
There is a charge per copy for medical notes or X-ray films, of up to a maximum of £50. If records are computerised the fee is £10. Under the Data Protection Act, access is free if a permanent copy is not required (ie, a photocopy) or if the information in the records has been added to in the past 40 days.

If records have not been made or added to within the past 40 days prior

to the application, there is a fee of £10 plus a charge per copy and postage, if applicable. Once notes have been located, and the fee has been paid and identity verified, the GP practice or hospital has 40 days to provide a copy of the records.

Patients have direct access to the Information Commissioner (Richard Thomas) who can investigate any aspect of information contained within the health records. The restricted access to records created prior to 1991 (under the Access to Health Records Act 1990) no longer applies. The Data Protection Act allows access to the complete record regardless of whether this is held electronically or on paper.

Data Protection Act principles
There are eight principles in the Data Protection Act. Personal data must be:
- processed fairly and lawfully
- processed for limited purposes
- adequate, relevant and not excessive
- accurate and where necessary up-to-date
- kept for no longer than necessary
- processed in accordance with individuals' rights
- secure
- not transferred outside the European Union to any country with inadequate protection.

Health records and data protection review group
Formed in 2002, the health records and data protection review group comprises representatives from patient groups, health and social care professionals and regulatory bodies. The group advise the government on the:
- costs for patients to access their health records
- conditions for when patients' records have to be screened

- handling of information in patients' records concerning family and family history
- conditions needed relating to the use of the NHS number (a unique number allocated to individuals).

Clinical disputes forum

The Woolf reforms of the medicolegal system originated from the publication of *Access to justice* by Lord Woolf in 1996. The inquiry involved lay and professional people with medical litigation experience, from judges to nurses.

In the same year, Lord Woolf established the clinical disputes forum and charged its 25–30 members with making recommendations for reform. A pre-action protocol was devised which set out a code of good practice for parties to follow when litigation became a possibility.

The objectives of the protocol are to:
- take the process out of the hands of lawyers and make the courts responsible
- streamline the litigation process
- avoid litigation where possible by

agreeing settlement of claim prior to proceedings
- support efficient management of litigation proceedings when this cannot be avoided.

The aims of the protocol are to encourage:
- early communication of the perceived problem
- patients to voice their concerns/ dissatisfaction early
- early reporting of serious adverse outcomes
- early resolution by disclosure of sufficient information by both parties to ensure that they understand each other's perspective and case.

Retention of health records

Guidance on the retention and disposal of records, including a detailed retention schedule, is given in an appendix to HSC 1999/053. *For the record: managing records in NHS trusts.* An important consideration is the retention of health records for possible medicolegal purposes. It should be noted that the health services circular applies to *all* types of NHS records not just health records.

However, the circular does not cover GP medical records (which are covered in HSC 1998/217) or family health services forms (which are set out in ECL 2/68).

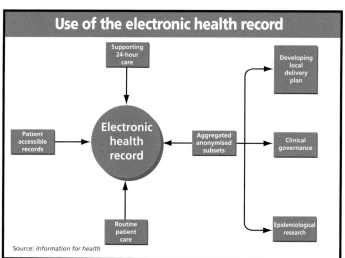

Use of the electronic health record

Source: *Information for health*

Wellard's NHS Handbook 2006/07

Wellard's NHS Handbook 2006/07

Freedom of Information Act

The Freedom of Information Act 2000 has superseded the code of practice on access to government information. All public authorities must adopt and maintain a publication scheme, specifying the type of information that they publish and whether there is charge for the information. The Information Commissioner must approve each scheme.

Further information

Clinical disputes forum
www.clinical-disputes-forum.org.uk

Information Commissioner, Wycliffe House, Water Lane, Wilmslow, Cheshire SK9 5AF. Tel: 01625 545 745.
www.informationcommissioner.gov.uk

Patient confidentiality and Caldicott guardians. www.dh.gov.uk/PolicyAndGuidance/InformationPolicy/PatientConfidentialityAndCaldicottGuardians

Data Protection Act 1998
www.legislation.hmso.gov.uk/acts/acts1998/19980029.htm

HSC 1999/012. *Caldicott guardians*

HSC 1999/053. *For the record: managing records in NHS trusts and health authorities*

Freedom of Information Act 2000
www.hmso.gov.uk/acts/acts2000/20000036.htm

Department of Health. *Confidentiality: NHS code of practice*. November 2003.

NHS library and knowledge services

NHS library services play a leading role in developing effective knowledge management in the NHS. They are natural learning centres and act as a key resource for evidence-based decision-making, clinical governance, education, training and research.

Information for health implementation guidance outlined the need for local investment plans for libraries as part of local implementation strategies.

Improving access for all NHS staff to information on effective clinical practice remains an important target for all library and knowledge services. This reflects the main principles

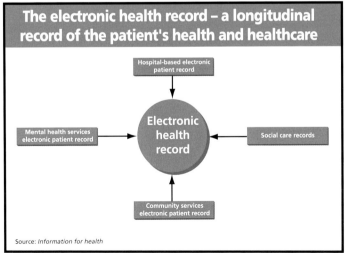

The electronic health record – a longitudinal record of the patient's health and healthcare

Hospital-based electronic patient record

Mental health services electronic patient record

Electronic health record

Social care records

Community services electronic patient record

Source: *Information for health*

for library service development as per the 1997 health service guideline *Library and information services*, which set out the need for regional professional leadership and direction of services and better coordination of funding streams. The aim is for multiprofessional library services open to and meeting the needs of all NHS staff.

There are some 600 libraries in NHS organisations. The majority of these are professionally managed and multiprofessional in scope, offering users enquiry services, online searching, book and journal loans, current awareness services and access to intranets and the internet. NHS libraries work closely with related knowledge services in higher education, local authorities and the voluntary sector as well as other NHS services such as NHS Direct and medicines information services. The emphasis on seamless access for clinicians and patients expressed in the NHS Plan and priority areas gives a fresh impetus to these long-standing relationships. Many NHS Direct sites are employing qualified librarians.

Roles of NHS library and knowledge services include:
- teaching information and critical appraisal skills
- developing outreach services for primary healthcare teams
- creating web pages and intranet services
- establishing clinical librarian posts in specialist teams
- searching the internet on behalf of users.

Regional library units are established in seven of the former eight English regions. They organise and promote resource sharing, continuing professional development opportunities and support information communication technology and information

initiatives such as knowledge management, clinical librarian projects, 24-hour access to electronic resources and web site development.

The NHS Regional Librarians Group encourages the accreditation and benchmarking of library services across the UK and publishes annual statistics related to library use and resources.

As direct access to knowledge increases librarians will act as 'infomediaries', finding the right evidence in the fastest possible time and by providing services such as document delivery.

Increasingly funding for library services in England has become the responsibility for the strategic health authorities, which work with regional library directors to achieve best value and coherence in NHS knowledge services.

In Wales, a review of NHS library services has ensured that responsibility for them is embedded in National Assembly structures. The aim is to enable every health professional to access information at or close to their point of need.

The National Library for Health

The National Library for Health (NLH) was launched in electronic format in November 2000. NLH provides clinicians, managers and patients with fast and easy digital access to the best current knowledge. The web-based system (www.nlh.nhs.uk) provides access to a range of quality information resources to support better patient care and choice.

In its current stage of development NLH is bringing digital and traditional library services together into a single national library. There are plans to add electronic resources from regional and local collections, so that NHS staff can use the NLH website as the gateway to all the resources that are available to

Healthcare information — 13

them. Other plans include links to individual libraries, so that NHS staff can move seamlessly between electronic resources and the library staff who can help them with their information needs.

For patients, carers and the public the best gateway to the library is through NHS Direct Online. Among other resources on offer are an A–Z guide to the NHS, a healthcare guide and information on conditions and treatment.

Components of the library include:
• a news service
• clinical guidance, such as that put out by NICE
• evidence-based information, such as the Cochrane Library
• clinical databases
• journals and books
• health management innovations.

There are disease specific branch libraries within NLH, professional portals for individual health professions, and a reference section covering topics such as quality and clinical governance, medicines and anatomy.

NLH comprises a comprehensive web resource, rather than being a centralised service, and library staff continue to have a central role in the development and delivery of knowledge and information services. The NLH programme director is Dr Ben Toth.

Further information

HSC 1999/154. *Continuing professional development: quality in the new NHS.*

HSG (97)47. *Library and information services.*

Cochrane Library user's group.
www.york.ac.uk/inst/crd/clug

National Library for Health.
www.library.nhs.uk

Health on the net Northern Ireland.
www.honni.qub.ac.uk

NHS Scotland e-library.
www.elib.scot.nhs.uk

Health of Wales information service.
www.wales.nhs.uk

NHS Direct

In England in April 2004 NHS Direct became a special health authority, with primary care trusts responsible for commissioning its services. The organisation is chaired by David Edmonds and its chief executive is Ed Lester.

NHS Direct provides people with prompt and comprehensive access to health information and advice. Launched in March 1998, nurses and other health professionals advise callers, suggest the best courses of action and are also able to pass calls directly to the emergency services. Callers may be advised as to what they can do at home, to visit a GP or other health professional or go to a hospital emergency department. Callers are provided with ready access to information about health, illness and the NHS so that they are better able to care for themselves and their families. Clinical advice supports self-care and appropriate self referral to NHS services.

The service covers the whole of England and Wales, with lines open 24 hours a day, 365 days a year. NHS Direct handles over 650,000 calls to the telephone service and over one million visits to the website every month.

From December 2006, the NHS Direct number will provide a single point of access for out-of-hours care. Calls will be passed on, where necessary, to the emergency services, appropriate GP co-operative or deputising service.

The telephone helpline has been used to develop the *NHS Direct self-help*

284

guide: not feeling well, which provides advice on the 44 most common symptoms about which people contact the service. It can be used on its own or alongside the telephone service. The guide is free and is sent to callers when NHS Direct nurses think it will be helpful. It is also available from pharmacies, primary care trusts and Jobcentre New Deal agencies.

NHS Direct can be contacted by telephone on 0845 4647 (calls charged at local rates) and online at www.nhsdirect.nhs.uk. A textphone number is available for deaf people, those who are hard of hearing and those with speech difficulties (0845 606 4647).

The telephone service is also available in Wales. NHS Direct Wales/ Galw lechyd Cymru also caters for Welsh speakers. There is also a separate website for NHS Direct Wales with information in English and Welsh (www.nhsdirect.wales.nhs.uk).

Scotland has its own system called NHS 24, available from 08454 242424 (www.nhs24.com).

Online and TV interactive services

NHS Direct Online was launched in 1999 and attracts over a million visitors a month, making it the most popular UK-based health website. The site contains healthy living advice, an A to Z guide to the NHS, accredited information about hundreds of diseases and self-care groups, a database of local NHS services and an interactive self-help guide.

From May 2001, three pilot digital TV projects allowed patients to access health advice and information via television. From December 2004, the NHS Direct interactive service became available nationally to households with digital satellite TV, and it is being rolled out to other digital TV platforms, such as Freeview and cable.

By pressing the interactive button on their remote control and scrolling down the menu to 'NHS Direct interactive', viewers can find about 3,000 pages of content.

A number of NHS Direct information points have been located in public places (such as pharmacies and libraries), to allow people access to health information. The terminals provide touch screen access to the information contained on the NHS Direct Online website. The NHS Plan made a commitment to provide 500 NHS Direct information points by 2004.

Web links

NHS Direct
www.nhsdirect.nhs.uk

NHS 24
www.nhs24.com

NHS Direct Wales
www.nhsdirect.wales.nhs.uk

Further reading

NHS Direct: a new gateway to healthcare (2001).

NHS Direct four years on (2002).

National Audit Office report into NHS Direct (2002).
www.nao.gov.uk/publications/ nao_reports/01-02/0102505.pdf

Developing NHS Direct: A strategy for the next three years (2003).

Healthcare information — 13

The national network for the NHS

NHSnet (the NHS intranet) was first established in the early 1990s. It is a secure national network for exclusive use by the NHS — it is not available to the public. Managed by Connecting for Health, it supports a number of national services including:

- high-speed internet access
- e-mail
- electronic data interchange of information, such as pathology and radiology results from hospitals to GPs
- access to NHS gateway
- online patient bookings.

A rapid growth in messaging traffic has indicated hospital and primary care staff have been using NHSnet to change the way they work.

The contract for a new national broadband network (N3) for the NHS was awarded to BT in February 2004. N3 is replacing NHSnet in England and Scotland. The N3 network enables transmission of voice and video information as well as data including e-mails, medical information, test results and GP payment information. The combined voice and data network allows NHS organisations to use the network for their telephone systems, enabling the NHS to make significant savings on its telephone bill.

All confidential medical information transmitted over the network will be secured using industry standard security protocols. In addition, confidential medical information will be protected by further security measures built into the NHS care records service.

The network has also been specifically designed to reflect the critical nature of the services that run on it. This means that the network has high levels of resilience built in to minimise any potential impact on patients. Electronic information can be re-routed around any faults and back-up connections will be provided for key sites.

The safety alert broadcast system

The safety alert broadcast system (SABS) is an electronic system developed by the Department of Health, the Medicines and Healthcare Products Regulatory Agency (MHRA), the National Patient Safety Agency and NHS Estates. It e-mails safety and device alerts to nominated leads in NHS trusts and primary care trusts, who are asked to disseminate the message to those who need to take action. They also are asked to complete a feedback form to confirm that action has been taken.

The aim of SABS has been to bring together all alerts into one electronic system and improve the way they are issued to the health service.

www.info.doh.gov.uk/sar/cmopatie.nsf

Telemedicine

Telemedicine allows patients to receive treatment — or healthcare professionals to seek advice from specialists and colleagues — over long distances using communication technologies ranging from standard telephone lines to wireless networks.

So operations have been performed in Europe by surgeons in the US using robotic technology, and pregnant women have been e-enabled to monitor their health at home and receive advice via a computer or television screen.

Telemedicine technology is increasingly being used in the UK. Telemedicine and telecare are likely to change the place of care and the configuration of health services, with more care provided at home and in the community and less in hospitals. If realised as an integral part of the way in which services are delivered, this could reduce inpatient stays, A&E and outpatient attendances, also home visits. Patients can benefit from reductions in the amount and cost of their time and travel. Assessment and discharge can be speeded up, and waiting lists reduced. This implies significant productivity gains. The main difficulties appear to be that these technologies bring with them the need for changes in the way people work.

The cost effectiveness has been demonstrated of teleradiology, the technique for obtaining a specialist radiological opinion by transmitting digital medical images to a radiologist elsewhere, and telenursing where patients with chronic diseases are monitored via home videophones.

Video-conferencing between clinicians also shows promise as a means of sharing scarce expertise and providing professional development and education.

In the future, the internet is likely to play an increasingly important role in telemedicine, especially as wireless access improves.

In January 2001 the British Library launched its telemedicine information service funded by the Department of Health which aims to improve take-up of telemedicine technology in the UK. It is run by the University of Portsmouth and its work has been supported by the NHS (www.teis.nhs.uk).

The Health & Social Care Information Centre

The role of the Health and Social Care Information Centre (HSCIC), launched as a special health authority on 1 April 2005, is to coordinate and streamline the collection and sharing of data about health and social care. It has assumed responsibility for the regulation of all requests for information from the NHS. By simplifying data gathering, HSCIC aims to reduce the burden on frontline staff. The idea is to collect information only once in the most efficient manner. The DH review of central returns function has been transferred to HSCIC.

The centre has taken on some of the work of the former NHS Information Authority and some statistical and information management functions of the Department of Health. Some 250 staff have been transferred from the Department and 107 from the information authority.

Smaller independent collections of data are being brought into one omnibus survey. The frequency of monitoring returns is being reduced and returns from allied health service professionals are being stopped. Some workforce returns are also being stopped and the scope of others reduced.

Mike Ramsden, a former chief executive of Leeds Health Authority, is the centre's chair, and the chief executive is Professor Denise Lievesley.

www.ic.nhs.uk

Healthcare information — 13

NHS gateway

In November 2003, the NHS gateway website for the NHS in England was relaunched. www.nhs.uk is to designed to connect users to their local NHS services and provides general information about the NHS. There are sections dealing with recent developments, performance, the patient's voice and working for the NHS, and a portal to all NHS organisations.

The information available can help people find walk-in centres, or find out about waiting times. It can tell them about their local hospital and the services it provides. In some cases the public can send an e-mail to patients in hospital.

nhs.uk is expected to play an important role in facilitating the patient choice initiative. It is accessed by over five million users a year.

Links are provided for the NHS in Scotland, Wales and Northern Ireland.

Health Space

Health Space is a national service from Connecting for Health which will provide members of the public with a secure and personal health portal accessed via the internet. The system, once fully operational, will allow people to view their own individual electronic care record. People wanting this type of access will be required to register with the service, in order to prove who they are. This is to protect the privacy and confidentiality of all individuals using the service.

Once registered, each person will be given a unique user name and be able to generate their own personal password. They will also get their own token-grid, which will be used to prove who they are, when accessing their care record later on. This process ensures that only the registered person, or others designated by that person to act on their behalf, will be able to see their care record. The care record will also be available in printable format through Health Space, so that people will be able to print out their own copy for future reference.

The NHS estate and facilities management

In 1995, half of the buildings in the NHS were older than the NHS itself. Today, that figure stands at fewer than a quarter, and this level of investment in infrastructure is having a huge impact on services for patients.

The efficient management of the estate and its support facilities, in both financial and quality terms, is a crucial element of the successful provision of direct patient care services by NHS trusts. It is important that there is recognition at board level of the impact that the estate and its associated non-clinical support services have on a trust's ability to deliver effective patient care and achieve its strategic direction.

Between 20–30 per cent of the annual expenditure of the NHS is spent on its infrastructure — the estate and its non-clinical support facilities. These facilities cover a diverse range of activities including estates and asset management, all hotel services and many specialist support functions including maintenance, waste management and clinical records.

Department of Health directorate

Under the Department of Health's review of arm's length bodies NHS Estates has been wound up, with a small core estates team being brought into the Department of Health and other NHS estates expertise transferred to the wider NHS. The core services moved to the DH cover policy on design, costings and construction, technical services, policy and strategy, strategic estate management and facilities management. The National Patient Safety Agency has taken the lead on hospital food, cleanliness and safe hospital design.

The engineering, technology and environment part of the DH estates and facilities directorate provides support to help NHS organisations drive forward specialist healthcare engineering, embrace new ideas and technologies and deliver quality patient care. The design and costing section provides expertise to improve the design of the healthcare built environment. Information available covers design guidance and standards, capital investment and costing advice.

The NHS estate

The existing estate in the NHS in England is worth some £24bn and would cost three times that to replace. With few exceptions trusts own their assets, land, buildings, and other property, so that most of the operational buildings in the NHS are under their direct control. Trusts, however, remain part of the NHS and the Health Secretary is accountable to Parliament for the effective management of the estate in their charge. Hospitals and other healthcare premises owned by NHS trusts occupy approximately 9,500 hectares.

In 2002/03 over £150m was generated from the sale of redundant land.

Managing the estate. Capital investment is enabling the modernisation of the NHS with the emphasis on greater efficiency and more consumer responsiveness. The estate is in variable condition with a growing number of new and refurbished buildings and a reducing number of older buildings which need disproportionately high levels of ongoing maintenance. The importance of fairness in allocating capital resources is being improved through national prioritisation of major projects, use of local delivery plans and the activities of the spearhead primary care trusts.

NHS trusts have a statutory responsibility for the management of their assets. Each chief executive ensures that an estate strategy is developed, considered and approved by the trust board, implemented and reviewed annually. Strategic health authorities set top-level targets for the performance of the estate of trusts. In addition, where major capital investment projects may result, the SHA and the Department of Health will need to approve a strategic outline case and the subsequent business case.

Risk management is an important element of the implementation of the estate strategy. Controls assurance assumes that control of risk is part of the work of everyone involved in the provision of healthcare. The Healthcare Commission standards provide a framework which can be used by NHS organisations to identify problems, assess risk and determine actions to reduce or eliminate risk.

Significant risks which prevent or pose a threat to the trust fulfilling its obligations to patients, visitors and staff might be generated in a number of areas including:
• estate management
• fire safety
• managing medical devices
• health and safety
• controlling contractors
• infection control
• decontamination
• waste management
• information management and technology
• security.

Every trust is responsible for identifying areas of significant risk and preparing a prioritised action plan to manage or eliminate them.

Property transactions. Trusts manage their own estate in accordance with the directions of the trust board

and are free to manage and sell land, buildings, and other assets subject to certain restrictions:
• the Health Secretary has a reserve power to prevent the disposal of property where this would be against the interests of the NHS. However, this power applies only to assets and land valued at £1m and over. Trusts have an additional duty to notify the Department of Health of any planned disposals in their strategic plans or capital development proposals
• where a trust wishes to purchase land or property compulsorily, it must seek approval from the Health Secretary before doing so
• where a trust proposes taking a lease on property which has an open market value in excess of £1m it must obtain the consent of the Department of Health.

Methods of capital procurement. Capital procurement includes new buildings, refurbishment schemes for existing buildings and major equipment purchases. Each trust will determine its requirements for capital on the basis of the overall strategic direction set out nationally and regionally and in the local health delivery plan.

For construction projects of any significant size or importance, trusts must appoint a named and appropriate individual as project director to undertake the project ownership role. The project director is required to assume responsibility for the cohesive management, direction and discipline of the project.

Capital investments can be delivered through public sector routes or through public-private partnerships (PPPs). Since 1992 the NHS has been encouraged to seek collaborative funding for public works through the private finance initiative (PFI). The aim is to attract private sector capital into the NHS by testing capital schemes to determine if there is an opportunity for private sector investment. To improve primary care premises in England, NHS local improvement finance trusts (NHS LIFTs) were initiated in the NHS Plan. This allows the NHS to enter into a public-private partnership within a new equity stake company. Under this scheme 3,000 family doctors' premises are being refurbished or replaced and 500 one-stop primary care centres developed.

In response to the NHS Plan, between 2001 and 2004 there was nearly £8bn of capital investment. It is expected that within ten years, more than 25 per cent of hospitals will have been replaced or upgraded.

Capital charging. Capital charges were introduced to increase awareness in health service managers of the cost of capital, provide incentives for the efficient use of capital and recognise the cost of capital. Capital charges consist of a 3.5 per cent return on the value of all net assets plus depreciation.

Non-clinical support services

The value of operational costs to run NHS non-clinical/facilities management services is £11bn. These services include site operations and maintenance, cleaning, catering, laundry and linen, security, grounds and garden maintenance, space management, energy management, medical engineering, reception and portering, residential accommodation, transport, sterile services, pest control, waste management, sustainability/environmental issues, safety, and contracting.

Among these, a number of areas have been prioritised for increased investment in the NHS Plan:
• **better hospital food** — *new NHS menu*. A new NHS menu has been

designed by leading chefs.
— *24 hour service*. The 24-hour element of the new NHS menu is designed to ensure that, for whatever reason, patients do not go hungry while in hospital. Patients may miss meals because they are undergoing treatment at the time meals are served or because their time of admission does not coincide with meal serving or ordering. To facilitate the introduction of the service in all hospitals, £4m was allocated to trusts in December 2000. The funds allowed hospitals to purchase refrigerated storage facilities, microwave ovens and toasters.
• **consumerism** — *clean hospitals*. The patient environment programme was launched in 2000 to address the need to improve standards of cleanliness in NHS hospitals. Patient environment action teams (PEATs) were set up to conduct planned hospital visits to produce a nation-wide assessment of the patient environment. Reports confirmed a wide range of improvements throughout the NHS which have had a positive impact upon the patient environment.
• **patient power** — *bedside television and telephone services*. The NHS Plan challenges all major hospitals to install bedside television and telephone services. These services improve the experience of patients by giving them control over their entertainment and by keeping them in touch with friends and families. Services are being installed and managed at no cost to trusts and with costs recovered by making a charge to patients.

A healthy environment

Another area of increasing activity is in sustainable development and the environment. The NHS is aware that a healthy environment is an aid to a healthy population and is committed to following sound environmental practice in the day-to-day conduct of its business. Hospitals inevitably produce emissions to land, water and air. The NHS needs to limit these potentially harmful pollutants, and to improve environmental performance by complying with guidance and regulations and specifying that its contractors do the same.

Waste production, water consumption and energy usage are being reduced by trusts and they are also considering the related issues of transport volumes and the disposal of clinical waste. Best environmental management practice needs to be applied to improving existing healthcare services, and to making significant improvements in the way facilities are designed, built and operated. The *Capital investment manual* takes account of these aspects.

Further opportunities are presented by:
- the more efficient use of resources, for example, more combined heat and power
- investment in energy efficiency measures
- use of alternative materials
- re-use
- recycling
- innovative purchasing.

Conclusion
The effective management of the healthcare estate and its support facilities is increasingly recognised as a major contributor to the development and maintenance of a modern dependable NHS.

Further reading
Building for the future. Modernising the fabric of the NHS. DH/NHS Estates.

September 2003.

Capital investment manual. NHS Executive

Concode. NHS Estates

Firecode. NHS Estates

Estatecode. NHS Estates

Reducing food waste in the NHS. NHS Estates

Strategic guide to clinical waste management. NHS Estates

Developing an estates strategy. NHS Estates.

Sterile services and decontamination

The effective cleaning and sterilisation of reusable surgical instruments between operations is essential in reducing the risk of cross-infection. This relies on high standards of decontamination. Decontamination can be defined as a combination of processes, including cleaning, disinfection and/or sterilisation. In order to sterilise medical devices effectively, all organic debris (for example, blood, other body fluids and tissue) have to be removed from the item prior to sterilisation. Two factors that affect the ability to clean instruments are the performance of the washer-disinfector and the condition of the instruments to be processed.

Devices designated for a single episode of use should be discarded after use and never reprocessed.

There are 182 NHS trusts covering 249 hospitals with central sterile services departments in England. Each year about 6.5m surgical procedures take place. The surgical instruments for these procedures must be routinely and effectively decontaminated in order to minimise the risk of transmitting infection.

Effective decontamination requires the implementation of a number of processes, from purchasing instruments, through effective washing and disinfection, to sterilisation, delivery and use.

The Department of Health issued revised guidance and advice to the NHS in 1999 on how to reduce the risk of vCJD transmission, and on the importance of adhering to decontamination standards (HSC 1999/178 and 1999/179).

A survey in 2001 illustrated that earlier efforts to improve the management of decontamination services had been successful and enabled NHS Estates to rate all the services as acceptable or better than acceptable. A follow-up report in June 2005 showed that there had been a step change in progress towards compliance with best practice guidance.

The Department has recently spent £200m on improving the services. This has been invested in equipment and facilities that can decontaminate surgical equipment to the highest standards. Over 300 pieces of decontamination equipment and significant numbers of surgical instruments have been provided as part of the investment programme.

Training programmes have been instituted and the technical guidance available to the NHS has been reviewed. Web-based tools have been developed to assist organisations with ongoing programmes of improvement.

Decontamination is a topic covered by the Healthcare Commission standards. NHS trusts need to ensure that their organisations meet a series of criteria concerning the environment in which decontamination is carried out, the equipment used for it, and the

management of the whole process.

The government says it is taking action to ensure that the rate of improvement in decontamination standards is maintained into the future.

Department of Health. *The decontamination of surgical instruments in the NHS in England update report: a step change.* June 2005.

www.decontamination.nhsestates.gov.uk

NHS supplies and procurement

A typical hospital will be packed with thousands of individual supplies: bandages, syringes, wheelchairs, heart monitors, coffee machines, pillows, trolleys, telephones … the list goes on.

Every year the NHS spends over £14bn on these so-called non-pay items and services, making it a significant area of health service spending.

In 1999, a Cabinet Office review of procurement led to the launch of the NHS Purchasing and Supply Agency, and an improvement of trust performance. NHS trusts need to coordinate their purchasing activities and collect reliable data on the supplies and suppliers they use. They need sufficient suitable storage space, well-trained supplies managers, and an interest in procurement issues at the top management level.

Trusts are expected to achieve yearly procurement efficiency savings, have a lead director for procurement and produce an approved procurement strategy. In addition, primary care trusts should take account of procurement performance when commissioning services.

Support services — 14

The NHS Purchasing and Supply Agency

The NHS Purchasing and Supply Agency (PASA) for England, launched in April 2000, took over most of the functions of NHS Supplies. It is an executive agency of the Department of Health. NHS Logistics concentrates on wholesaling and distribution.

The agency's responsibilities are to:
• coordinate and guide NHS procurement policy and strategy and ensure that procurement issues are fully taken into account in national policy development
• develop and improve the national purchasing function, and explore the scope for mandatory national contracts
• provide expert advice on procurement policy and strategy to NHS trusts and health authorities
• develop common terms and conditions for procurement across the NHS
• collate and disseminate information on procurement performance for benchmarking
• maintain a market overview of procurement and advise NHS organisations on market issues.

It addresses critical procurement matters such as medical gases, energy, information and baby milk.

PASA works with around 400 NHS trusts and health authorities and manages 3,000 national purchasing contracts.

Recently the supply chain excellence programme has involved three strands:
• the national contracts procurement project
• the development of collaborative procurement hubs
• the market testing of of NHS Logistics and related procurement functions.

The collaborative procurement hub project aims to save the NHS £270m a year by 2007/08 by accelerating the growth of collaborative procurement across the NHS. Pathfinders began implementation of their hubs in February 2005.

NHS Logistics

NHS Logistics was formed in April 2000, as the main supply route for consumable products into the NHS. It operates out of six distribution centres with a fleet of over 200 vehicles that make, on average, 1,200 deliveries a day, serving over 10,000 delivery points. It directly employs over 1,300 people.

Wales

Welsh Health Supplies (WHS) is a service provider to to the NHS in Wales and is managed by Bro Morgannwg NHS Trust. Its role is to provide two links in the supply chain to Welsh NHS trusts — the negotiation of contracts and a materials management service. The business operates from three locations in Cardiff, Bridgend and Denbigh.

Scotland

Procurement in Scotland is organised on two levels — nationally, by Scottish Healthcare Supplies (SHS), and locally, within the NHS boards. SHS is a division of National Services Scotland and provides procurement and technical services to the NHS in Scotland and private sector organisations.

Northern Ireland

The Regional Supplies Service, set up in 1992 as part of the Central Services Agency, is the sole provider of supplies services to the health and social services boards, trusts and special agencies, as well as nursing homes and GP surgeries. It charges a management fee based on an organisation's annual use of the service. It supplies everything from basic hospital commodities to major capital items.

Further information
NHS Purchasing and Supply Agency, Premier House, 60 Caversham Road, Reading RG1 7EB. Tel: 0118 980 8600. www.pasa.doh.gov.uk

NHS Logistics Authority, West Way, Cotes Park Industrial Estate, Alfreton, Derbys DE55 4QJ. Tel: 01773 724000. www.logistics.nhs.uk

Scottish Healthcare Supplies, Gyle Square, 1 South Gyle Crescent, Edinburgh EH12 9EB. Tel : 0131 275 6000. www.show.scot.nhs.uk/shs

Welsh Health Supplies, PO Box 183, Bevan House, 25 Lambourne Crescent, Cardiff CF14 5GT. Tel: 029 2031 5500. www.whs.wales.nhs.uk

The NHS Purchasing and Supply Agency. *Modernising supply in the NHS.* April 2002. www.pasa.doh.gov.uk/ modernisingsupply

Security in the NHS

The NHS has a duty to protect its patients and their property in a secure environment, also safeguarding visitors, staff and NHS property. Yet it must balance this with the overarching duty of providing comfortable and easily accessible services. Healthcare premises cannot become fortresses and must not exclude genuine visitors or contractors.

It is important that all NHS staff be aware of and conform with security procedures, be involved in crime prevention and receive appropriate training in crime prevention techniques.

The NHS faces many security problems: patients have been attacked

by intruders; staff assaulted and occasionally seriously injured; babies abducted from maternity units; and every day the NHS loses thousands of pounds through theft and vandalism.

Security is a responsibility for all chief executives, boards should keep security strategies under review and they should define objectives and draw up policy which is delegated to operational managers. Managers must gain the commitment of staff to implement policies and everyone should feel that it is in their interests to make policies work.

NHS trusts are legally bound to provide a safe and secure environment for patients and staff. Effective security depends on all staff being aware of their responsibility to follow security procedures, be observant, record all incidents and encourage crime prevention.

Operational managers should ensure that procedures take account of security issues and that staff have appropriate training. A clear reporting mechanism needs to be developed. In most trusts there will be an operational services security department with professional security managers and staff with whom security matters will rest.

Primary care trusts also need their own security arrangements. GPs and other health practitioners employ staff and run their own practices and therefore have their own responsibilities for the security of patients, staff and property under their control (including medicines). Individual healthcare staff can be particularly vulnerable when delivering care to the homes of patients.

The NHS security management service
The Counter Fraud and Security Management Service was launched in April 2003 with a remit encompassing the

'policy and operational responsibility ... for the management of security in the NHS'. The service is committed to the delivery of an environment for those who use and work in the NHS that is properly secure so that the highest possible standard of clinical care can be made available to patients.

The strategy document *A professional approach to managing security in the NHS* was published in December 2003 and explains the distinctive strategic approach the NHS should take in seeking to raise standards of security work in a comprehensive manner. Action is taken through a national structure, founded on NHS local security management specialists.

Criminal and civil liability

Legal responsibilities. A hospital or other NHS body is criminally liable under the Health and Safety at Work Act 1974 if it fails to ensure, so far as is reasonably practicable, the safety at work of its employees. This duty would cover lapses of security leading to incidents which arose as a result of the NHS body failing to provide a safe system of work. The duty includes the requirement for a written policy pointing out areas of risk and the safe procedure for dealing with them. An organisation must provide:
• a safe system of work
• a safe working environment
• safe premises
• adequate training and instruction
• information which allows employees to ensure their own safety at work.

Security policy should be communicated to all staff. It is not enough merely to set out a policy for members of staff, there is a duty to ensure that it is carried out. All employees have a duty under the Act to take reasonable care of their health and safety and that of their colleagues.

The Occupiers Liability Act 1984 imposes a duty of care upon an occupier of premises to ensure that visitors and property are reasonably safe. The duty is more onerous in the case of children since an occupier must be prepared for children to be less careful than adults. The concept which governs the duty is foreseeability. As violence and crime are foreseeable occurrences all healthcare bodies must employ all reasonable security measures to reduce the risk.

An occupier may discharge the duty by giving a warning of any danger, but it must be in a form to enable a visitor to avoid danger. The mere fact that a warning is given may not be sufficient.

An NHS employer may be liable to pay compensation if it fails sufficiently to protect patients and other members of staff from the possibility of a criminal act by its employees. For a victim to have a case against a health board, trust or PCT it is for them to prove that:
• the NHS institution has a duty of care to attempt to prevent the criminal act occurring
• it did not perform that duty
• the victim suffered loss or damage
• this loss or damage was a foreseeable result of the failure.

Sufficient protection could be seen to be given by methods such as proper interview, vetting and selection of employees, as well as supervision of staff and a general awareness of the potential for criminal conduct.

Neither the public, nor members of staff, can be searched without consent. Members of a security team have the right to arrest in certain situations, so it is essential that they are fully trained in the powers of arrest and best procedures. Arrestable offences are defined within the Police and Criminal Evidence Act 1984 and include theft, criminal damage, assaults and so on. If the powers of arrest are exceeded or ignored civil actions for assault and false imprisonment may follow.

Under the provisions of The Protection of Children Act 1999 staff working with children have to undergo vetting by the Criminal Records Bureau at selection stage with regard to past criminal records, particular attention is paid to any record of offences against children.

A security strategy. Each NHS body needs to set its own strategy for security, devised by senior management in discussion with the full board, line managers, security staff and all other staff. It should clearly allocate responsibilities and outline:
• risk management
• reporting and recording
• access controls
• designing out dangers
• identification
• financial controls and training.

Training. Security issues and induction into security procedures need to be part of all staff training. Specific training topics could include personal safety awareness and conflict reduction, as well as preventing and reporting crime in the workplace.

Reporting and recording crime. All NHS institutions must have in place appropriate reporting and recording procedures. Up-to-date information of incidents provides a picture of the scale of the problem. The compilation of an inventory of all assets, not just those above asset register minimum values, is important.

Systems must be in place to manage stocks and control assets in all areas. Any discrepancies should be reported and investigated initially internally, and where appropriate reported to the police.

Reporting crimes should be in the job descriptions of all managers and supervisors. In the case of violent crimes, security or other staff who record such incidents should have appropriate skills in dealing with distressed people.

An effective feedback mechanism is paramount as many crimes are not reported. Information should be provided on all progress on security matters and individuals who have been the victims of crime should be made aware of the outcome.

Crimes against staff should be reported to the police but only if the victim has requested this.

Identification. Identification badge systems are a key element of a comprehensive security regime. It is important that all staff, including the most senior managers and clinical staff, wear identity badges at all times.

Basic badge systems for identification purposes only can be used or advanced systems for identification and access control. Pass systems for authorised visitors and contractors can also be employed.

Devolution of budgets. Along with ownership of devolved budgets at departmental level comes accountability and the need for financial probity. This means having procedures in place to reduce the loss of assets and strict controls over the procurement and use of supplies.

Access controls. Where NHS premises have multiple access points consideration should be given to restricting access via some of those points at certain times. The points should be classified as:
• essential at all times
• necessary for certain hours and open for convenience only.

Security professionals should be

Support services — 14

consulted on the design of new NHS buildings to eliminate risk zones and vulnerable areas in existing premises; for example, reusing space and improving lighting.

Aggression and violence

There were 84,273 reported violent or abusive incidents in the NHS in England in 2000/01. The number of violent incidents varied by trust type, for example, the average for mental health/learning disabilities trusts was two an a half times the average for all trusts.

NHS zero tolerance zone. To reinforce the message about the unacceptability of violence against staff, the Department of Health launched the cross-government campaign 'NHS zero tolerance zone' in 1999. It is designed to stamp out incidents where staff are assaulted, abused or threatened during the course of their work.

The initiative requires that NHS staff report all incidents of violence to their managers at the time they occur or as soon as possible thereafter. All NHS trusts should have systems in place to record such incidents and have published strategies for reducing them. A national target was set for curtailing occurrences of violence against NHS staff by 30 per cent.

In addition, an action plan was formulated to lower violence and abuse against social care staff by at least 25 per cent by March 2005.

During 2004/05 there were 759 prosecutions against those who physically assaulted NHS staff.

Conflict resolution. Under the auspices of the NHS security management service, over 250,000 frontline staff are expected to have been trained in conflict resolution by March 2006. This suggests the service is on schedule to train 750,000 staff by 2008.

Highest risk categories. Incidents of violence are highest in four main areas: ambulance and primary care staff, NHS community workers and those working in mental health.

Guidance published by the Department of Health in October 2000 gives specific recommendations designed to tackle violence in these areas. As a result, more NHS staff who work away from the office have been issued with pagers and mobile phones so they can stay in contact with colleagues, improvements are being made to staff training and tougher action is being taken against patients who threaten NHS staff.

Accident and emergency departments. Accident and emergency departments normally have high, stressful peaks of activity during which they deal with a large mix of patients. Therefore there may be an enhanced risk of aggression and violence and loss of, or damage to, equipment.

Factors identified as being conducive to aggression include inappropriate attitudes, poor environmental conditions and facilities and lack of information for staff and visitors. Aggression can also be a component of a physical condition, psychological distress, alcohol or drug use.

Staff should be trained to manage stress. They need to adopt a calm, considerate, confident and even-tempered approach and should learn to recognise and control their own prejudices and emotions and resist countering anger with anger.

The manner in which furniture is arranged, as well as the sufficiency of lighting and choice of colour schemes, can have a positive effect on patient behaviour and safety. Attempts should be made to reduce noise levels and premises should be designed to prevent staff being isolated in any part of them.

Appropriate facilities can help relieve anxiety during long periods of waiting and the adequate provision of information, particularly in situations of acute distress or long waiting periods, can be crucial in lessening the risk of assault. Closed circuit television, alarm bells, personal alarms and the presence of security staff can all be considered as additional measures.

Primary care. In December 1999 the government put in place regulations to help combat violence in GP surgeries. The changes mean that persistently violent patients can be seen in a location which provides a secure environment for GPs and NHS staff. This could range from a nearby hospital site with security guards to a local police station. The regulations also mean that primary care trusts are no longer required in law to provide a patient with the most local GP service in cases where that patient has a history of violent or abusive behaviour.

Withholding treatment. Department of Health guidelines on the withholding of NHS treatment from violent and abusive patients in NHS trusts were issued to NHS employers in November 2001. The guidelines are intended to ensure that the need to protect staff is properly balanced with the need to provide healthcare to individuals. Trusts were asked to introduce local policies in line with the guidelines.

Infant abduction

NHS maternity units. NHS maternity care aims to support safe, high quality services within an atmosphere which helps parents enjoy childbirth. Parents must feel that they and their children are in a safe and secure environment yet achieving the right level of security

should not be at the expense of a positive overall experience of childbirth. Generally, maternity units offer open visiting for immediate family, such as partners and children, with more restricted visiting for others such as family and friends. Most units demonstrate a great deal of flexibility about allowing people to stay.

Maternity units face problems of the unauthorised removal and abduction of infants and wider security issues. To help to tackle such problems, *Safe and sound in NHS maternity units* was published in 1995 by the NHS Confederation's predecessor NAHAT. It includes examples of good practice from units throughout the NHS and a self-assessment tool with which units can audit their own performance.

Infants may be abducted innocently by a family member who forgets or neglects to inform relatives and staff. They may fall victim to a family dispute or may be registered as at risk with social services. Finally, infants may be the victim of an abduction. Because of the potential harm to the infant and the devastating effects on parents and staff, it is vital that abductions are prevented.

Solutions to these issues can be found in controlling access to maternity units and making staff and parents aware of security arrangements.

Maternity units can raise parents' awareness of security issues in a number of ways. Information can be included in maternity unit handbooks, leaflets and posters. Verbal advice can be given during antenatal classes, upon admission and as the need arises during their stay.

Security arrangements should be the subject of consultation. Parents, visitors and staff should all be provided with opportunities to comment on security policies.

An infant should be identified by two name labels during their stay in hospital and these should be placed on them shortly after birth. The mother must be shown the labels as soon as possible so that she can check that the information on them is correct. Electronic tagging can be used as part of the overall strategy against infant abduction.

Preventing infant abduction. Infants should be in view of parents whenever possible or in the presence of a person known to the parents. If parents need to be away from their baby from any length of time security coverage should be made available.

Any abnormal visitor behaviour should be immediately investigated by security staff and/or senior management. Other maternity units in the area should be given a description of the people involved and the event.

Some units have a security-orientated discharge policy. Parents may be given a discharge pass or be escorted out of the hospital by security staff or other members of staff. Anyone leaving the hospital and not following the correct procedures can then be challenged.

Dealing with unauthorised removal or abduction. A critical incident plan for dealing with an unauthorised removal or abduction should be devised, covering items such as instructions for parents on raising the alarm, and instructions for ward staff on controlling the situation, for example, by closing the ward and keeping on the scene all those present at the time of the alarm.

Primary care settings
Much healthcare is delivered away from large hospitals and in a wide range of community and primary care settings.

Each of these will have its own security needs and duties similar to those summarised above. Where they differ will be in the less formal nature of the organisations and in the physical surroundings involved. In particular, the question of safety of the lone professional attending patients in their homes.

A number of solutions have been suggested for ensuring the safety of such individuals, including:
• visits in pairs
• alarm systems
• systems for communication with the staff base when a visit is about to begin and when it has ended
• specific training.

Other considerations include the protection of property in buildings which are small scale but just as prone to theft and damage as larger institutions. Here all the solutions such as closed circuit television, access control, identification badges and design apply.

Improving working lives
An important emphasis today is the improvement of the quality of the working lives of staff. NHS employers are expected to have:
• systems in place to record and monitor workplace accidents and violence against staff, and strategies to achieve a reduction in such incidents
• policies and procedures to tackle harassment by staff and service users, supported by monitoring and reporting arrangements to measure progress
• occupational health services and counselling available for all staff
• training and development plans for the majority of health professionals.

Conclusion
It is clear that effective security arrangements are essential in the NHS and that

for all staff constant vigilance and ongoing determination to improve security arrangements are important commitments.

Further information

EL[97]34. *Security in the NHS.*

Health Services Advisory Committee of the Health and Safety Commission. *Violence and aggression to staff in health services: guidance on assessment and management.* HSC, 1997. ISBN 0 11 883917 9.

Department of Health. *Stopping violence against staff working in the*

NHS. We don't have to take this. Managers' guide. 2002.

Department of Health. *Primary care — preventing violence and abuse against general practitioners and their staff.* 2002.

Department of Health. *A professional approach to managing security in the NHS.* December 2003.

NHS England. *Directions to NHS bodies on security management measures 2004.* March 2004.

Counter Fraud and Security Management Service. www.cfsms.nhs.uk

NHS fact file — 15

This section provides some useful facts and figures relating to the NHS including UK population and vital statistics, the financing of the NHS and NHS resources and activities.

Most of the figures have been derived or taken from the *Compendium of Health Statistics (www.ohecompendium.org)* published by the Office of Health Economics. Other sources of data include the *Economic Forecast* report by the HM Treasury, *Social Trends* (ONS) and the *Annual Abstracts of Statistics* (ONS).

This section has been contributed by Peter Yuen, Statistician, Office of Health Economics, London

UK population and vital statistics

Life expectancy at birth, England and Wales, 1841 - 2020

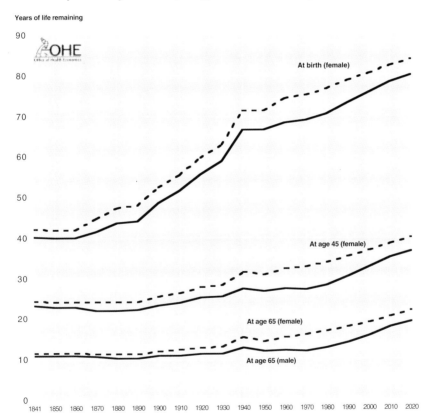

Age standardised mortality rates from coronary heart disease, men and women aged under 75, in selected OECD countries, circa 2003

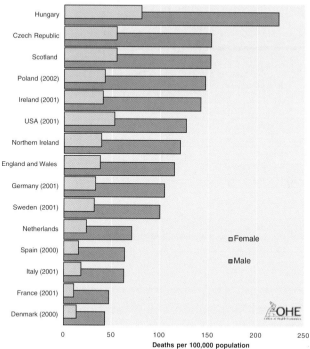

Deaths per 100,000 population

Source: OHE calculation based on WHO Mortality Database (WHO).

Days of certified incapacity by cause, Great Britain, 2002

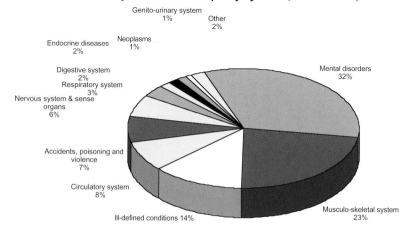

Infant and childhood mortality rates, UK, 1948 - 2003

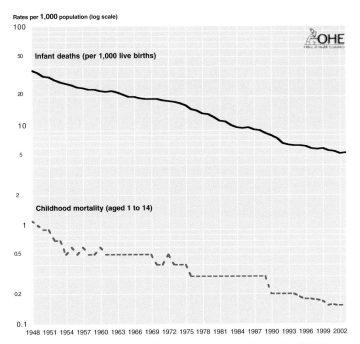

UK resident population and projections to 2051

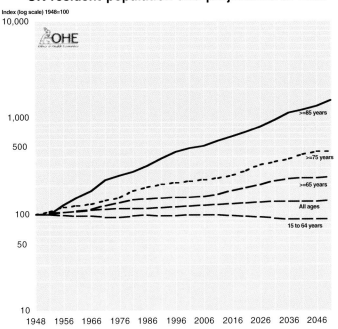

Health expenditure as a percentage of GDP, 2003

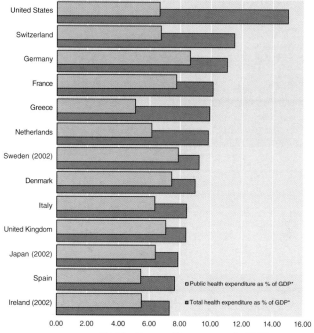

Note: *Gross Domestic Product at market prices.
Source: OECD Health Database.

Gross cost of NHS in real terms, UK, 1949 - 2005

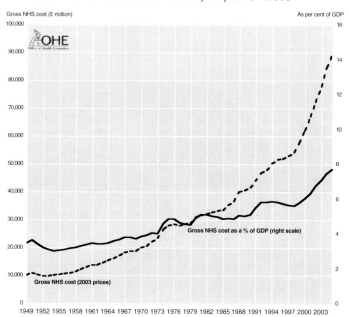

305

UK spending on healthcare at constant prices, 1973 - 2003

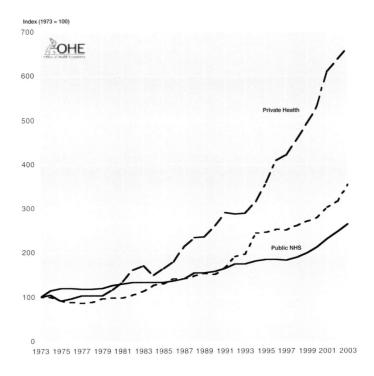

Index (1973 = 100)

Private Health

Public NHS

1973 1975 1977 1979 1981 1983 1985 1987 1989 1991 1993 1995 1997 1999 2001 2003

NHS gross expenditure - proportion spent on each service, UK, 2002/03

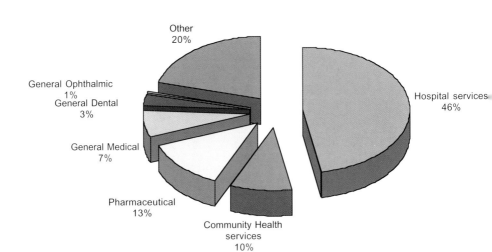

Other
20%

General Ophthalmic
1%
General Dental
3%

General Medical
7%

Pharmaceutical
13%

Community Health
services
10%

Hospital services
46%

Percentages

UK NHS Sources of Finance, 1988 to 2003

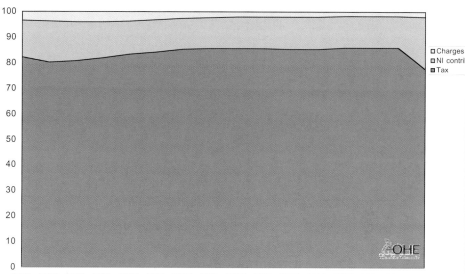

☐ Charges
☐ NI contributions
■ Tax

1988 1989 1990 1991 1992 1993 1994 1995 1996 1997 1998 1999 2000 2001 2002 2003

NHS resources and activities

NHS hospital workforce, UK, 1951 - 2003

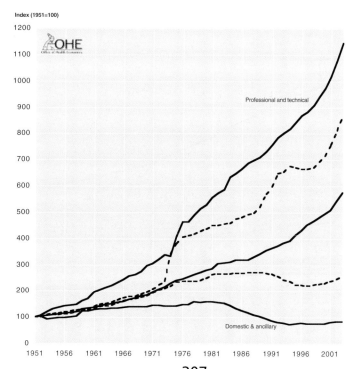

Index (1951=100)

Professional and technical

Domestic & ancillary

1951 1956 1961 1966 1971 1976 1981 1986 1991 1996 2001

307

Number of staff employed in NHS hospitals by category, UK, 2003

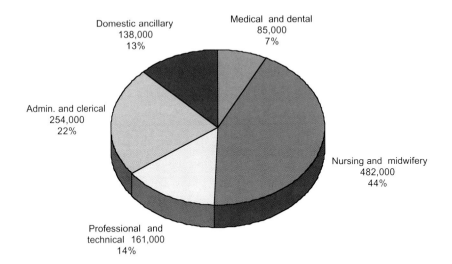

Medical and dental
85,000
7%

Domestic ancillary
138,000
13%

Admin. and clerical
254,000
22%

Nursing and midwifery
482,000
44%

Professional and
technical 161,000
14%

Average daily available acute beds in NHS hospital, Great Britain, 1980-2003/04

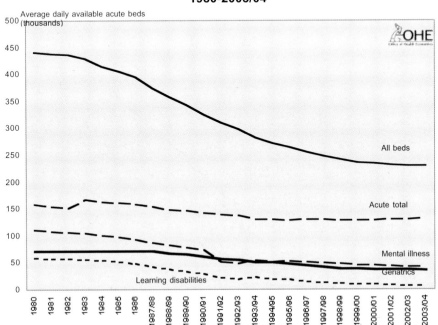

308

Available beds by ward classification, England, 2003/04

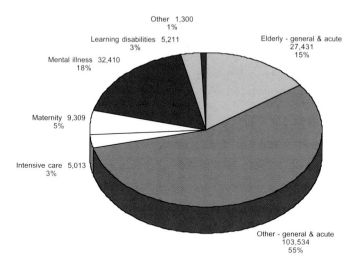

Other 1,300
1%

Learning disabilities 5,211
3%

Mental illness 32,410
18%

Elderly - general & acute
27,431
15%

Maternity 9,309
5%

Intensive care 5,013
3%

Other - general & acute
103,534
55%

Total number of persons waiting for hospital admission, England, 1984 - 2005

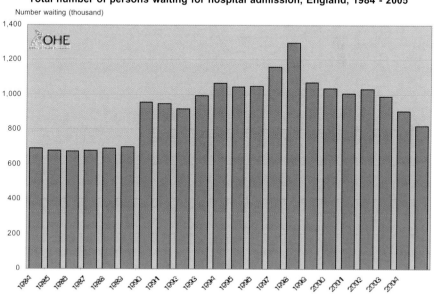

Number waiting (thousand)

309

Hospital outpatient attendances, UK 1980 to 2003/04

Outpatient attendances per 1,000 population

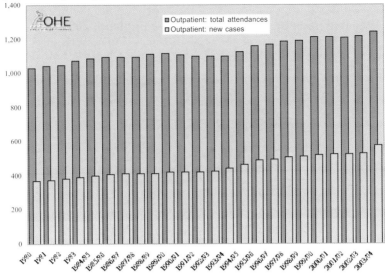

Legend:
- Outpatient: total attendances
- Outpatient: new cases

Notes: Figures from 1984/85 relate to financial year ending 31 March.

Average list size of unrestricted GP principals by country, UK, 1964 - 2003

Average list size

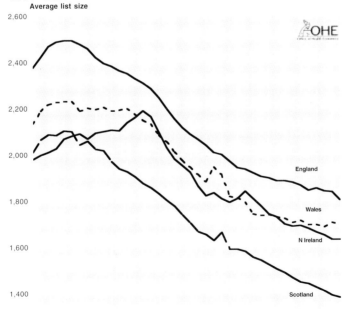

England

Wales

N Ireland

Scotland

Percentage of prescription items dispensed by age group, England, 1980-2004

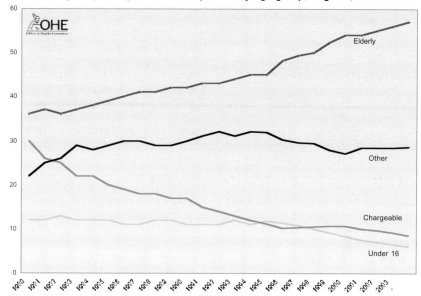

Prescription items dispensed by major therapeutic group, UK, 1991 - 2003

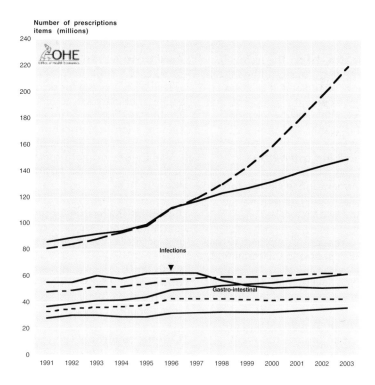

Acute care: Traditionally seen as secondary or hospital-based healthcare services, to which patients are referred to by GPs, or to which people refer themselves by going to an accident and emergency department.

Agenda for change: The new pay system set out in *Agenda for change* has been applied to all directly employed NHS staff, except senior managers and doctors and dentists. A structure has been used based on job evaluation and two pay spines and pay bands. It has also introduced a common set of core conditions of employment.

Allied health professions: A group of staff including dieticians, physiotherapists, orthoptists, occupational therapists, podiatrists, radiographers, speech and language therapists, who used to be know as the professions allied to medicine.

Annual health check: The system for assessing the performance of healthcare organisations in England. It is based on core and developmental standards, and compliance with the standards is monitored by the Healthcare Commission.

Area prescribing committees (APCs): Act as a filter for new drugs entering primary and secondary care and encourage common policies between the two sectors.

Assertive outreach: An approach to care of mentally ill people in the community which involves having specialist teams dedicated to keeping track of severely mentally ill people around the clock.

Business plan: A plan setting out the goals of an organisation and identifying the resources and actions needed to achieve them.

Caldicott guardian: Their role is to safeguard and govern the use of confidential patient information within NHS organisations. Each NHS body appoints a senior health professional as guardian. They get their name from Dame Fiona Caldicott's review of the use of patient-identifiable information, published in 1997.

Calman-Hine framework: A tiered network of care for cancer patients to ensure that the severity of the patient's condition is matched by the degree of specialist care that is available.

Capital charges: Internal NHS charges (depreciation and interest) made against land, building and fixed assets.

Carer: Six million informal carers look after relatives or friends who are elderly, ill or disabled.

Care trust: An NHS body, evolving from primary care trusts or NHS trusts, which is responsible locally for securing a range of primary and community healthcare and social care for older people and/or other client groups, such as children. Local councils delegate one or more functions such as personal social services to the care trust.

Casemix: The mixture of clinical conditions and severity of condition met in a particular healthcare setting.

Cash limit: A limit imposed by the government on the amount of cash which a public body may spend during a given financial year.

Chronic condition: Long-term disease with typically little change in severity over time.

Clinical audit: A cyclical evaluation and measurement by health professions of the clinical standards they are achieving.

Clinical directorate: A unit within an NHS trust providing specific clinical services, frequently led by a consultant.

Clinical governance: The process by which each part of the NHS assures its clinical decisions. It involves a commitment to improving clinical practice through peer review and the use of evidence about effectiveness. It aims to safeguard high standards of care and create a working environment where excellence can flourish.

Clinical network: Health professionals from different NHS organisations working together across institutional and local boundaries, to provide optimum care for a particular disease or patient group. Involves the sharing of information and resources to smooth the patient pathway through the system.

Clinical outcome: The effect on health status of a healthcare intervention, or lack of intervention.

Cochrane Library: This online collection of documents is the work of the Cochrane Collaboration, an international non-profit organisation, dedicated to making available up-to-date, accurate information about the effectiveness of healthcare. The library contains systematic reviews of healthcare interventions and promotes the search for evidence in the form of clinical trials and other studies.

Collaborative: Shared work programme involving different NHS

organisations designed to help local clinical teams to improve the outcomes and experiences of care for groups of patients. Collaboratives have been created in emergency care, cancer and coronary heart disease, orthopaedics and primary care.

Commissioning: The process by which the health needs of the population are defined, priorities determined and appropriate services purchased and evaluated.

Community care: Social care and treatment to patients/clients outside hospital, with an identified physical or mental illness or disability.

Community health partnership: Local Scottish NHS organisation that is responsible for community health and primary care provision, including GP services, pharmacy and community nursing.

Community nurse: A generic term for health visitors, community midwives and district nurses.

Controlled drugs: These are substances named under the Misuse of Drugs Act 1971. They include: opiates and their synthetic substitutes, stimulants such as cocaine and pemoline and hallucinogens (LSD and cannabis). If a practitioner needs to prescribe these drugs, specific requirements must be fulfilled, and only certain people are allowed to prescribe them.

Consultants' contract: The revised consultants' contract, implemented in 2003/04 across the UK, is time sensitive and is based on an agreed schedule of four-hour programmed activities. Clinical duties, out-of-hours commitments and service objectives have to be included in mandatory individual job plans.

Day cases: Patients who have an investigation, treatment or operation and are admitted and discharged on the same day.

Delayed discharge: A patient occupying a hospital bed whose acute treatment has been completed and who should be, and wishes to be, located elsewhere but their transfer is delayed due to lack of appropriate social care services.

Elective admission: A patient who is admitted to hospital in a planned way from a waiting list.

Electronic care record: A record detailing all the health and social care an individual has received. Under government plans, these records will be linked in a single secure national system of more than 30,000 GPs and 270 acute, community and mental health NHS trusts.

Emergency admission: A patient admitted on the same day that admission is requested.

Epidemiology: Study of the distribution and determinants of disease in human populations.

Evidence-based medicine/ healthcare: The systematic analysis of information on the effectiveness of treatments and its use to provide optimum results.

External financing limit: A cash limit set by the Department of Health on net external financing for an NHS trust.

Finished consultant episode (FCE):

An episode where the patient has completed a period of care under a consultant and is either discharged or transferred to another consultant.

Formulary: A list of medicines that has been approved for use in either a primary or secondary care setting.

Foundation trust: NHS hospital trusts which have achieved two or three star status are able to apply to become an NHS foundation trust. The first foundation hospitals were in operation from April 2004 as independent public interest organisations. Their assets remain within public ownership. Local people elect their representatives to serve on the trust's board of governors. From 2005 mental health and other specialist trusts have also been able to apply for foundation status. The government expects all NHS trusts to become foundation trusts by 2008.

General medical services: General practitioners contract with the NHS to provide general medical services for patients registered with their practice.

Health and social services board (HSSB): There are four HSSBs in Northern Ireland. They are responsible for commissioning health and social services for their region.

Health and social services trust: A body that provides healthcare and social services in Northern Ireland. Some provide both primary and secondary care, some provide primary care only and some provide secondary care only.

Health board: The Scottish health boards are strategic and operational bodies. They commmission primary care from primary care operating divisions and secondary care from hospitals.

Healthcare Commission: Monitors standards in every part of the NHS in England. It conducts annual reviews of NHS organisations, rates them, and can also be called in to examine problem areas.

Healthcare resource groups (HRGs): Are a tool classifying patients into a manageable number of groups of cases that are clinically similar

Health gain: The improvement of the health status of a population.

Health needs assessment: The process of determining the healthcare needs of a population or group within a population. It involves studying the health status of the population, the incidence of disease and mortality rates.

Health outcome: The effect on health status of a healthcare intervention, or lack of intervention.

Health promotion: Encouraging people to improve their own health by picking up better lifestyle habits. These could include initiatives to help people give up smoking; eat a more nutritious and balanced diet; take more exercise.

Health service price index: Takes the NHS 'shopping basket' of goods and services (excluding pay of employees) and weighs them according to use to measure price movements.

Health status: A measure of the overall health experience of an individual or a defined population.

Healthy living centres (HLCs): Aim to help people become healthy, both physically and mentally.

Hospice: NHS, voluntary or private residential premises for the provision of palliative care to people who are terminally ill.

Hotel costs: The accommodation costs of keeping a patient in hospital, excluding treatment costs.

Independent prescribing: Prescribing by a doctor or other health professional who is able to act independently.

Inpatient: A patient who has gone through the full admission procedure and is occupying a hospital bed.

Intermediate care: Services designed to assist the transition for a patient or client from medical and social dependence to day-to-day independence. A range of services can be involved as people move from hospital to home, where the objectives of care are not primarily medical, the patient's discharge destination is anticipated, and a clinical outcome of recovery (or restoration of health) is desired. Excluded are services such as convalescence or hotel beds that do not have therapeutic input.

International Classification of Diseases (ICD): Published by the World Health Organization for the statistical classification of morbidity and mortality.

Intubate: Treatment by insertion of a tube.

Joint investment plan (JIP): Aims to help vulnerable groups (eg, older people and adults with mental problems) through interagency funding.

Local delivery plan (LDP): a three-year plan which outlines how resources will be deployed and which healthcare services a primary care trust will invest in. The local delivery plan for a strategic health authority area is formed by putting together the plans of its PCTs.

Long-term condition: Chronic disease with typically little change in severity over time.

Medical outlier: A hospital medical patient in a surgical bed.

MEDLINE: Electronic database summarising thousands of published biomedical studies.

Meta-analysis: A method of combining the findings of a number of studies in a clinical area, with different weightings given to individual trials, to allow firmer conclusions to be drawn.

Monitor: The independent regulator of foundation trusts.

Morbidity rate: The relative incidence of a particular disease in a specific locality.

Mortality rate: The ratio of deaths in a specified area/group, to the population of that area/group.

National Institute for Health and Clinical Excellence (NICE): A special health authority that produces formal advice for NHS clinicians and managers in England and Wales on the clinical and cost-effectiveness of new and existing medicines, clinical guidelines, interventional procedures and public health measures.

National Prescribing Centre (NPC): Based in Liverpool and led by pharmacists, the centre provides the NHS with advance details about new treatments. Its primary role is to encourage high quality, cost-effective prescribing.

National service framework: Evidence-based programme that spells out what patients can expect to receive from the health service in a major care area or disease group. Issued by the Department of Health in conjunction with the National Institute for Health and Clinical Excellence, they specify the type of services that should be available in all primary care, local hospital and specialist centres.

National tariff: A standard national price list for NHS treatments which is being used to implement the payment by results system.

NHS Direct: 24-hour (telephone/internet) advice service for the English public.

NHS LIFTs: Local improvement finance trusts. Public-private partnership projects, set up to improve primary care premises.

NHS Plan: Published in July 2000, this is the main ten-year plan for the NHS, with the emphasis on the needs and convenience of the patient.

NHS trust: Self-governing NHS body which provides hospital, mental health or ambulance services. They obtain most of their income from service agreements for patient care with primary care trusts.

Non-medical prescribing: Prescribing by a suitable trained and accredited health professional who is not a doctor.

Number needed to treat (NNT): The number of patients who need to be given a particular treatment for a positive result to be achieved in one of them.

Nurse practitioner: Nurse with advanced training able to undertake much healthcare without reference to a doctor. They typically work to pre-agreed clinical protocols.

Obstetric: Care of women during pregnancy, childbirth and up to six weeks following the birth.

Out-of-hours care: Care that is provided outside of the normal working day. The new general medical services contract defines the out-of-hours period as 6.30pm to 8.00am on weekdays, the whole of weekends, Bank Holidays and public holidays.

Outpatient: A patient attending for treatment, consultation and advice, but not staying in a hospital.

Out-turn prices: The prices prevailing when the expenditure occurs, as distinct from the estimated prices.

PACT data: Prescribing analysis and cost tabulation on the name and cost of medicines prescribed by individual GPs.

Palliative care: The management of pain and symptoms in seriously ill patients so as to improve and maintain their quality of life.

Paramedics: Ambulance personnel qualified to provide pre-hospital care.

Parenteral nutrition: Feeding by means other than by the mouth.

Patient advice and liaison service (PALS): Set up in NHS trusts and primary care trusts to provide information to patients, their carers and families and to help to them through the system and to resolve any immedi-ate problems and complaints.

Patient-centred care: Care and treatment is designed around the needs of the patient, and their convenience, and patients and users are fully con-sulted on the performance of health services and their future development.

Patient pathway: The route followed by the patient into, through and out of NHS and social care services.

Patient and public involvement forum: Set up in each NHS trust and primary care trust and responsible for representing the views of patients and users of the services provided.

Patient spell: A continuous period of time spent as an inpatient. It may include more than one finished consult-ant episode.

Pay bed (private bed): A bed occu-pied by a patient who pays the whole cost of accommodation, medical and other services.

Payment by results: A method for standardising healthcare commission-ing. A fixed price tariff is being introduced for all healthcare treat-ments which will be employed across the NHS.

Performance assessment frame-work: A framework introduced by the Department of Health designed comprehensively to measure and improve standards of performance, efficiency and patient care within NHS organisations.

Personal medical services (PMS): Are an approach to providing primary care that allow health professionals to deliver services in a targeted manner to suit local conditions. They often focus on local problems such as high levels of illness or inequalities in access to services. Over a third of GPs work under PMS.

Prescription Pricing Authority (PPA): A special health authority which makes payments to pharmacists and dispensing doctors in England for NHS prescriptions. It provides detailed information on prescribing trends (in the form of PACT reports), to the Department of Health, NHS organisations and GPs. It also detects prescription frauds.

Practice-based commissioning: GP practices, singly or in partnerhsip, commission services for their patients from hospitals and other organisations. They do this using a budget and in the context of the PCT local delivery plan. Any savings made can be ploughed back into the practice.

Primary care: Care provided in the community by GPs, the practice team and associated health professionals.

Primary care organisation: NHS body which organises NHS primary care in the UK (eg, primary care trusts in England and local health boards in Wales).

Primary care trust (PCT): NHS body (with its own budget) that is responsible for delivering healthcare and commissioning hospital services for its local population. They are responsible for improving the health of their community and developing l ocal primary care services.

Private finance initiative (PFI): A government system of encouraging private capital to be employed in public

sector projects so as not to add to the total public sector borrowing requirement.

Private patient: A patient who pays the full cost of all medical and other services.

Professional executive committee (PEC): Comprising a majority of health professionals (eg, GPs, nurses and allied health professionals), the PEC is responsible for running the PCT on a day-to-day basis.

Provider: A healthcare organisation, such as an NHS trust, which provides healthcare and sells its services to purchasers (commissioners).

Purchaser: A healthcare body, such as a primary care trust, which assesses the health needs of a population and buys services to meet those needs.

Quality and outcomes framework: Part of the general medical services contract for GPs which sets out targets concerning clinical and managerial outcomes. Achievement of the targets by GPs earns them points and fees.

QUALY: Quality adjusted life year — an economic measure which assesses variations in the quality of life for the patient resulting from an intervention in relation to cost and length of life.

Randomised control trial: A research trial in which a cohort of patients are randomly allocated to a group receiving treatment or a control group receiving no or conventional treatment.

Service level agreement (SLA): Typically these agreements for the delivery of health services between purchasers and providers last for three years. They set out the responsibilities of the parties on issues such as the cost, volume, quality, efficiency and effectiveness of the services to be provided.

Skill mix: The mixture of skill levels of individual members of staff that are available to perform a particular task or group of tasks.

Specialty: A branch of medicine such as orthopaedics, paediatrics, and so on.

Standardised mortality ratio: The number of deaths in a given year as a percentage of those expected.

Strategic health authorities (SHAs): Strategic health authorities performance manage NHS trusts and primary care trusts in England. They are expected to secure improvement in services and encourage local NHS organisations to work together.

Supplementary prescribing: Supplementary prescribers take responsibility for the continuing care of patients who have already been clinically assessed by a doctor. Trained nurses and pharmacists prescribe medicines, based on care management plans.

Tertiary care: When a hospital consultant refers a patient with an unusual condition or one needing highly specialised treatments on again to a specialist centre such as a teaching hospital or a regional hospital.

Throughput: The number of patients using each bed in a given period (also termed bed turnover).

Treatment centre: Help the NHS to increase the number of NHS elective operations and diagnostic procedures performed. They enable routine

surgery to be separated from emergency work, and are often being financed in partnership with the private sector.

Turnover interval: The average number of days that beds are vacant between successive occupants.

Virement: The transfer of resources from one budget heading to another.

Waiting list: The number of people awaiting admission to hospital as inpatients.

Waiting time: The time which elapses between (1) the request by a GP for an appointment and the attendance of the patient at the outpatients' department, or (2) the date a patient's name is put on an inpatients' list and the date they are admitted.

Wanless reports: The first Wanless report (*Securing our future health*) is a study of long-term UK health trends, written by Sir Derek Wanless in 2002. It successfully called on the government to devote a larger share of the national income to healthcare over the next 20 years. A second report in 2004 (*Securing good health for the whole population*) concentrates on public health and argues that preventing poor health, rather than treating it, can reduce NHS spending. Its recommendations were fed into the 2004 public health White Paper *Choosing health*.

Weighted capitation: Sum of money provided for each resident in a particular locality.

AAA	Annual accountability agreement
A&C	Administrative and clerical
A&E	Accident and emergency
ABC	Activity based costing
ABHI	Association of British Health-Care Industries
ABM	Activity based management
ABPI	Association of the British Pharmaceutical Industry
AC	Audit Commission
ACAS	Advisory, Conciliation and Arbitration Service
ACCEA	Advisory committee on clinical excellence awards
ACD	Appraisal consultation document
ACDP	Advisory committee on dangerous pathogens
ACGT	Advisory committee on genetic testing
ACIS	Advanced clinical information system
ACPC	Area child protection committee
ACRA	Advisory committee on resource allocation
ACTR	Additional cost of teaching and research
ADA	Annual delivery agreement
ADC	Automatic data capture
ADL	Activities of daily living
ADP	Automatic data processing
ADR	Adverse drug reaction
ADSS	Association of Directors of Social Services
AfC	Agenda for change
AFR	Annual financial return
AGH	Advisory group on hepatitis
AHCPA	Association of Health Centre and Practice Administrators
AHHRM	Association of Healthcare Human Resource Management
AHP	Allied health profession
AIM	Activity information mapping Advanced informatics in medicine
AIP	Approval in principle
ALA	Association of Local Authorities
ALARM	Association of Litigation and Risk Managers
ALB	Arm's length body
ALE	Auditor's local evaluation
ALERT	Auditor's local evaluation and reporting tool

ALOS	Average length of stay
AMA	Association of Metropolitan Authorities
AMP	Annual maintenance plan
AOP	Association of Optometrists
APC	Area prescribing committee
APH	Association for Public Health
APMS	Alternative provider medical services
AQH	Association for Quality in Healthcare
ARC	Arthritis and Rheumatism Council
ASA	Ambulance Service Association
ASC	Action for Sick Children
ASH	Action on Smoking and Health
ASSIST	Association for Information Management and Technology Staff in the NHS
ASW	Approved social worker
ATLS	Advanced trauma life support (procedures/courses)
AVG	Ambulatory visit group
AVMA	Action for the Victims of Medical Accidents
AWMEG	All-Wales Management Efficiency Group
AWMSG	All-Wales medicines strategy group
BAEM	British Association for Accident and Emergency Medicine
BAMM	British Association of Medical Managers
BAMS	Benefits Agency Medical Service
BAOT	British Association of Occupational Therapists
BASICS	British Association of Immediate Care Schemes
BASW	British Association of Social Workers
BaTA	Blood and Transplant Authority
BCS	British Computer Society
BDA	British Dental Association British Dietetic Association
BEAM	Biomedical equipment assessment and management
BMCIS	Building maintenance cost information system
BMA	British Medical Association
BMI	Body mass index
BMJ	British Medical Journal

BMS   Booking mangement service
BNF   British National Formulary
BPAS   British Pregnancy Advisory
         Service
BPMF   British Postgraduate Medical
         Federation
BRCS   British Red Cross Society
BSI   British Standards Institution
BTA   Blood and Transplant Authority
BTS   British Thoracic Society
BUPA   British United Provident
         Association

CAB   Clinical advisory board
CAD   Computer aided design
CAP   Controls assurance project
CAS   Clinical assessment service
         Controls assurance statement
CASP   Critical Appraisal Skills
         Programme
CAT   Computerised axial tomography
         (Health and social care)
         Change agent team
CBA   Cost benefit analysis
CBS   Common basic specification
CCDC   Consultant in communicable
         disease control
CCE   Completed consultant episode
         (also FCE)
CCSC   Central Consultants and
         Specialists Committee
CCST   Former certificate of completion
         of specialist training (doctors)
CCT   Certificate of completion of
         training (doctors)
CCU   Coronary care unit
         Critical care unit
CD   Clinical director
         Clinical directorate
CDC   Center for Disease Control (USA)
CDM   Chronic disease management
CDO   Chief dental officer
CDP   Clinical disputes protocol
CD-ROM   Compact disc read only memory
CDSC   Former Communicable Disease
         Surveillance Centre
CDSM   Committee on Dental and
         Surgical Materials
CDSS   Computerised decision support
         system
CE   Chief executive

CEA   Clinical excellence award
         Cost effectiveness analysis
CEDP   Chief executive development
         programme
CEMACH   Confidential enquiry into
         maternal and child health
CEN   Comité Europeen de
         Normalisation (European
         Standards Organisation)
CEPPI   Centre for excellence in patient
         and public involvement
CES   Community equipment service
CfH   Connecting for Health
CfI   Centre for Infections
CFSMS   Counter fraud and security
         management service
CGSDU   Clinical governance support and
         development unit
CGST   Clinical governance support team
CHAI   Commission for Healthcare Audit
         and Inspection (Healthcare
         Commission)
CHI   Community health index
         Former Commission for Health
         Improvement
CHM   Commission on Human Medicines
CHP   Community health partnership
         (Scotland)
CHRE   Council for Healthcare
         Regulatory Excellence
CHS   Child health surveillance
CI   Clinical indicator
CIO   Chief information officer
CIC   Common information core
CIM   Capital investment manual
CIMP   Clinical information management
         programme
CIP   Cost improvement programme
CIPFA   Chartered Institute of Public
         Finance and Accountancy
CIS   Clinical information system
CM   Community midwife
CMDS   Contract/core minimum data set
CME   Continuing medical education
CMHN   Community mental handicap
         nurse
CMHT   Community mental health team
CMMS   Case mix management system
CMO   Chief medical officer
CMS   Community midwifery service
         Contract management system

CN	Charge nurse	CRL	Capital resource limit
CNM	Clinical nurse manager	CRS	Care records service
CNO	Chief nursing officer	CSA	Children's services adviser
CNS	Clinical nurse specialist		Child Support Agency
	Community nursing service	CSASHS	Common Services Agency for the
CNST	Clinical Negligence Scheme for		Scottish Health Service
	Trusts	CSCI	Commission for Social Care
COI	Central Office of Information		Inspection
COMEAP	Committee on the medical effects	CSD	Committee on the Safety of
	of air pollutants		Devices
COPD	Chronic obstructive pulmonary	CSIP	Care services improvement
	disease		partnership
COREC	Central office of research ethics	CSIW	Care Standards Inspectorate for
	committees		Wales
COSHH	Control of Substances Hazardous	CSM	Former Committee on Safety of
	to Health (1999 Regulations)		Medicines
COSI	Central open system	CSP	Chartered Society of
	interconnection		Physiotherapy
CPA	Care programme approach	CSSD	Central sterile services/supplies
	Clinical Pathology Accreditation		department
	Critical path analysis	CT	Computerised tomography
CPAG	Capital prioritisation advisory	CTO	Compulsory treatment order
	group	CU	Casualties Union
CPD	Continuing professional		
	development	DAC	Dental access centre
CPEP	Clinical practice evaluation	DDA	Disability Discrimination Act
	programme	DDRB	Doctors and Dentists Review
CPH	Collaborative procurement hub		Body
CPHL	Central Public Health Laboratory	DEB	Dental Estimates Board
CPHM	Consultant in public health	DEC	Development and evaluation
	medicine		committee
CPMP	Committee for proprietary	DES	Direct enhanced services
	medical products (EU)	DF	Director of finance
CPPIH	Commission for Patient and	DfES	Department for Education and
	Public Involvement in Health		Skills
CPN	Community psychiatric nurse	DFT	Distance from target
CPR	Child protection register	DGH	District general hospital
CPS	Centre for public scrutiny	DH	Department of Health (also DoH)
CQI	Continuous quality improvement	DHSC	Directorate of health and social
CRD	(NHS) Centre for Reviews and		care
	Dissemination	DHT	District handicap team
CRDB	Care record development board	DI	Director of information
CRDC	Central research and	DIPC	Director of infection prevention
	development committee		and control
CRE	Commission for Racial Equality	DIPG	Drug Information Pharmacists
CRES	Cash releasing efficiency savings		Group
CRHP	Former Council for the	DIO	District immunisation officer
	Regulation of Healthcare	DMD	Drug misuse database
	Professionals	DN	District nurse
CRIR	Committee for regulating	DNA	Did not attend
	information requirements	DNS	Director of nursing services

DOA	Dead on arrival
DOB	Date of birth
DoF	Director of finance
DoH	Department of Health (also DH)
DPH	Director of public health
DRG	Diagnosis/diagnostic related group
DRS	Dental Reference Service
DSC	Disablement service centre
DSCA	Defence Secondary Care Agency
DSS	Decision support systems Department of Social Security
DSD	Database of service delivery
DSU	Day surgery unit
DTC	Drug and therapeutics committee
DTI	Department of Trade and Industry
DV	Domiciliary visit (by consultant)
EAN	European article number
EBM	Evidence-based medicine
EBS	Emergency Bed Service
ECDL	European computer driving licence
ECP	Emergency care practitioner
ECST	Emergency care strategy team
EDI	Electronic data interchange
EDIFACT	Electronic data interchange for administration, commerce and transport
EFL	External financing limit
EHIC	European health insurance card
EHMA	European Healthcare Management Association
EHO	Environmental health officer
EHR	Electronic health record
EIS	Executive information system
EL	Executive letter
EMAS	Employment Medical Advisory Service
EMDS	Email and directory service
EMEA	European Medicines Evaluation Agency
EMI	Elderly mentally infirm
ENP	Emergency nurse practitioner
ENT	Ear, nose and throat
EOC	Equal Opportunities Commission
EPP	Expert patient programme
EPO	Emergency planning officer
EPR	Electronic patient record
EPS	Electronic prescription service

EQUIP	External reference group on effectiveness and quality in practice
ERDIP	Electronic record development and implementation programme
ESAT	Emergency services action team
ESMI	Elderly severely mentally infirm
ESR	Electronic staff record
ETA	Enabling technology application
ETD	Education, training and development
ETP	Electronic transfer of prescriptions
EWTD	European Working Time Directive
FBC	Full business case
FCE	Finished consultant episode (also CCE)
FCS	Financial control system
FDL	Finance directorate letter
FHS	Family health services
FIS	Financial information system
FM	Facilities management
FMIS	Financial management information systems
FMP	Financial management programme
FNC	(NHS) funded nursing care
FOI	Freedom of information (legislation)
FPA	Family Planning Association
FPHM	Faculty of Public Health Medicine
FPS	Family planning services Family practitioner services
FRS	Financial reporting standards
FSA	Food Standards Agency
FSO	Forum support organisation
FT	Foundation trust
FTE	Full time equivalent
FTN	Foundation Trust Network
GCC	General Chiropractic Council
GDC	General Dental Council
GDP	General dental practitioner Gross domestic product
GDS	General dental services
GHS	General household survey
GM	General manager
GMC	General Medical Council
GMP	General medical practitioner

GMS	General medical services
GNP	Gross national product
GOC	General Optical Council
GOsC	General Osteopathic Council
GOS	General ophthalmic service
GOsC	General Osteopathic Council
GPC	General Practitioners Committee
GPFC	General Practice Finance Corporation
GPRD	General practice research database
GPSI	General practitioner with special interest
GRE	Glycopeptide-resistant enterococci
GSCC	General Social Care Council
GTAC	Gene therapy advisory committee
GUM	Genitourinary medicine
HA	Health authority
HAN	Hospital at night
HAI	Healthcare associated infection Hospital acquired infection
HAZ	Health action zone
HB	Health board
HBG	Health benefit group
HC	Healthcare Commission
HCA	Hospital Caterers Association
HCAI	Healthcare associated infection
HCHS	Hospital and community health services
HDA	Former Health Development Agency
HEFCE	Higher Education Funding Council for England
Hefma	Health Facilities Management Association
HELMIS	Health Management Information Service (Nuffield Institute, Leeds)
HEO	Health education officer
HES	Hospital episode statistics Hospital eye service
HFC	Healthcare Facilities Consortium
HFEA	Human Fertilisation and Embryology Authority
HFMA	Healthcare Financial Management Association
HGC	Human Genetics Commission
HHT	Hand held terminal
HIA	Health impact assessment

HIBCC	Health Index Bar Code Council
HIS	Health information service Health informatics service
HISS	Hospital information and support system
HIW	Healthcare Inspectorate Wales
HLC	Healthy living centre
HLPI	High-level performance indicator
HMR	Hospital medical record
HMO	Health maintenance organisation (USA)
HO	House officer
HOSC	(Local authority) health overview and scrutiny committee
HPA	Health Protection Agency
HPC	Health Professions Council
HPR	Health process re-design
HPS	Health Protection Scotland
HR	Human resources
HRA	Human Rights Act
HRG	Healthcare resource group
HSAC	Health Service Advisory Committee (of HSE)
HSC	Health and Safety Commission Health service circular Health Service Commissioner Horizon Scanning Centre (University of Birmingham)
HSCIC	Health and social care information centre
HSDU	Hospital sterile and disinfection unit
HSE	Health and Safety Executive Health survey for England
HSG	Health service guideline
HSI	Health service indicator
HSJ	Health Service Journal
HSPI	Health Service Prices Index
HSSB	Health and social services board (Northern Ireland)
HSW	Health & safety at work
HSWA	Health & Safety at Work Act 1974
HTA	Health technology assessment Human Tissue Authority
HTM	High technology medicine
HV	Health visitor
IBD	Interest bearing debt
IC	Information Commissioner
ICAS	Independent complaints advocacy service

Wellard's NHS Handbook 2006/07

ICD	International Classification of Diseases
ICF	Intelligent customer function (information technology)
ICN	Infection control nurse
ICP	Integrated care pathway
ICR	Injury costs recovery
ICT	Infection control team
ICU	Intensive care unit
ICWS	Integrated clinical work station
IG	Information governance
IHE	Institute of Hospital Engineering International Health Exchange
IHF	International Hospital Federation
IHM	Institute of Healthcare Management
IHRIM	Institute of Health Record Information Management
IIP	Investors in People initiative
ILAF	Independent local advisory forum
IMCA	Independent mental capacity advocate
IMLS	Institute of Medical Laboratory Sciences
IM&T	Information management and technology
IOG	Improving outcome guidance
IP	Inpatient
IPAS	Improvement partnership for ambulance services
IPM	Institute of Personnel Management
IPR	Individual performance review
IRP	Independent Reconfiguration Panel
ISSM	Institute of Sterile Services Management
ISTC	Independent sector treatment centre
IT	Information technology
ITU	Intensive therapy/treatment unit
IWL	Improving working lives
JCC	Joint Consultants Committee Joint consultative committee
JCVI	Jont committee on vaccination and immunisation
JDC	Junior Doctors Committee
JFC	Joint Formulary Committee
JIF	Joint investment fund (Scotland)
JIT	Just in time (supplies delivery)

JIP	Joint investment plan
JPAC	Joint planning advisory committee
KF	King's Fund
KI	Key indicator (social services)
KSF	Knowledge and skills framework
LAS	London Ambulance Service
LCR	Local care record
LDC	Local dental committee
LDDF	Learning disabilities development fund
LDP	Local delivery plan
LEAP	Local exercise action pilot
LHB	Local health board
LHC	Local health community
LHE	Local health economy
LHG	Local health group (Wales)
LIFT	Local improvement finance trust
LIS	Local implementation strategy
LMC	Local medical committee
LOS	Length of stay
LPI	Labour productivity index
LPS	Local pharmaceutical services
LREC	Local research ethics committee
LSCB	Local safeguarding children board
LSMS	Local security management specialist
LSP	Local service provider (IT) Local strategic partnership
LTA	Long term agreement
LTC	Long term condition
LTPS	Liability to third parties scheme (NHS insurance)
LTSA	Long term service agreement
LYS	Life year saved
MAAG	Medical audit advisory group Multidisciplinary audit advisory group
MAC	Medical advisory committee
MAF	Management accountancy framework
MAS	Minimal access surgery
MASC	Medical Academic Staff Committee
MAU	Medical assessment unit
MBA	Master of business administration
MC	Medicines Commission

MCN	Managed clinical network	NAAS	National Association of Air Ambulance Services
MCO	Managed care organisation		
MCP	Medical care practitioner	NACS	National administrative code service
MDD	Medical Devices Directorate		
MDO	Mentally disordered offender	NAGPC	National Association of GP Co-operatives
MDS	Minimum data set		
MDT	Multidisciplinary team	NAHCSM	National Association of Health Care Supplies Managers
MDU	Medical Defence Union		
MEC	Management executive committee	NAHSSO	National Association of Health Service Security Officers
MEL	Management executive letter (Scotland)	NALHF	National Association of Leagues of Hospital Friends
MESOL	Management Education Scheme by Open Learning	NAO	National Audit Office
		NAPC	National Association of Primary Care
MFF	Market forces factor		
MFS	Market forces supplement	NAPP	National Association for Patient Participation
MHAC	Mental Health Act Commission		
MHE	Mental health enquiry	NASP	National application service provider (IT)
MHRA	Medicines and Healthcare Products Regulatory Agency	NATN	National Association of Theatre Nurses
MIMS	Monthly Index of Medical Specialties	NatPaCT	National primary and care trust (development programme)
MISG	Mental illness specific grant	NBA	Former National Blood Authority (for England)
MIT	Minimally invasive therapy		
MIU	Minor injuries unit	NBAP	National booked admissions programme
MLA	Medical laboratory assistant		
MLSO	Medical laboratory scientific officer	NBI	National beds inquiry
MLTC	Managing long term conditions	NBTS	National Blood Transfusion Service
MMC	Modernising medical careers		
MOP	Mobile optical practice	NCA	Non contract activity
MPET	Multi-profession education and training (budget)	NCAA	Fomer National Clinical Assessment Authority
MPS	Medical Protection Society	NCAS	National clinical assessment service
MRC	Medical Research Council		
MRI	Magnetic resonance imaging	NCCHTA	National Coordinating Centre for Health Technology Assessment
MRO	Medical records officer		
MRSA	Methicillin-resistant *Staphylococcus aureus*	NCEPOD	National Confidential Enquiry into Patient Outcome and Death
MSAC	Maternity Services Advisory Committee		Former National Confidential Enquiry into Perioperative Deaths
MSLC	Maternity Services Liaison Committee		
MSF	Manufacturing Science and Finance (technical staff trade union)	NCHOD	National Centre for Health Outcomes Development
		NCISH	National Confidential Inquiry into Suicide and Homicide by People with Mental Illness
MUR	Medicines use review		
MWCS	Mental Welfare Commission for Scotland	NCMO	National Case Mix Office
MWSAC	Medical workforce standing advisory committee	NCPC	National Council for Paliative Care

NCRI   National Cancer Research Institute
NCR   National care record
NCRS   NHS care records service
NCVO   National Council for Voluntary Organisations
NCVQ   National Council for Vocational Qualifications
NDPB   Non-departmental public body
NDT   National Development Team for People with Learning Disabilities
NDTMS   National drug treatment monitoring system
NEAT   New and emerging applications of technology
NED   Non-executive director
NeLH   National electronic Library for Health
NES   National Health Service Education for Scotland
NET   New and emerging technologies
NF   Nuffield Foundation
NFA   No fixed address
NHSAC   National Health Service Appointments Commission
NHSAR   National Health Service Administrative Register
NHSBSA   National Health Service Business Services Authority
NHSBT   National Health Service Blood and Transplant
NHSCCC   National Health Service Centre for Coding and Classification
NHSCR   National Health Service Central Register
NHS CRS   National Health Service care records service
NHS CTA   National Health Service Clinical Trials Adviser
NHSE   Former National Health Service Estates
NHS EED   NHS Economic Evaluation Database
NHSFT   National Health Service foundation trust
NHSIA   Former National Health Service Information Authority
NHSiS   National Health Service in Scotland
NHSIII   National Health Service Institute for Innovation and Improvement
NHSISB   National Health Service information standards board
NHSL   National Health Service Logistics
NHSLA   National Health Service Litigation Authority
NHS LIFT National Health Service Local Improvement Finance Trust
NHSP   NHS Professionals
NHSPSA   National Health Service Purchasing and Supply Agency
NHST   National Health Service trust
NHSTU   National Health Service Training Unit
NHSQIS   National Health Service Quality Improvement Scotland
NHSU   Fomer National Health Service University
NICARE   Northern Ireland Centre for Health Care Co-operation and Development
NICE   National Institute for Health and Clinical Excellence (formerly National Institute for Clinical Excellence)
NICON   Nothern Ireland Confederation of Health and Social Services
NIH   Nuffield Institute for Health (Leeds)
NIHR   National Institute for Health Research
NIMHE   National Institute for Mental Health in England
NINSS   Nosocomial infection national surveillance scheme
NISP   National infrastructure service provider (IT)
NKS   National knowledge service
NLH   National Library for Health
NMC   Nursing and Midwifery Council
NNH   Number needed to harm
NNT   Number needed to treat
NOM   Non officer member
NPA   National Pharmaceutical Association
NPAT   National patients access team
NPC   National Prescribing Centre
NPfIT   National programme for information technology
NPG   National priorities guidance

Wellard's NHS Handbook 2006/07

NPHT	Nuffield Provincial Hospitals Trust		(London)
NPIS	National Poisons Information	OHS	Occupational health service
	Service	OHSC	Occupational health smart card
NPSA	National Patient Safety Agency	OJEC	Official Journal of the European
NPT	Near patient testing		Community
NRCI	National reference cost index	OLIT	Organisational lead for
NRE	Non-recurring expenditure		information technology
NRLS	National reporting and learning	OMP	Ophthalmic medical practitioner
	system	ONS	Office for National Statistics
NRPB	Former National Radiological	OOH	Out of hours
	Protection Board	OP	Outpatient
NRR	National research register	OPD	Outpatient department
NRT	Nicotine replacement therapy	OPM	Office of Public Management
NSAID	Non-steroidal anti-inflammatory	OSC	(Local authority) overview and
	drug		scrutiny committee
NSC	National screening committee	OT	Occupational therapist/therapy
	(UK)	OU	Open University
NSCAG	National specialist commissioning		
	advisory group	P&T	Professional and technical
NSF	National service framework	PA	Patients Association
NSPF	National strategic partnership		Programmed activity
	forum	PAC	Public Accounts Committee
NSRC	National schedule of reference	PACS	Picture archiving and
	costs		communications system
NSTS	NHS strategic tracing service	PACT	Prescription analysis and cost
NSV	National supplies vocabulary		tabulation
NTA	National Treatment Agency (for	PAF	Performance assessment
	Substance Misuse)		framework
NTO	National training organisation	PALS	Patient advice and liaison service
NTTRL	National Tissue Typing Reference	PARC	Prescription audit reports and
	Laboratory		catalogue (Wales)
NVQ	National vocational qualification	PAS	Patient administration system
NWCS	Former NHS-wide clearing service	PAT	Performance assessment toolkit
NWN	NHS-wide networking	PBC	Practice based commissioning
		PBR	Payment by results
OAT	Former out of area treatment	PCAG	Primary care audit group
OBC	Outline business case	PCIP	Primary care investment plan
OCR	Optical character recognition	PCT	Primary care trust
OCS	Order communication system	PCTE	Primary care trust executive
ODA	Operating department assistant	PCTMS	Primary care trust medical
ODP	Operating department		services
	practitioner	PDC	Public dividend capital
ODPM	Office of the Deputy Prime	PDP	Personal development plan
	Minister	PDS	Personal demographics service
OECD	Organization for Economic		Personal dental services
	Cooperation and	PEC	Professional executive committee
	Development		(of PCT)
OGC	Office for Government	PEAT	Patient environment action team
	Commerce	PEM	Prescription event monitoring
OH	Occupational health	PES	Property expenses scheme (NHS
OHE	Office of Health Economics		insurance)

	Public Expenditure Survey
PET	Positron emission tomography
PEWP	Public Expenditure White Paper
PF	Patients' forum
PFC	Patient focused care
PFI	Private finance initiative
PFU	Private finance unit
PGD	Patient group direction
PGEA	Postgraduate education allowance
PGMDE	Postgraduate medical and dental education
PHA	Public Health Alliance
PHC	Primary health care
PHCDS	Public health common data set
PHCT	Primary health care team
PHL	Public health laboratory
PHLS	Fomer Public Health Laboratory Service
PHO	Public health observatory
PHSS	Personal health summary system
PI	Performance indicator
PIAG	Patient information advisory group
PIC	Paediatric intensive care
PIF	Patient Information Forum
PIL	Patient information leaflet
PMCPA	Prescription Medicines Code of Practice Authority
PMETB	Postgraduate medical education and training board
PMI	Performance management indicator
	Private medical insurance
PMR	Physical medicine and rehabilitation
PMS	Personal medical service
	Post marketing surveillance (medicines)
PODs	Patient's own drugs
POM	Prescription only medicine
POMR	Problem oriented medical records
POPP	Partnerships for older people projects
POPUMET	Protection of persons undergoing medical examination (regulations)
PPA	Prescription Pricing Authority
PPC	Promoting Patient Choice
PPF	Priorities and planning framework

PPG	Patient participation group
PPI	Patient and public involvement
PPIF	Patient and public involvement forum
PPM	Planned preventive maintenance
PPP	Private Patients Plan
	Public-private partnership
PPO	Preferred provider organisation
PPRS	Pharmaceutical price regulation scheme
PQ	Parliamentary question
PRB	Pay review body
PREPP	Post registration education and preparation for practice (nurses)
PRP	Performance related pay
	Policy research programme
PSA	Public service agreement
PSBR	Public sector borrowing requirement
PSNCR	Public sector net cash requirement
PSI	Policy Studies Institute (London)
PSNC	Pharmaceutical Services Negotiating Committee
PSO	Patient safety observatory
PSPP	Public services productivity panel
PSS	Personal social services
PTS	Patient transport services
PVC	Prime vendor contract
QA	Quality assurance
QALY	Quality adjusted life year
QMAS	Quality management and analysis system
QOF	Quality and outcomes framework
QUANGO	Quasi-autonomous nongovernmental organisation
R&D	Research and development
RA	Registration authority
RAFT	Regulatory Authority for Fertility and Tissue
RAM	Registration authority manager
RCA	Royal College of Anaesthetists
RCCS	Revenue consequences of capital schemes
RCGP	Royal College of General Practitioners
RCM	Royal College of Midwives

RCN	Royal College of Nursing		medicines (guidelines)
RCOG	Royal College of Obstetricians	SAP	Single assessment process
	and Gynaecologists	SAS	Standard accounting system
RCP	Royal College of Physicians		Scottish Ambulance Service
RCPCH	Royal College of Paediatrics and	SAU	Surgical assessment unit
	Child Health	SCBU	Special care baby unit
RCPath	Royal College of Pathologists	SCIEH	Former Scottish Centre for
RCPsych	Royal College of Psychiatrists		Infection and Environmental
RCS	Royal College of Surgeons		Health
RCT	Randomised controlled trial	SCM	Specialist in community medicine
REC	Research ethics committee	SCODA	Standing Conference on Drug
RDU	Regional dialysis unit		Abuse
RFA	Requirements for accreditation	SCOPME	Standing Committee on
	(GP computers)		Postgraduate Medical
RGN	Registered general nurse		Education
RHI	Regional head of information	SCOTH	Scientific Committee on Tobacco
RIPA	Royal Institute of Public		and Health
	Administration	SCP	Surgical care practitioner
RMO	Resident medical officer	SDAC	Standing dental advisory
	Responsible medical officer		committee
RMN	Registered mental nurse	SDO	Service delivery and organisation
RN	Registered nurse	SDP	Service delivery practice (NHS
RNHA	Registered Nursing Home		Web database)
	Association	SDU	Service delivery unit
RNMH	Registered nurse for the mentally	SEHD	Scottish Executive Health
	handicapped		Department
ROCE	Return on capital employed	SERNIP	Former safety and efficacy
ROE	Regional office for Europe (WHO)		register of new interventional
RPSGB	Royal Pharmaceutical Society of		procedures
	Great Britain	SFA	Statement of fees and allowances
RPST	Risk pooling scheme for trusts	SfBH	*Standards for better health*
RRAP	Regulatory reform action plan	SFE	Statement of financial
RSCG	Regional specialist commissioning		entitlements (for GPs)
	group	SFI	Standing financial instructions
RSCN	Registered sick children's nurse	SHA	Strategic health authority (or
RSH	Royal Society of Health		StHA)
RSI	Repetitive strain injury		Special health authority
RSM	Royal Society of Medicine	SHARE	Scottish Health Authorities
RSU	Regional secure unit		Revenue Equalisation
RTA	Road traffic accident	SHO	Senior house officer
		SHOT	Serious hazards of transfusion
SABS	Safety alert broadcast system	SHPIC	Scottish Health Purchasing
SACAR	Specialist advisory committee on		Information Centre
	antimicrobial resistance	SHRINE	Strategic human resource
SACN	Scientific Advisory Committee on		information network
	Nutrition	SHS	Scottish Healthcare Supplies
SaFF	Former service and financial	SI	Statutory Instrument
	framework	SIC	Statement on internal control
SAHC	Scottish Association of Health	SID	Sudden infant death
	Councils	SIFT	Service increment for teaching
SAMM	Safety assessment of marketed	SIGN	Scottish intercollegiate guidelines

network

SITREP Situation report
SIS Supplies information system
SLA Service level agreement
SMAC Standing Medical Advisory Committee
SMAS Substance Misuse Advisory Service
SMC Scottish Medicines Consortium
SMR Standardised mortality ratio
SNMAC Standing Nursing and Midwifery Advisory Committee
SNOMED Systematized nomenclature of human and veterinary medicine
SPA Scottish prescribing analysis
SPG (NHS) Security Policy Group
SPS Standard payroll system
SR Society of Radiographers Specialist registrar
SRD State registered dietician
SSA Standard spending assessment
SSC Shared service centre
SSD Social services department
SSI Former Social Services Inspectorate
  Surgical site infection
SSIS Surgical site infection surveillance service
STEIS Strategic executive information system
StHA Strategic health authority (or SHA)
STI Sexually transmitted infection
STG Special transitional grant
STP Short-term programme
SUS Secondary uses service
SWOT Strengths, weaknesses, opportunities, threats (analysis)

T&O Trauma and orthopaedics
TC Treatment centre
TEC Training and enterprise council
TEL Trust executive letter
TIP Trust implementation plan (Scotland)
TOD Took own discharge
TOPSS Training organisation for

personal social services

TPCT Teaching primary care trust
TQM Total quality management
TSO The Stationery Office (formerly HMSO)
TSSU Theatre sterile supplies unit
TUPE Transfer of Undertakings (Protection of Employment) Regulations 1981

UKCHHO United Kingdom Clearing House on Health Outcomes (Leeds)
UKCRC UK clinical research collaboration
UKXIRA UK Xenotransplanation Interim Regulatory Authority
ULC Unit labour cost
ULTRA Unrelated Live Transplant Regulatory Authority
UNISON Public sector trade union

VDU Visual display unit
VFM Value for money
VSC Voluntary service coordinator

WAIS Wide area information server
WAN Wide area networking
WHO World Health Organization
WHCSA Welsh Health Common Services Agency
WDC Former workforce development confederation
WHDI Welsh Health Development International
WHS Welsh Health Supplies
WIC Walk-in centre
WIMS Works Information Management System
WO Welsh Office
WONCA World Organization of National Colleges, Academies and Academic Associations of General Practitioners
WTE Whole time equivalent
WTEP Whole time equivalent posts

YCS Young chronic sick
YDU Young disabled unit

ZBB Zero based budgeting

Wellard's NHS Handbook 2006/07

Index

A&E 76, 298–9
abduction, infant 299–300
access
  control of 288, 297–8
  improvement of 39, 79, 84, 275
  and inequality 77, 178, 186
  to records 275, 280
  to services 182, 186, 191
accidents 68, 119–20, 127, 161, 178
accountability 13, 17–18
  in care networks 152
  of care trusts 27
  code of 17, 231, 270, 271, 273
  financial 297
  of NHS trusts 21, 28, 233
accreditation programmes 109, 198–9
Acheson report 133, 134, 157
Action for Sick Children 164
activity, physical 118, 128, 177, 246
acute hospital trusts 29, 38, 183
acute services 143–7
administrative staff 64–5
admissions' reductions 217
adult protection protocols 245
advanced pharmacy services 204
adverse events 93, 110–12
ageism 245, 246
Agenda for change 41–2, 43, 47
AIDS 178, 221
Alberti, Sir George 241
ALBs (arm's length bodies) 34–5
alcohol misuse 77, 122, 167
All-Wales Risk Pool 110
allied health professions 39, 62–5, 66
Alzheimer's disease 101
ambulance services 213–16, 242
anaesthetic gases 71
ancillary staff 65–6, 66
angina 241, 242
annual health check 229
annual meetings and reports 232–4
antibiotic resistance 137
anxiety 166
APMS (alternative provider medical
  services) 24, 254
Appleby, Professor Louis 171, 244
appointments 78, 87, 88, 144
appraisal 54, 56, 104
assessment 67, 72, 120–1, 129, 229, 245

assurance framework 231–2
Audit Commission 73, 97, 212, 228, 264
Audit Scotland 266
auditing 53–4, 69, 71, 95, 136–8, 215
  clinical audit 54, 93–4, 99
awards 53, 54, 109
AWMSG (All-Wales medicines strategy
  group) 10, 105
Aynsley-Green, Professor Al 163–4

babies 155–6, 160, 165, 178, 299–300
BAMM (British Association of Medical
  Managers) 54
banking system 266–8
Barnes, Dr Ian 199
Barnett, Steve 47
Barron, Kevin 34
Beasley, Chris 139
beds 72, 144, 148, 168, 187
Behan, David 253
Best research for best health 101
*Better information, better choices,
  better health* 87–8
biochemistry, clinical 195
birth 153–4, 158
black minorities 79, 161, 171–2, 175–80
blood testing 198
blood transfusion services 35, 225–6
BMA (British Medical Association) 110–
  11
BNF (British National Formulary) 206
boards
  annual meetings 234
  of DH 1–2
  of HAZs 125
  of Monitor 30
  of NHS 5–6, 12–19
  of NICE 105
  roles of 48
  of trusts 22, 27, 28, 29, 54, 260, 271
  see also LHBs
booking systems 88, 144, 276, 277
borrowing, by FTs 29
Bottomley, Virginia 17
Bourn, Sir John 267
Boyle, Dr Roger 117, 243
Bradley, Peter 213
breast screening 77–8, 182, 238
Breckenridge, Professor Sir Alasdair 210

budgets
  for dental services 190
  devolution of 297
  for Institute for Innovation and
    Improvement 47
  for NHS 256
  pooled budgets 268
  programme budgeting 263–4
  for research 99, 101
  for staff training 75
  see also costs; funding
Building on the best 87, 188
Building a safer NHS for patients 107,
  110, 205
buildings 289, 290
Business Services Authority 34–5

Caldicott guardians 279–80
Calman-Hine report 236–7
CAMHS (child and adolescent mental
  health services) 172
cancer 96, 127, 177, 184, 185–8
  screening programmes 77–8, 121–2,
    177, 182, 238
cancer plan 77–8, 119, 188, 235, 236–9
Cancer Services Collaborative 238
Cancerlink 185
capital finance 29, 266–8
capital procurement 290–1
cardiologists 78
Care Direct 182
care home market 255
care practitioners 63–4
care services see community care
  services; integrated care services
care trusts 26–7, 36–7, 74, 183, 250, 252
career structures 39, 41, 52, 67
carers 38, 91–2, 181
Carter, Lord 198
case management 218
cataracts 87, 193
catering services 65, 78, 129–30, 291
Cayton, Harry 86, 87
census reports 91, 158, 175
centralisation 145–6
cervical cancer 77–8, 177
chairman, of NHS board 12–14
change, ten high impact changes 80
Changing childbirth 153, 154–5

charges
  capital charging 291
  for community care services 38
  for dental services 62, 189, 190–1
CHCs (community health councils) 10
CHD (coronary heart disease) 78, 117–
  20, 241–3
  death rate reduction 127
  in ethnic minorities 177, 179
  heart surgery 86–7, 245
  screening programme 123
CHI (Commission for Healthcare Improvement) 35, 37, 97, 228
chief executive 14, 48, 49, 95, 271
  of NICE 105
  of PCT board 22
child health services 77, 118–19, 158–
  66, 252
  mental health 172–3
  see also babies
children 91–2, 155, 239–41, 297
Children Act 2004 162, 163, 252
children's trusts 27, 85, 164, 252
choice see decision-making; patient
  choice
choose and book 88, 276, 277
Choosing a better diet 119, 124
Choosing better oral health 190
Choosing health 103, 117, 119, 123–4,
  125, 170
CHPs (community health partnerships)
  6, 49
CHRE (Council for Healthcare Regulatory Excellence) 2, 38, 42, 56
chronic conditions 89, 103, 216–19
CIMP (clinical information management
  programme) 278
civil liability 296–8
claims, clinical negligence 112, 113
clean hospitals scheme 129–31, 138, 291
cleanliness 65, 72, 78, 129, 138–9, 292–3
clerical staff 64–5
Climbie inquiry 161–2
clinical assistants 51
clinical audit 54, 93–4, 99
clinical care networks 8, 146, 151–2
clinical directorates 2, 52, 117
  for cancer 117, 238
  for CHD 117, 243

Index

for children 163, 241
for learning disabilities 174
for mental health 243–4
for older people 183, 246
for patients and public 86
clinical effectiveness 96–9, 215
clinical excellence awards 53, 54
clinical governance 20, 28, 48, 93–116, 278
clinical guidelines 75, 78, 100, 102–5, 184, 191, 206
clinical matrons 60, 79
clinical negligence 111–16
Clinical Pathology Accreditation (UK) Ltd 198
clinical practice guidance 103, 196
clinical priorities 77–8, 79
clinics 50, 78, 81
CMHTs (community mental health teams) 168
CNST (Clinical Negligence Scheme for Trusts) 110
Code of conduct and code of account-ability 17, 231, 270
codes of conduct 16–18, 231–2, 233, 270
coding 206–7, 278–9
collaborating centres 104
Commission for Health Improvement see Healthcare Commission
Commissioner for Children 163–4
commissioning
  black and ethnic minorities 179
  NHS dentistry 190
  of PMS schemes 24–5
  role of hospital doctors 74
  role of PCTs 20–1, 37, 260
  specialised services 32
  strategy for 81, 275–6
  Welsh NHS 9–10
commissioning groups 11
Commissioning a patient-led NHS 19, 20, 21, 81
committees, local representative 37
communicable disease 134, 142
communications 68, 75, 86, 112, 270–4
  ambulance radio communications 215–16
communications specialists 273–4

Community Care (Delayed Discharges etc) Act 2003 38
community care services 20–1, 38, 81, 287
  dental 62, 191
  nurses' role 60
  for paediatrics 159–60
  palliative care 187
  pharmacy 202–4
community hospitals 81, 143
community matrons 50, 60, 79, 124, 218–19
community pharmacy contracts 203–4
compensation, for negligence 112
complaints 85–6, 112–16
complaints manager 113, 114
computerisation see electronic systems; websites
confidentiality 106, 279–82
configuration of services 74, 146
conflict resolution 298
Connecting for Health 2, 275
consultant nurses 79
consultants 51–2, 74, 78
  recruitment of 39, 49, 146
consultants' contract 47, 51, 53, 74, 254
contact (e-mail/directory service) 276
contraception 117, 178, 209–11
contracts
  community pharmacy contracts 203–4
  consultants' contract 47, 51, 53, 74, 254
  dental contracts 61–2, 189, 190–1
  GP contract 47, 55–6
  honorary 51
copying letters to patients 89
COREC (Central Office for Research Ethics) 108
corporate governance 231
cost structures 267
cost-effectiveness 96, 104
costs
  of accidents 68
  of care home fees 255
  and efficiency 28, 233, 292
  of GDS 189
  of hospital infections 135
  of human resources 6–7, 39
  and inflation 257–8
  of laboratory medicine services 196

of medication errors 205
of mental health services 166, 170
national schedule of reference costs
261
of non-clinical support 291
of prescribing 203, 205–6
reference costs index 261
of research 101
of sight tests 192
Counter Fraud and Security Management Service 295–6
Court of Protection 171
CPA (care programmes approach) 168
CPD (continuing professional
development) 49, 94
CPPIH (Commission for Patient and
Public Involvement in Health) 2, 37–8, 84
CRD (Centre for Reviews and
Dissemination) 96–7, 98, 99, 102
criminal liability 296–8
crisis resolution teams 78
Crisp, Sir Nigel 1, 19, 20, 80–1, 126–7
CsCDC (consultants in communicable
disease) 134, 135
CSCI (Commission for Social Care
Inspection) 2, 252–3, 255
CSIP (care services improvement
partnership) 251
Cumberlege, Baroness Julia 153

Data Protection Act 1998 279, 280
databases 98–9, 102
Davies, Professor Sally 99
day care 187
day surgery 145, 196
death, end of life care 87, 187–8
death rate
accidental death 127
babies and children 158, 161, 178
from cancer 177, 239
from hospital infections 135–6
suicides 127, 178, 244
decision-making 15, 278
decontamination 138, 292–3
delayed discharge payments 38, 183
Delivering choosing health 124
dental contracts 61–2, 189, 190–1
dental services 62, 189–91, 191
dental staff in NHS hospitals 53

dentists 61–2, 189, 190
Denton, Erika 201
depression 166
Designed for life 10, 83
devolution 5, 268–9
DH (Department of Health) 1–2, 32,
81–2, 289
DHSSPS (Department of Health, Social
Services and Public Safety) 11
diabetes 101, 103, 123, 177, 178
diagnostic testing 200–1
digital imaging 201, 287
directorates 9, 289
see also clinical directorates
disabled children 91–2
disciplinary procedures 113
disease programmes 117, 133, 161, 177,
292–3
disease-specific care management 218
disputes forum 281
dissemination of information 96–8
distance learning programmes 49
district nurses 218
dm+d (definitive dictionary of
medicines and devices) 206–7
doctors 35–6, 40, 53–4, 57–8, 74–5
see also consultants; GPs; hospital
doctors
doctors in training 44, 52–3, 145
Doing less harm 110
domestic staff 65–6
Donaldson, Professor Sir Liam 54, 107,
111, 131, 140
donation, organs and blood 35, 225–6
drug misuse 77, 167, 220–1, 251
Drug Tariff 203, 212
drug and therapeutics committees 105
drugs (pharmaceutical) 35, 77, 105–6,
204–5, 206–7, 215
see also prescribing
DSSs (decision support systems) 278
Duerden, Professor Brian 199

e-mail/directory service 276
early intervention teams 78
earned autonomy 73
Edmonds, David 284
education and training
of allied health professions 64

Index

for ambulance crews 215
and CPD 94
for dentists 190
in genetics 219
of GP registrars 50
for H&S 68–9
health education bodies 132–3
of hospital doctors 52–3, 74–5
of managers 49
in NHS Plan 42
of nursing staff 59, 72
ophthalmic 62, 194
of optometrists 62
in palliative care 188
for pathology services 196
in PDPs 43
for pharmacists 203
in Scotland 6
for security 297
sex education 117
strategies for 42, 72, 73, 75
teaching PCTs 23
for user-led self management 89
Effective Health Care bulletins 98
efficiency 28, 233, 292
EFL (external financing limit) 268
elective surgery 33, 254, 263
electronic systems
  booking 88, 276, 277
  ESRs 57, 67, 265
  for medicines coding 206–7
  patient records 87, 275, 276, 277, 281–2, 288
  and patient/public access 288
  prescribing 79, 204, 205–6, 208, 276
  priority despatch systems 215
  for radiology 201
  recruitment 67
  test reporting to wards 198
  see also N3; NHS Direct online; websites
EMEA (European Medicines Evaluation Agency) 211
emergency care 143–4, 164, 242
emergency care practitioners 63–4
emergency services 213–16
employees *see* staff
employment, by NHS 36, 40, 41
end of life care 87, 187–8

enhanced pharmacy services 204
environmental quality 37, 251, 291–2
epidemiology 120, 178–9
EPS (electronic prescription service) 79, 204, 205–6, 208, 276
equality 126–7, 175–80, 186, 233
  see also inequalities
ESRs (electronic staff records) 57, 67, 265
essential pharmacy services 204
estate management 289–90
ethnic minorities 65, 79, 161, 171–2, 175–80
Every child matters 27, 162, 164, 241, 252
Everybody's business 173, 184
EWTD (European working time directive) 44, 52, 145
exclusion, social 170, 251
executive directors 12, 14, 105
expenditure 6–7, 39, 258, 263–4, 289
expert patient programme 78, 89, 128, 218–19
eye surgery 193

Facing up to the difference 179
failing organisations 30, 73–4
Fair shares for all 7
falls 71, 246
Family Health Services Appeals Authority 36
FCSD (Finance and Central Services Department) Scotland 6
fertilisation treatment 154
finance 22, 29, 73, 233, 256–70
A first class service 93, 110
five high impact interventions 138
five-a-day programme 77, 79, 118, 238
folic acid campaign 155
food in hospitals 65, 72, 78, 129–30, 291
forensic psychiatric services 167
Forget me not 173
formulae, financial 77, 258
forums, patients 37, 76, 84
foundation programme 52–3, 75
foundation trusts (FTs) 29–31, 115, 171
frameworks *see* legal frameworks; NSFs; PAFs
Freedom of Information Act 2000

270–1, 282
Fritchie, Dame Renee 18
fruit campaign 77, 79, 118, 238
Fullagar, Bill 225
funding 258
  of blood centres 226
  for carers 91
  for children's services 77
  for dentists 61
  for drug misuse prevention 220
  for eye surgery 193
  of FTs 29
  for GPSIs 51
  of health technologies 105
  for imaging services 201
  of laboratory medicine services 196, 197
  for learning disabilities 173, 175
  for library services 283
  for LMCA 92
  for maternity care 155
  of NHS 6, 10, 72, 256, 258
  of NHS trusts 28, 260, 268
  for nurse education 59
  for older people's care 182–3
  for ophthalmic training 194
  of PCTs 22, 37, 258–60
  for R&D 100–1
  for risk management 110
  for spearhead trusts 125
  for staff training 75
  for training and development 75
  for walk-in centres 25
  see also budgets; costs

GDC (General Dental Council) 190
general practitioners see GPs
genetic services 219
genetically determined conditions 177, 178
Gershon, Sir Peter, review 256–7
Getting ahead of the curve 139, 141, 199
Gibbons, Brian 8
GMC (General Medical Council) 50, 54–6
Gorham, Martin 225
GOS (general ophthalmic service) 192, 194

GP contract 47, 55–6
GP fundholding 20, 35
GP partnerships 50
GP practices 50–1
  child healthcare 159, 160
  commissioning role 21
  complaints procedures 114
  security measures 299
  staff numbers 40, 50
  and walk-in centres 25
GP referrals 49, 73, 145
GP registrars 50
GPs 49–51
  IT support for 276
  pharmacy advice for 206
  and PMS scheme 24
  recruitment of 39, 49
  remuneration and patient numbers 36
  training for 72
GPSIs (general practitioners with special interests) 51
Granger, Richard 275
Greig, Rob 174
GSL (general sale list) medicines 210
guidance
  on cancers 96, 184, 185–8
  for clinical practice 103, 196
  on intermediate care 150
  NICE guidelines 75, 78, 100, 102–5, 184, 191, 206
  for non-executive directors 15
  for quality improvement 7–8, 78, 96, 278

haematology 195
Hampel code 16
hanging, risk of 71
Hayman, Baroness 225
HAZs (health action zones) 125
HDA (Health Department Agency) 131
Health Act 1999 28, 35–6, 170, 183
health improvement programmes 20, 35, 127–8, 130–1
health plans, NHS Scotland 6
health promotion 117, 206, 238, 246
Health Promotion Agency, Northern Ireland 133
Health Protection Scotland 141

Health reform in England 82
health and safety 67–70, 107–8
Health and Safety at Work Acts 67, 68
health service commissioner 115–16
Health skills 128
Health and Social Care Act 2001 36–7
  and care trusts 27, 183, 250
  and ICAS 85
  and non-medical prescribing 207
  and patient–public involvement 5,
    28, 86
Health and Social Care (Community and
  Standards) Act 2003 9, 29, 30, 97, 190,
  228
Health and Social Care Information
  Centre 2, 34
Health Space 288
The Health survey for England 2004 118
health trainers 123–4
health visitors 72, 160
Health (Wales) Act 2003 132
healthcare assistants 60
Healthcare Commission 2, 72, 76, 78,
  228–30
  clinical governance role 93, 96, 97,
    104
  and CSCI 252–3
  and maternity services 156
Healthcare facilities cleaning manual
  129
heart disease *see* CHD
heart surgery 86–7, 245
hepatitis immunity status 71
HES (hospital eye service) 192, 193
Hewitt, Patricia 257
HFEA (Human Fertilisation and
  Embryology Authority) 2, 154
high impact changes 80, 138
highest risk categories 298
Higson, Peter 9
histopathology 195, 197
HIV 158, 178, 221–2
HIW (Healthcare Inspectorate Wales) 9
HLCs (healthy living centres) 118, 132
home care 187, 287, 300
honesty 13
honorary contracts 51
horizon scanning centres 106
hospices 187

hospital dental services 62, 190, 191
hospital doctors 52–3, 74, 145
hospital eye services 192, 193
hospital pharmacy services 211–12
hospitals 143–7
  A&E waiting times 76
  cleanliness programme 129–31, 138–
    9, 291
  infection control in 135–8, 292–3
  paediatric care 159, 164
  psychiatric care 168
  staff 51, 52–3, 60
  teaching hospitals 159
hours of work, junior doctors 52, 145
House of Commons Health Committee
  33–4
housekeepers 129
HPA (Health Protection Agency) 2, 134,
  141–2, 221
HPC (Health Professions Council) 63
HR in the NHS Plan 39, 40, 42–3
HRGs (healthcare resource groups) 263
HSCIC (Health and Social Care
  Information Centre) 2, 287
HTA (health technology assessment)
  98, 100, 106
HTA (Human Tissue Authority) 2, 34,
  225
Human Fertilisation and Embryology
  Act 1990 154
Human Genetics Commission 219
human resources 6, 39–46, 72–3
Hunt, Lord Philip 107

ICAS (independent complaints advocacy
  services) 85–6, 113–14
ICT (infection control team) 136
identification 297
imaging services 199–202, 287
immunisation 160–1
immunity status, hepatitis 71
Improving health in Wales 10, 83
incentives 73, 74, 80
Independent Reconfiguration Panel 74,
  78
independent sector *see* private and
  voluntary sector
inequalities 77, 80, 120, 126–7, 171–2,
  176–8

NSFs for 237, 241
partnerships for 77, 250
see also equality
infant abduction 299–300
infection control 103, 135–8, 196, 292–3
HIV strategy 77, 158, 221
inflation, and costs 257–8
information
  for carers 185–6
  for childbirth 153–4
  for clinical effectiveness 96
  on clinical governance 109
  on disease 120
  dissemination of 234
  for healthcare 275–88
  for long-term conditions 249
  for older people 183
  for patients 37, 75, 86, 87–8, 185–6, 270–1, 275
  and surveillance 229
  see also electronic systems
Information for health 275, 282
injury through mental illness 127
innovation 34, 47, 102
inpatient care 187
inspection 73, 85, 97, 252–3, 255
  accreditation programmes 109, 198–9
  for cleanliness 72, 129
insurance, private medical 255
integrated care services 26–7, 76, 147, 157, 158–61, 250
integrity 13
intellectual property 102
intensive care, paediatric 165
intermediate care 74, 78, 147–51, 183, 246, 252
internal market, removal of 28–9, 35
internet see electronic systems; websites
intervention strategy 73–4
interventional procedures 104, 152–3
intranet 276, 286
investment
  in estate 290–1
  in facilities 72
  priorities 7, 82
  in risk management 110
  in services 21, 166, 170, 238, 247, 277
ISTCs (independent sector treatment

centres) 254
IT strategy 275–7
IWL (improving working lives) 41, 45, 73, 300

Jewell, Dr Tony 11
joint finance 268
joint working 74
Jones, Trevor 5
journals 98, 273
junior doctors 52–3, 145

Kennedy, Sir Ian 97, 229
Kerr, Professor David, report 82–3
kidney patients 247–8

laboratories 141–2, 196, 197
Laming, Lord 162
language 156, 161, 179
latex sensitisation 71
leadership 13, 75, 126
learning disabilities services 173–5
Learning together 6
legal frameworks 167–8, 175–6
legal responsibilities 296–7
legionella precautions 70
Lester, Ed 284
Lewis, Gwyneth 156–7
LHBs (local health boards) 9–10, 10, 21
LHGs (local health groups) 49
liability, criminal and civil 296–8
library services 282–4
licensing 29, 56, 212
Lievesley, Professor Denise 287
life check 81
lifestyle programmes 81, 117, 118, 119, 123–4
lifting and handling 70
LISs (local implementation strategies) 277
Lloyd, Ann 9
LMCA (Long-Term Medical Conditions Alliance) 92
local authorities 26, 27, 38, 81, 91–2, 233
  scrutiny committees 36, 74, 79, 252, 272
local care networks 74, 146, 250
local delivery plans 32, 33, 242, 261
local health boards, Wales 83

Index

local plans 42, 79, 82, 163
local resolution process 114–15
local strategic partnerships 77, 250
long-term care 79–80, 181–2, 184–8,
    216–19
  carers' support 91–2
  expert patient programme 78, 89
long-term conditions 167, 248–9
low income groups 91, 181
LPS (local pharmaceutical services) 207,
    208

*Maintaining high professional standards
    in the modern NHS* 57
maintenance staff 65
Management of Health and Safety at
    Work Regulations 1999 67, 68
management teams 22
managers/management 47–9, 227–49
  complaints manager 113, 114
  doctors' role 54
  of health and safety 66–7, 69
  of imaging services 201–2
  of NHS estate 289–90
  of pathology services 197
  risk management 110–11, 198, 290
  see also boards
maternity services 87, 152–7, 239–41,
    299–300
  mother and child programmes 122–
    3, 128, 160, 179
A matron's charter 139
MCNs (Managed Clinical Networks) 8
MDOs (mentally disordered offenders)
    167
the media 272–3
medical devices 211
medical secretaries 64–5
medical staff 49–54
medicines *see* drugs; prescribing
Medicines Act 1968 210, 212
Medicines matter 207
men, as nurses 58
Mental Capacity Act 2005 171
mental health 78, 119, 124, 171–3, 243–4
  in ethnic minorities 177
  funding for research in 101
  and older people 173, 184, 246
  and suicide 127

Mental Health Act 1983 167
Mental Health Act Commission 2, 228
mental health services 26, 166–73, 179
MeReC Bulletin 206
MHRA (Medicines and Healthcare
    Products Regulatory Agency) 2,
    210–11
microbiology 195, 199
midwives 72, 75, 153, 157
Milburn, Sir Alan 148
minorities *see* black minorities; ethnic
    minorities
MiP (Managers in Partnership) 66–7
misconduct 58
MLSOs (medical laboratory scientific
    officers) 196, 197
Models of care 221
modernisation programmes 39–46, 80,
    101, 197
Modernising medical careers 52, 145
Modernising mental health services
    166, 170–1
Modernising NHS dentistry 189
Monitor 2, 29, 30
monitoring 15–16, 69, 115, 124–5, 179
Moore, Roger 17
morale, of staff 39, 42–3
mortality rate *see* death rate
mother and child programmes 122–3,
    128, 160, 179
MRCGP diploma 50
MRSA 79, 135, 138

N3 (new national network) 276, 286
NAO (National Audit office) 265
National Assembly for Wales 8–9, 10, 83
National Care Standards Commission
    97, 228
national clinical lead 201
national confidential enquiries 106
National Institute for Health Research
    101
national pathology adviser 199
national patient survey programme
    88–9, 230–1
national planning framework 79
national programme for information
    technology 275
National Public Health Service for Wales 9

national schedule of reference costs 261
national staff survey 44–5
national standards 79
  for cleanliness 129
  for mental health 243
  for older people 182, 246
  for renal services 247
National standards, local action 79, 163
NCA (non contract activity) 35
NCAS (National Clinical Assessment
  Service) 57–8, 75, 78, 108
NCPC (National Council for Palliative
  Care) 184–5
NDPBs (non-departmental public
  bodies) 2
needs, healthcare 114, 120–1
negligence, clinical 111–16
networks 8, 74, 146, 151–2, 237, 250
neuroses 166, 248
New Deal 170, 251
The new NHS 35, 48, 110
NHS 1–19
  as employer 36, 40, 41
  and independent sector 76
  inspection of 97
  and the press 272–4
NHS 24 5, 207
NHS Act 1977 213
NHS Appointments Commission 17, 18,
  23, 78
NHS Bank 266–8
The NHS cancer plan 77–8, 119, 188,
  235, 236–9
NHS (Complaints) Regulations 2004 115
NHS CRS 276, 277
NHS Direct 76, 79, 128, 191, 207, 214,
  278, 284–5
NHS Direct online 284, 285
NHS Direct Wales 285
NHS Employers 46–7
NHS gateway 288
NHS Health Scotland 5, 133
NHS improvement plan 42, 79–81, 217
NHS Institute for Innovation and
  Improvement 2, 34, 47
NHS LIFT 268, 291
NHS Litigation Authority 2, 112
NHS Logistics 294
NHS Plan for England 1, 72–82

  for child care 161
  clinical governance in 93
  human resources agenda 39–41, 59
  for independent sector 254
  for intermediate care 149
  for mental health care 172, 173
  for older people 182–3
  for partnerships 250, 252, 291
  for pharmacy 208–9
NHS Plan for Scotland 82–3
NHS Plan for Wales 83
NHS (Primary Care) Act 1997 191
NHS Professionals 2, 44
NHS Quality Improvement Scotland 5,
  97–8
NHS Redress Bill 2005 111
NHS Reform and Healthcare Professions
  Act 2002 37–8
NHS Scotland 5–8
NHS Shared Business Services Ltd 265
NHS trusts 4, 11, 28–9, 110, 260–1, 268
  see also care trusts; foundation trusts
NHS trusts manual for accounts 232
NHS Wales 5–11
NHSBT (NHS Blood and Transplant) 35,
  224, 225
NHSnet 286
NHSplus 76
NHSQIS (NHS Quality Improvement
  Scotland) 7–8
NIAO (Northern Ireland Audit Office)
  266
NICE (National Institute for Health and
  Clinical Excellence) 75, 78, 100, 102–5,
  184, 191, 206
NLH (National Library for Health) 283–4
NMC (Nursing and Midwifery Council)
  59
NNR (National Research Register) 102
non-emergency transport 216
non-executive board members 22–3
non-executive directors
  of NHS boards 12, 14–15, 22–3, 74,
    95, 260–1
  of NICE 105
non-medical prescribing 207–11
non-medical staff 40, 63, 64–7
Northern Ireland NHS 11–12, 133, 266,
  294–5

notifiable diseases 136
NPfIT (national programme for information technology) 275
NPSA (National Patient Safety Agency)
  2, 93, 107–8, 110, 205, 289
NRT (nicotine replacement therapy) 77,
  131
NSFs (national service frameworks) 10,
  45–6, 150, 171, 182, 188, 235–49
nurse practitioners 60
nursing staff 39, 40, 50, 58–61, 72, 75
nutrition 77, 79, 118, 124, 161
  see also food in hospitals

obesity 77, 118
objectivity 13
observatories, public health 124–5
obstetric care 153–6
Occupiers Liability Act 1984 296
older people 148–9, 173, 181–4, 244–6
ombudsman 115–16
OMPs (ophthalmic medical
  practitioners) 62, 192, 193–4
one-stop shops 24, 76
online systems see, electronic systems
openness 13, 18, 270, 273
ophthalmic services 62, 191–4
optometrists (opticians) 62, 192, 193–4
oral health 190
organ donations 35, 224
An organisation with a memory 93, 107
organisational commitment 178
orthopaedic project, national 147
Our health, our care, our say 81
Our national plan 82
out-of-hours care 21, 76, 83, 284
outpatients 49, 73, 76, 144, 196
overview see, scrutiny committees

P (pharmacy) medicines 210
PACS (picture archiving and
  communications system) 201, 276
paediatric care 159–60, 164–5
PAFs (performance assessment
  frameworks) 72–3, 93, 227
palliative care 103, 184–8
PALS (patient advice and liaison
  services) 75–6, 79, 84, 85, 113
Partnership for care 7

partnerships 250–3
  GP partnerships 50
  healthcare 83, 89, 170, 174, 183–4,
    252
  local 77, 125, 180, 233, 250
  NHS–independent sector 29, 76
  NICE partners' council 105
PAs (programmed activities) 53
PASA (Purchasing and Supply Agency)
  294
Patel, Lord Naren 97
Patel, Professor Kamlesh 172
Paterson, Dr Kenneth 106
pathology services 194–9
patient choice 29, 39, 75, 86–8, 153,
  185–6, 263
patient involvement see PPI
patient records 245, 280
  electronic 87, 275, 276, 277, 281–2,
    288
Patient safety and clinical risk 110–11
patient-led services 80–1
patient–public involvement 5, 28, 86
patients 75–6, 84–93
  health and safety of 71, 200, 296–
    300
  information for 37, 75, 86, 87–8,
    185–6, 270–1, 275
  non-emergency transport 216
  numbers, and GP remuneration 36
  safeguards 30–1
  supported self care 89, 208, 217, 218
  views of 76, 230–1
  violent and aggressive 298–9
  women-centred maternity care 153–
    4
  see also access; patient choice; PPI
pay system
  for dentists 61–2
  health professionals 36, 50, 53, 61–2,
    203, 204
  modernisation of 41–2, 43, 72, 78
  see also low income groups
payments
  delayed discharge 38, 183
  direct payments 245
  guide to good practice 233
  to dentists 61, 62
PbR (payment by results) 30, 261–3

PCIPs (primary care investment plans)
21, 277
PCPs (personal care plans) 182, 217
PCTs (primary care trusts) 4–5, 19–23, 37
boundaries of 81
and care trusts 26
clinical governance duties 95–6
complaints procedures 114
dental services role 191
employees 36
GPs as members of 49
health action zones 125
patients prospectuses 79, 86
and PMS schemes 24
practice-based commissioning 81
public health role 134, 142
revenue allocations 22, 37, 258–60
security arrangements 295
and service agreements 29
spearhead trusts 125
and specialised services 32
PEATs (patient environment action
teams) 129, 130, 291
pensions 45, 91, 181
performance assessment 72–3, 93, 227
performance management 227–49
performance reviews 56, 57–8, 69, 76,
193
performance standards 69, 73, 93, 96,
214–15, 227–8
person-centred care 153–4, 246
PFI (private finance initiative) 266–8,
290
pharmacists 75, 76, 206, 209
Pharmacy in the future 203, 208, 209
pharmacy services 37, 202–12
PHCDS (Public health common data set)
120
Philp, Professor Ian 183, 246
physical activity 118, 128, 177, 246
planning populations 32
plans/planning 53, 69, 79–80
see also NHS Plan
Platt, Dame Denise 253
PMETB (Postgraduate Medical Education and Training Board) 2, 53, 75, 77,
78–9
PMS (personal medical services) 24–5,
50–1, 74, 78

point of care testing 198
POMs (prescription only medicines) 210
pooled budgets 252, 268
poor performers 57–8, 96
POPP (partnerships for older people)
183–4
population statistics 32, 158, 175, 277
Positively diverse 41, 176, 233
PPA (Prescription Pricing Authority)
203, 212
PPI (patient and public involvement)
forums 37, 76, 84–5
PPI (patient and public involvement) 5,
30, 47, 82, 84–95, 101–2, 252
in Wales 10, 83
practice nurses 50, 59–60, 75
practice-based commissioning 81
pregnancy, teenage 117, 158, 222
prescribing 76, 79, 87, 203–12
in Wales 10, 105
prescribing rights 37
the press 272–4
preventive programmes 81, 117
Prevention better than cure 58
price regulation 35, 262–3
primary care professionals 20, 21, 166
primary care services
for children 159, 240
clinical governance 95–6
investment plan 21, 277
private 192
in Scotland and Wales 82–3
security arrangements 299, 300
see also community care services;
PCTs; PMS
primary healthcare teams 49–50
priority despatch systems 215
private finance 266–8, 290–1
private and voluntary sector 254–5
healthcare 187, 189, 192, 193
inspection of 85, 97
partnerships with NHS 76, 79, 291
use of ambulance services 216
voluntary care workers 91
probity 18, 270
procurement 292–5
professional & technical staff 40, 62–6,
72
A professional approach to managing

Wellard's NHS Handbook 2006/07

Index

security 296
professional self-regulation 36, 42, 56, 94
programme budgeting 263–4
property transactions 290
prospectuses, for patients 79, 86
providers
    alternative 24, 29, 82, 254
    choice of 86–7, 88, 263
psychiatry services 159, 167, 168, 177, 178
psychoses 167
public guardian 171
public health 103, 117–42, 152, 157, 170
public health observatories 124–5
Public Interest Disclosure Act 1998 16
public involvement see PPI

quality of care 15–16, 28, 53–4, 93, 95–6
quality improvement 7–8, 9, 78, 96, 228–9, 233, 235, 278

Race Relations Acts 127, 175, 177
racial equality 126–7, 175–80
radiological techniques 199–201
RAFT 34, 35, 154
Ramsden, Mike 287
rating system 73, 130
Rawlins, Professor Sir Michael 105
reconfiguration of services 74, 78
records 278–9, 280–1, 297
    see also ESRs; patient records
recruitment
    of allied health professionals 39
    of cancer specialists 237
    of consultants 39, 49, 146
    electronic 67
    of GPs 39
    international 73
    for laboratory services 197
    of mental health workers 78
    of nursing staff 39, 60–1
    see also staff
redress 76, 111–12
ReFeR (Research Findings electronic Register) 102
reference cost index 261
referrals 49, 73, 114, 144, 248
Reforming emergency care 143

regional development agencies 102
Regional Supplies Service, Northern Ireland 294–5
registrars 50, 53, 72, 74
regulation
    of allied health professions 63
    for complaints procedures 115
    of doctors 75
    independent (Monitor) 2, 29, 30
    of nursing staff 59
    price regulation 35, 262–3
    role of CHRE 38, 42
    role of GMC 54–6
    self-regulation 36, 42, 56, 94
rehabilitation 147–51, 245
Reid, John 125, 138, 176, 216, 219, 239
renal services 247–8
repeat dispensing 207, 208
research and development 53, 99–106
residential care, independent 255
resource allocation formula 77, 258
restoration and transition 148
revalidation 54, 56
revenue allocations 22, 37, 258–60
review teams 76, 280–1
Richards, Professor Mike 117, 237–8
rights, of patients 76, 111–13, 164
risk assessment 67
risk management 110–11, 198, 290, 298
risks 71, 200
Royal College of Nursing 60
RPSGB (Royal Pharmaceutical Society of Great Britain) 203
RSCGs (regional specialised commissioning groups) 32

SABS (Safety Alert Broadcast System) 108, 286
safety
    health and safety 67–70, 107–8
    medicines safety 204–5
    security systems 295–301
Saving lives 117, 127–8, 170, 223
scalding, risks of 71
scanning services 201
school fruit scheme 77, 79, 118, 238
Scotland 5–8, 82–3
    community health partnerships 6, 49
    national carers strategy 91

pharmacy strategy 208–9
poorly performing doctors 58
primary care in 21
public health agenda 133
the SMC 105–6
supplies and procurement 294
screening programmes 121–3, 160, 161, 201, 222
cancer 77–8, 121–2, 177, 182, 238
scrutiny committees 36, 74, 79, 252, 272
secondary care see acute hospital trusts; hospitals
security 295–301
SEHD (Scottish Executive Health Department) 5, 58
self care 89, 206, 208, 217, 218–19
selflessness 13
seven principles of public life 13
sex education 117
sexual health 77, 82, 124, 221–3
shared service initiative 264–6
Sharma, Surinder 126, 176–7
sharps and needlesticks 70
SHAs (strategic health authorities) 2–4, 19, 37, 95
Shribman, Dr Sheila 163, 241
SHRINE (strategic human resource intelligence) 43
SHS (Scottish Healthcare Supplies) 294
SIC (statement on internal control) 232
sight tests, free 192
SIGN (Scottish Intercollegiate Guidelines Network) 7–8
single-handed practices 74
skills escalator 41
SLAs (service level agreements) 261
smart cards 57, 279
SMC (Scottish Medicines Consortium) 8, 105–6
Smith, Dr Jim 204, 209
Smith, Dr Marie 102
smoking 77, 79, 117, 124, 130–2, 238
SNOMED 207, 278
social care 81, 152, 157, 186
social exclusion agenda 170, 251
social services 38, 74, 252, 253
spearhead primary care trusts 125
special health authorities 2, 44, 47
special interests, GPs with 51

specialised services 32, 76, 187–8
specialist registrars 53, 72, 74
spending reviews 256
see also costs; funding
sports strategy 118, 128
staff
administrative and clerical 64–5
ambulance service 214
care practitioners 63–4
communications specialists 273–4
consultant pharmacists 204
development of 41, 43, 72–5
earnings 256
ESR system 57, 67
from ethnic minorities 65, 179
health and safety duties 67–8, 70
in NHS Plan 78
night cover in hospitals 146–7
non-medical staff 40, 63, 64–7
numbers of 39–40, 49, 50, 53, 61, 64
nursing staff 39, 40, 50, 58–61, 72, 75
older people's care 245
pathology services 196, 197
professional and support staff 62–3
safety 300
shortages 157
X-ray and imaging services 199
see also education and training; human resources; recruitment
standards see national standards; NSFs; performance standards
Standards for better health 73, 105, 227–8, 229, 232
sterile services 292–3
Stewart, Sir William 142
stress 70
stroke 101, 123, 127, 177, 246
Stroke Association 92
suicide rates 127, 178, 244
supply-side reforms 82, 293–5
support services 289–301
support staff 40, 62–6
supported living 174
supported self care 89, 208, 217, 218
supportive care 103, 184–8
Sure Start 77, 126, 128, 157, 161, 251
surgery 33, 86–7, 145, 193, 201, 223
surveillance programmes 160, 229, 230–1
sustainability 291–2

Tackling drugs to build a better Britain 220, 251
Tackling health inequalities 176
Taking healthcare to the patient 213
targets
  health 127–8, 130–1, 144, 217, 220–1, 242
  management 72, 79, 87, 115, 257
tariffs, elective 263
taxation 72, 258
TCs (treatment centres) 33, 143, 145, 254
teaching hospitals 159
teaching PCTs 23
technical & professional staff 40, 62–6
technologies 103, 104, 105, 144
teenage pregnancy 117, 158, 222
telemedicine 276–7, 286–7
Ten high impact changes 80
tertiary centre teaching hospitals 159
therapists 72, 75
Thomas, Richard 280
thrombolysis treatment 243
time limits, for complaints 113
trades unions 66–7
training *see* education and training
transfusion services 35, 225–6
transition and restoration 148
transplant services 223–4, 247
treatment, withholding 299
triage systems 215
Troop, Dr Pat 142
trusts *see* care trusts; children's trusts; foundation trusts; NHS trusts; PCTs
TV interactive services 285
24 hour food service 291

unified NHS boards, Scotland 5–6, 82
urgent cases 214
user-led self management 89, 206, 208, 217, 218–19
users' councils 168
utilisation of services 178, 181–2

vaccination 160
Valuing people 173, 174
violence 70, 298–9
A vision for pharmacy 209
voluntary services *see* private and voluntary sector
voucher schemes 192

waiting times 87, 144, 193, 238, 243
  maximum 76–7, 79
Wales 8–11, 83
  Audit Office 267
  local health groups 49
  library services 283
  medicines strategy group 105
  national carers strategy 91
  NHS Direct Wales 285
  pharmacy strategy 10, 208
  primary care in 21
  public health agenda 132, 141
  supplies and procurement 294
Wales Centre for Health 132
walk-in centres 25–6, 78, 191, 288
Walker, Anna 97, 229
Wanless, Derek, review 257
Warner, Lord 198
waste disposal 71
Webb, Sir David 106
websites
  for carers 92
  for long-term conditions 249
  NHS 86, 88, 102, 224, 285, 288
  NICE 105
  NLH 283–4
  see also electronic systems
Wells, Sir William 17
WHS (Welsh Health Supplies) 294
Winning ways 140
Winterton Report 153
women 50, 51, 58, 65, 181, 222
  see also mother and child programmes
women-only day centres 78
Woodward, Shaun 11
Woolf, Lord 281
workforce planning 42, 45–6, 197
  see also staff
working conditions 94
Working together: securing a quality workforce for the NHS 39
Working together, learning together 41, 94

X-ray and imaging services 199–202

young people 165, 220, 239–41, 252